D0968464

A CONCEPTUAL FRAMEWORK FOR THE MANAGEMENT SCIENCES

McGRAW-HILL SERIES IN MANAGEMENT

KEITH DAVIS, **Consulting Editor**

A CONCEPTUAL FRAMEWORK FOR THE MANAGEMENT SCIENCES

MARVIN E. MUNDEL, Ph.D. M. E. Mundel and Associates

Management and Industrial Engineering Consultants
Silver Spring, Maryland

McGRAW-HILL BOOK COMPANY   New York   St. Louis

San Francisco   Toronto   London   Sydney

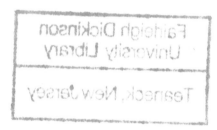
A CONCEPTUAL FRAMEWORK FOR THE MANAGEMENT SCIENCES

Library of Congress Catalog Card Number 67-17202

44035   1 2 3 4 5 6 7 8 9 0   M P   7 4 3 2 1 0 6 9 8 7

PREFACE

This book is designed to present, from an analytical viewpoint, a framework for information about industrial management and the management sciences and technologies. It is intended to serve the basic needs of beginning students as well as to stimulate a broader view in experienced managers and experienced specialists.

The book begins by carefully defining the activity of management not from the view of a few isolated examples, but in terms of the fundamental characteristics. A basic method of solving problems is also discussed. This is followed by a series of chapters devoted to the components which appear in the typical industrial enterprise, defining these components, describing their characteristics, and presenting ways of classifying them to aid in problem solving. These chapters are followed by one describing time and money as two basic dimensions in most managerial problems. The introductory section concludes with a discussion of the society of the industrial plant, the setting in which managers work. The focus of this discussion is on extracting the essential features of such a society rather than dealing with a few examples. These chapters are designed to aid in the understanding of essentials rather than to describe specific ways of reacting to specific situations.

The next group of chapters returns to the components of the industrial enterprise and takes these one by one, examining the manner in which the desired characteristics are designed or selected. The emphasis is on the general method rather than the specific and on an understanding of the factors involved and their interrelationships rather than on isolated, special examples. Even though the components are treated in individual chapters, care is exercised to indicate their interdependence.

The subsequent chapter is devoted to a discussion of the concept of control as fundamental to managerial activity. The basic features of all control situations are developed completely apart from any particular example or application. Any terminology necessary for full understanding is carefully defined. This chapter is followed by a series of chapters dealing with specific types of control, pertaining to the components discussed in related chapters in the introductory section but taken in the order of importance. As in the earlier section of the book, these are examined in a manner designed to increase the understanding of any situation rather than to describe the answer to a few specific situations. Details, where they are introduced, are designed to illustrate a broad or fundamental point rather than to describe some singular solution.

The final chapter returns to the problem of decision making. Drawing on the preceding chapters, it summarizes how the various technologies of management and management science are used to assist in performing the job of the manager. Again, the approach is broad and fundamental and of wide applicability.

An introductory text in physics does not make a physicist; an introductory book in chemistry does not make a chemist; there seems no reason why an introductory book on management should attempt to make a manager. This book departs from the common format of the introductory text, which usually contains a large amount of descriptive material divided in a mixed manner related to both the formal division of duties in a large American plant and the technologies involved, a large number of so-called principles of management, and a large number of specific approaches to special problems, all woven inextricably together. The result is usually overwhelming for the beginning student who has little, if any, background or experience to sort out the important from the trivial, the factual from the speculative, the principle from the specific case, the variables from the solution. This is not to deny the enormous importance of such books, but they are just not the place to begin. Some sort of overall preliminary orientation seems more appropriate.

At the end of each chapter I have appended a three-part list for the student who wishes to add additional information to the framework for knowledge provided by this book. First, under the heading of "Topics" I have listed subjects he will find in the index of most books on management, as well as in many of the handbooks. Thus, the student can seek additional relevant material in whatever books he has available without being limited to a specific bibliography. Second, at the end of each chapter there is a list of "Themes" or more specific topics he may wish to think or write about and examine in relation to the content of that particular chapter. Third, a number of simple case-problem books are given with specific cases indicated as pertinent to the material presented.

There were two main influences in writing this book. First, for approximately fifteen years I either taught college classes in industrial management and industrial engineering or directed the teaching of such classes. Judging from the students' reactions I frequently felt that the introductory material we presented on industrial management either failed to fill their needs or turned them away from the subject. Second, during the last fifteen years, most of my time has been devoted to consulting work on industrial and governmental industrial management and engineering problems. This has taken me from the western border of the "Iron Curtain" to the eastern border of the "Bamboo Curtain"; from work concerning the most economical formulation of sausages to the construction of outsized oil tankers; from the handicraft shops of Sweden and Japan to the Executive Office of the President and the Bureau of the Budget (of the United States); and from the industrial giants of Europe, America, and Japan to the small family-owned plants of the American Midwest. In all of these activities there seemed to be certain fundamental similarities which permitted the knowledge gained in one place to be used in others. These similarities seemed most related to objectives and the factors which create problems. These two aspects of management emerged as basic and much more important than technique. It is this which I have stressed in this book. After all, without objectives there are no problems; without problems, there is no need for techniques. It seemed appropriate to develop a need for the application of techniques before the description of the details of technology.

Those who go on far beyond this book into the more complicated areas of management science and become expert in one or more areas will still have a need to understand the totality of a situation and thereby to identify the problem standing in the way of achieving the objective and then to search for the technique to assist in solving the problem rather than hunting for problems for which they already have a technique. This book is designed to provide the fundamental framework for holding the more specialized areas of management science in their proper perspective relative to the whole of an industrial plant.

It is utterly impossible to thank by name all of the people who have made this book possible. The list would include everybody I have worked with, in one fashion or another, over a thirty-year span. Besides, at this point, it is impossible to determine which event, person, or conversation led to which view or conclusion. I can only say that I have learned much from many people and that I am trying to put some "back in the pot."

Marvin E. Mundel

CONTENTS

1

INTRODUCTION

2

**DESIGNING THE
COMPONENTS OF
THE INDUSTRIAL
ENTERPRISE**

3

CONTROL

4

CONCLUSION

PART 1 INTRODUCTION

1 INDUSTRIAL MANAGEMENT AND THE SCIENTIFIC APPROACH

This book is concerned with a fundamental conceptual structure for information about *industrial management* and the management sciences and technologies. It will be presented from an analytical viewpoint designed to facilitate the use of a procedure called the *scientific approach*. Hence, it would seem reasonable to start with definitions of the italicized parts of these sentences. This introductory chapter will then conclude with an explanation of the rationale of the remaining chapters of this book.

The careful definition of words is vital to clear thinking, particularly when dealing with specialized aspects of concepts denoted by words which have other meanings when used in everyday common contexts. The word *management* has many uses in current conversation, so many as to lead one writer to make the following statement:

One source of confusion is the variety of different meanings which are given to the term Management. Take the following sentence, which if ambiguous, is nevertheless an example of current usage:—The *management* (a) of the Nameless Company Ltd. are convinced that good *management* (b) is an important factor in the prosperity of every business; they have, therefore, decided that the study of *management* (c) and particularly of relations between *management*

(d) and labour, should be encouraged among all members of *the management* (e); for this purpose the term *the management* (e) does not include the foremen.

In this sentence the word management is used in five quite distinct meanings. Taking these in order:

(a) *The management* means those responsible for the day by day conduct of the business, the few people who make the ultimate decisions; it is a synonym for the Governing Body, the Board or the Management Committee.

(b) *good management* here means effective direction by all those responsible for the work of others—an activity.

(c) *management* here means a body of knowledge; it is not possible to study an activity as such, only the knowledge available about the activity.

(d) *management* here means as in (a), a group of people, but an indeterminate group—all those identified with nployers vis-a-vis those identified as wage-earners.

(e) *the management* here also means a group of people, but again a different group, larger than (a) but smaller than (c), all those in the company exercising managerial functions or described as "managers."[1]

Even if one restricts the use of the word management to the description of an activity, there are still many levels at which this activity takes place. The activity at the different levels will differ markedly. One may speak of home management and factory management. Without doubt, a case could be made for the similarities between these two activities, but there are also essential differences which, for the most part, are more than what might be called differences of degree. By way of explanation, the activity of a man lifting a 10-pound weight differs in degree from the activity of a man lifting a 50-pound weight. However, when the weight is 2,000 pounds, something new must enter. Hence, to avoid confusion, we shall give a specific definition for the activity of industrial management.

Industrial management is the performance of the task of designing, predicting the results of, providing the resources for, and controlling an integrated human-group activity, the related physical facilities, and the interrelationships between these two when the activity concerns the creation and distribution of goods or services to meet an external objective.

The above definition can perhaps be more fully understood if one examines the individual terms and their implications. Let us first restate the definition of industrial management in a form which permits the identification of separate aspects of the definition so that it will be easier to discuss.

Industrial management is:

    A.   The performance of the task of
        1. Designing
        2. Predicting the results of

[1] L. Urwick, "Is Management a Profession?" n.d.

      3. Providing the resources for
      4. Controlling
B. With
      1. An integrated human-group activity
      2. The related physical facilities
      3. The interrelationships between the above two items (*B*1 and 2)
C. When the activity concerns the creation and the distribution of goods
    or services
D. To meet an external objective

Let us examine these items, term by term.

Designing. This word should be given the meaning "making plans, in detail, for work to be accomplished," or "selecting a course of action from alternative courses." The word designing was picked to imply a carefully determined plan based on applicable facts, relationships, or principles, and prior knowledge concerning the probable behavior of all of the parts or components affected by the plan.

Predicting the results of. Although this may be implicit in the word designing, it has been explicitly stated to emphasize this feature of real industrial management. The plans made for work to be accomplished must, for effective use, be accompanied by a realistic anticipation of the results.

Providing the resources for. In the usual industrial management design, various facilities, e.g., men, equipment, product, materials, and money, are involved. It is part of the industrial management activity to make these available (procure and dispense) for use in the designed manner.

Controlling. Three phases of control should be recognized as being implicit in this term: (1) to have goals or objectives to serve as criteria of constraint, (2) to keep a record of work being accomplished by the people and facilities in the design, as compared with the expected results, and (3) to correct, if necessary, by adjusting either the design or the factors affecting compliance with the design (or both) so that design and performance conform with each other.

An integrated human-group activity. This should be understood as referring to "the joint labor of at least several people working at tasks which have been assigned in a manner such that the performance of each member of the group, in general, has a bearing on the success of each other member." Indeed, it is this aspect which is vital to an understanding of most twentieth-century industrial management activity. This precludes certain common uses of the word management while at the same time it more carefully delineates the major types of problems with which this book is concerned. Therefore, let us look further into the background of this aspect.

Prior to this century, industrial management, as herein defined, was relatively nonexistent. However, a type of management that was similar, except in outputs or objectives, was exercised upon occasion by the military in formal undertakings of an urgent nature, such as migrations and expeditions, or in the occasional use of large quantities of slave labor. Certainly these did not enter so deeply into the daily life of most citizens as does industrial management today. The normal manner of earning a livelihood was either in self-employment or in simple groupings in which a few men worked for one man but as semi-independent units, e.g., the hired hand who took care of the crops or the household worker who ran the household. It is to be noted that this was the normal or usual, but not the invariable, state of affairs; some sizable integrated enterprises did commonly exist, such as ship crews, mine crews, and so on. In most cases, however, the integration, as compared with modern practice, was very limited. The activity of industrial management and the integrated human-group activity with which it deals have affected the very structure of our society; these relationships call for a whole host of new behavior patterns. It should be noted that one of the problems of industrializing a so-called "underdeveloped nation" is not so much the introduction of industrial technology or the funding of enterprises, but the creation of the behavior patterns which are necessary for the operation of industrial management, i.e., the altering of the basic form of society. I refer not to the form of government but to the day-to-day relationships, attitudes, and motivations of people.

The change in our way of life created by the widespread use of the pattern of integrated human-group activity and the tremendous scope of integration is most easily understood by considering its effect upon another type of activity apart from the industrial scene; let us consider farming. The farmer of the 1800s was largely self-sustaining. Indeed, in many cases, he lived in relative isolation. He raised his own seed, made his own equipment or bought it from some nearby individual, and fed most of his crops to livestock which he used for both power and food. His land was fertilized with the by-product of his livestock. He raised his own food and sold his surplus only when he had crops over and beyond his own needs. It could be said, in the common use of the word, that he managed his land, but there was not the problem of the integrated human group.

The farmer in the U.S.A. today uses equipment, fuel, seed, and fertilizer produced in distant places and bought on the open market. He depends on the proper functioning of the people in these industries for his own existence. To a large extent, he raises a cash crop rather than a sustenance crop. He is dependent for his food on the marketing of this crop and on the people involved in marketing. He is a member of an integrated group. Although the group is not under his direct control, it must be considered, when he makes his decisions, to an extent so great that it is difficult to really compare with former eras.

Integrated group activity has become a major aspect of the modern way of life. In the typical manufacturing plant or service organization, internal relationships repeat, in close contact and in an intensified fashion, this aspect of the pattern of the outside world. The performance of almost every member of the group depends for success upon the successful performance of other tasks by other men. This is true for large plants and small plants.

Organizations such as General Motors Corporation, General Dynamics Corporation, and the U.S. Army Materiel Command in the United States; Imperial Chemical Industries and Lucas Ltd. of Great Britain; and Mitsubishi, Hitachi, and Tokyo Shibaura Electric Company in Japan directly employ within their close control from 100,000 to 300,000 or more people in a vast, complex, integrated human-group activity. These are extreme cases. Smaller plants, however, employ the same manner of operation. The difference, using our present frame of reference, is primarily a matter of degree. The integrated human-group activity is primarily a twentieth-century development. It is an essential and important aspect of industrial management as the term is used in this book.

The related physical facilities. This phase refers to the buildings and equipment and includes, for the purpose of this definition, stocks of material. Concomitant with the introduction of the integrated human-group activity we have had tremendous basic changes in the adjuncts to the performance of work, with both of these changes stimulating each other. Present-day facilities are very different from those of previous centuries, and they have a great bearing on our present form of industrial management.

Our present facilities are the direct result of four unique but complementary innovations introduced during the eighteenth and nineteenth centuries. These four innovations are simple in concept and far-reaching and revolutionary in effect, and they are predominant features of present-day industrial activity. They are:

1. Mass production and interchangeable manufacture
2. Jigs, fixtures, dies, and gauges
3. Mechanical and electrical power on a widely available basis and on a vast scale
4. Increased variety of "raw materials" as outputs of enterprise

The first of these innovations consisted of the idea of manufacturing complex goods by having each worker either producing one part or performing a single operation on a part but so carefully controlling his actions that for all intents and purposes each part could be substituted for any other of the same type. Under such a system, a worker could easily become both skilled (know the motions of the job) and productive in a shorter time than a man learning to produce the whole complex object by himself. Also, he produced many pieces.

The second innovation facilitated the type of activity created by the first innovation as well as being itself stimulated by the first. In many ways, it was a natural concomitant. Inasmuch as each job represented a simple problem, it was natural that the tools which made the jobs easier or more productive could be created faster under a system of mass production than under previous arrangements. The tools would receive greater use when used in mass production; hence they would be more feasible from the economics of the situation. They tended to be more specialized. A jig or fixture made to accurate dimensions would reduce the demands for skill from the user. Such tools, jigs, fixtures, and gauges (single-purpose measuring tools) enhanced the value of the integrated group system and tended to increase both the number and size of such working groups.

Widely available power (using the term to include both mechanical and electrical power) could have tended to reduce the size of the groups engaged in an undertaking if merely used to reduce the strength required from men, even though the mechanical power was not as adaptable as men. For example, a bulldozer could replace a considerable number of shovelers if the task remained unchanged. However, the two innovations previously referred to made the introduction of mechanical power convenient and appropriate because the typical scope of activity and the variety of the task to which the power was applied had been greatly reduced, bringing the task within the limited capability (variety-wise) of the machine. Mechanization, therefore, enhanced and accelerated the formation of group activity. It also made many larger tasks economically feasible.

The fourth innovation stems from the preceding three; the new concepts created a need for new materials and made them possible.

It should be noted that these innovations did not appear either spontaneously or in smooth order. In addition, it should not be thought that society calmly adjusted itself to the great changes these innovations wrought in both the individual and group ways of life. Indeed, at times people doubted the feasibility of these concepts. For instance, Eli Whitney, when attempting to sell mass-produced muskets with interchangeable parts to the U.S. government purchasing groups just prior to the War of 1812, had great difficulty in convincing them that his samples were not trick showpieces.

These four innovations have had effects upon such diverse phenomena as "the amount of money in circulation," "the number of people attending school," "union membership," and so forth. Countless other factors could be correlated with the use of these four monumental ideas, showing the marked changes in social and economic factors. These four innovations are now accepted practice to such extent that we seldom realize how recently they were introduced, but these are the factors which have made possible the typical present-day collection of plant and equipment.

The interrelationships between the group activity and the facilities. It should be obvious at this point that the effective use of the equipment is intimately related to the group activity and vice versa and that management must include the consideration of this relationship.

When the activities concern the creation and distribution of goods and services. The outputs for which a human group and its related facilities have been created may be classified, in the words of the economist, as being a form or a service utility. For convenience, the discussion of industrial management, in this book, will center on activities whose output is a form utility: the physical conversion of material from one state or form to another.

However, a service utility, wherein the objects do not change but ease of access to them is modified, e.g., a retail mail-order house or a government bureau, may present a management problem so akin that it need not be distinctly differentiated. A bank, which provides a service in respect to the access to money, may have many areas of activity similar to the manufacturing plant although it will have unique emphasis on some of them. The same may be said of a library, a hospital, or an airline. However, in this book, in order to avoid excessive dilution, the main direction of the discussion will be toward manufacturing plants. Reference to other types of activity will occasionally be made. In many of the items discussed, the similarities and differences will be obvious.

To meet an external objective. It should be noted that the definition of industrial management did not contain any reference to a specific objective. The industrial plant, in some countries, when privately owned may need to make a monetary profit to even exist; under other forms of government, the meeting of an assigned obligation or quota may be sufficient. This may be the objective of a government-owned facility, even in a country where free enterprise is normal. In this book, the discussion of industrial management will not always be oriented specifically toward any single objective. Much of that which will be discussed will be fundamental to any possible objective. Although the objective will, of course, influence actual actions, it will usually not have a bearing on many activities; it will not alter facts; it will not alter the means of collecting facts; it will only provide different criteria for selecting the action to be taken. Hence, the term industrial management is defined only in terms of directing the activities of the group and the facilities toward some external objective.

Thus we have a definition of industrial management. The present nature of the task, as defined, is one of relative recency and continually increasing importance.

The people who perform this activity are called managers. It is not to be thought that all managers perform all aspects of industrial management as it has been defined. Management activity itself usually is divided into smaller and smaller parts as the integrated group becomes larger. Inasmuch as there are many ways of dividing the activity, much more will be said about this later.

Up to this point management has been defined as an activity; managers, as those who are engaged in this activity. An activity is a "state of doing" which certainly implies "something to be doing with." To discuss meaningfully the problems of the activity and the manner of doing the activity, we must have some organized method of dividing "that with which the work is done." In our definition we referred to integrated human groups and facilities; for a really analytical discussion, we need a further breakdown.

A careful consideration of the definition of activity of industrial management and of the typical industrial establishment will show that all managerial activity can be related to four groups of observable "things." It can also be said that all management design activities and control activities relate to specific occurrences of these four kinds of things. The four groups are as follows:

1. Man-jobs—men and the work they do
2. Physical plant—all material adjuncts to productive activity not appearing in the outputs
3. Product—output of the work group
4. Materials—physical objects consumed by the work group in creating its outputs

This grouping has been selected because the groups are distinctly different; they are homogeneous divisions in that there are important similarities among all the items in any one group; the classification is physical and simple; the framework they represent will conveniently structure management knowledge; and also, they are such that management activity seldom takes place without all divisions being present or affecting the problem. Therefore, the assumption seems tenable that they are basic to management activity and to a study of this activity. As the prerequisite to learning how to perform management activity in a scientific fashion, one should become familiar with the basic features of each of these four components. However, even prior to this, one should become familiar with what is known as *the scientific method.* The application of the scientific method to management problems results in an approach quite properly called *scientific management.*

Unfortunately, this term has been abused even more than the term management; hence clarification is in order. The term was originated by Frederick Winslow Taylor (often referred to as "the father of scientific management") in 1903.

Taylor delivered a paper entitled "Shop Management" as his presidential address to the American Society of Mechanical Engineers. Taylor, in this paper, used the term scientific management and described the patterns of procedure he evolved by applying the scientific approach to his management problems. As we shall see later, some of Taylor's innovations were as far reaching as the four innovations of the so-called "industrial revolution," and have had an enormous influence on modern industrial management. However, most of the literature confuses Taylor's method of approaching problems with the solutions reached and misidentifies scientific management with the solutions rather than the methodology. How this could happen may be quite readily understood. The period from 1900 to 1920 witnessed so many far-reaching innovations in industrial management that one might properly call it the period of the "second industrial revolution." Carl Barth and Henry L. Gantt, two men who were closely associated with Taylor, introduced many techniques and procedures to make possible the general objectives outlined by Taylor. The same period witnessed the contributions of people such as Henry L. Town, H. K. Hathaway, Frank and Lillian Gilbreth, Dwight Merrick, Harrington Emerson, and Wallace Clark. There was a veritable flood of innovation, a great deal of which is still in widespread use. One can readily understand how the bulk of so much innovation at one time would cause confusion between method and results.

Even though the contribution of these pioneers was of great value, their greatest contribution really was in their approach to problems: their application of the logical or scientific method of thinking to the development of solutions as opposed to following patterns of thought based on tradition or emotion.

The scientific approach or method is simple. However, it is one of the most productive patterns ever devised for solving problems. It may be described in terms of a number of easily understood steps, as follows:

Steps of the Scientific Method

1. Statement of the objective (or criterion of success)
2. Statement of the problem
3. Analysis
4. Evaluation or critique
5. Synthesis or innovation
6. Test
7. Trial
8. Formalization
9. Application and follow-up[2]

Let us examine each of these steps, individually, so as to fully recognize the pattern.

[2] Different authors may describe this procedure in a different number of steps. There are many possible ways to break down the pattern for description; there is not necessarily any conflict.

Step 1.—Statement of the objective.   One must state what it is he is seeking to achieve or accomplish and, in so doing, define a criterion, or criteria, of success, i.e., a careful delineation of how one would know that the objective was achieved.

It should be noted that the performance of step 1 may require any one or a combination of the following: (*a*) the stating of a definite physical accomplishment which is desired; (*b*) the stating of a definite economic effect to be achieved; (*c*) the defining of the nature of the optimization of a factor or factors to be achieved; (*d*) the listing of a series of defects or undesirable aspects of a mechanism, action, structure, organization, action pattern, or social situation, which are to be remedied or eliminated; (*e*) the specifying of an understanding sought, and so forth. Further, the more substantively one states the units in which the accomplishment will be measured and the quantitative value sought, the more fully the objective will be defined. In addition, there may be certain limits to permissible action, e.g., one may wish to change productivity without altering the size of the work force. The second part of the previous statement is a limitation on the freedom of action feasible for achieving the objective. The limitations should be stated if we are to delineate the objectives fully.

The performance of the first step should not be confused with the second step; the exact meaning given to the words should be carefully noted.

Step 2.—Statement of the problem.   This step refers to the stating of the difficulties which must be overcome to achieve the objectives. With the meaning given here to the words, without objectives there can be no problems. Within the limitations of words, we are trying to separate the concept of a goal and the difficulties of reaching the goal. These are different things, and we should try to keep them separate in our mind. Of course, as will soon be seen, this step requires some insight into the situation. It consists, to some extent, in the formation of a working hypothesis, the selection of a place to start. How correct the working hypothesis is depends to some extent upon clues, hunches, and good guesses, derived from a realistic comparison with other situations which our insight indicates as containing real, pertinent elements of similarity. It must be understood that the scientific approach is not a substitute for human intellect; it is only a general guiding discipline.

Step 3.—Analysis.   One must carefully divide each problem into its components and collect facts concerning the details of these components, while at the same time recognizing the pattern of all the parts of the problem. To perform this step in an adequate manner, one must divide, or separate, all the available data, at the time of obtaining them, into carefully defined categories, so that past knowledge can be used to understand fully the significance of these facts.

This third step is of great importance because of the tremendous effect the manner in which it is performed has upon the steps which follow. Most of the great advances of science have resulted from the use of special ways of performing this step. Newton's laws of motion (physics), the definitions of trigonometry (mathematics), the periodic table of elements (chemistry), the Linnean system of nomenclature (biology), and Gilbreth's classification of human motions (motion study) each represent an important example of a successful approach to this step of analysis. One must realize, for example, that for Newton to have reached an intelligent conclusion concerning a relationship between action and reaction, each of these aspects of the problem had to be recognized, defined, and set up as a part of the problem. This is typical of this step. The parts or categories for analysis must be chosen so as to be thoroughly pertinent to the objective of the analysis as well as tending to be common to each occurrence of problems of the same general type. The parts or categories chosen should also be relatively singular in that they should be of such a nature as to reoccur as a small, unique totality. (It should be noted that our earlier discussion of the four groups of things connected with most managerial activity was a beginning of a framework for assistance in performing this step.)

Step 4.—Evaluation or critique.　　This usually involved the application to the problem of previously acquired knowledge or data concerning the parts, categories, or fractions into which the problem has been divided or analyzed. In contemplating this fourth step, one can readily see the importance of the nature of the parts, or divisions, chosen as an aid to understanding the problem. The parts or categories are the framework on which previously acquired knowledge or data is arranged, ordered, indexed, or related, so that it may be systematically employed. Difficulties encountered in the performance of step 4 may indicate some defects in the working hypothesis of step 2 and suggest the need to reperform steps 2 and 3 in some new manner.

Step 5.—Synthesis or innovation.　　(This may take one of several forms, depending upon the nature of the objectives and problems.) It may consist of the finalization of a hypothesis explaining the data observed in step 3 if we are working with data from a new situation which we are attempting to understand more fully or for which we are attempting to establish the general principles governing such situations. On the other hand, it may be the development of a plan (or alternative plans and the decision as to which one to select) for a course of action to achieve the objective formulated in step 1 and to overcome the problems indicated by our hypothesis of step 2 consistent with the data observed in step 3 and as suggested by our comparison to past knowledge in step 4. The plan or synthesis is usually devised in terms of a new arrangement of the same type of parts or categories as are used in the analysis.

Step 6.—Test. In this step we make a preliminary examination of the results of our synthesis to determine, "Does the proposed or synthesized solution meet the objective stated in step 1, and does it conform to all the limitations?" If our synthesis is in the form of a hypothesis, we will attempt to fit it to all of our data and examine the aptness of the hypothesis. If we have proposed a course of action, we may examine beforehand all of the probable consequences of following it. If it is an action of considerable importance, we may test it by discussion with other people concerned or by simulation, models, or in some cases, by using computers or other aids. Testing may assist in determining whether we correctly anticipated the problems when we performed step 2. It may indicate a need to return to that step and repeat our work in another fashion or direction.

Step 7.—Trial. This step may be either simultaneous with or separate from the preceding step, depending on the complexity of the situation, the type of problem, and the consequences of a mistake. The more complex the problem and the greater the consequences of a mistake, the more likely it is that the preceding step of test was separate and the more likely that this step of trial involves a sample run or real experiment with the actual device or action in a limited, controlled, and carefully evaluated situation, provided this is feasible. In those cases where the performance of synthesis yielded a hypothesis, because of the nature of the objectives and problems, trial will consist in attempting to apply it to additional data beyond that used for test.

In addition, in this seventh step, we will attempt to measure, more precisely than in the preceding step (but only within the limits of our requirements), whether the synthesized solution fulfills the requirements of the criteria originally formulated in the first step.

Step 8.—Formalization. In many cases, particularly with relatively minor problems, this step is barely recognizable. It may be, in such a case, the mere mental noting of the successful type of solution. As the objectives and problems increase in importance, so does the likelihood that all new data, or suggestions gleaned from the problem and its solution, will be prepared in written form. This is how our knowledge grows. To illustrate this eighth step: If an industrial process is faulty, the final remedy, when developed, will usually take the form of a new series of directives, policy statements, or a new set of drawings, as may be appropriate to the objective and the problems.

Step 9.—Application and follow-up. The solution selected or devised, after verification and formalization, will be used, and the results will be compared with those anticipated. This is after all the ultimate goal. The manager seeks not only understanding but accomplishment; accomplishment may even take precedence. However, it should be noted that we have no check on the correctness with which we have performed the steps until the final results are compared with the original intent. Without a check, one may perpetuate an error.

In order to fully understand the implications of the application of the scientific method which has been described, let us examine a simple application. Let us assume we have been driving a car. The car is stalled. This is the situation.

To perform step 1 of the scientific method, we must first determine what it is we want to do, e.g., (1) find help, (2) find a place to stay until we can get help, (3) determine what kind of help we need, or (4) attempt to repair the vehicle ourselves. Further, we must consider the limitations such as (a) the weather, (b) the possibility of soiling our clothing or hands, (c) the tools we have available, (d) our actual knowledge of cars, and (e) the amount of time we have. Before we can have a specific problem, we must have an objective. Let us say that the objective we select is "to attempt to repair the vehicle ourselves" and that this objective is compatible with our limitations. Implicit also is the criterion of success: a moving, operative car; controllable; with the absence, perhaps, of certain noises indicative of malfunctioning. So much for step 1.

Next we must identify the problem. Is the car operational but bogged down in mud? Is the traction surface satisfactory but the vehicle inoperative? Must the car be moved if we are to work on it? Sometimes we have several subproblems. The main problem-generating question is, "What are the specific difficulties we must overcome?"

To continue our simple illustration, let us assume that the road surface is fine and the car is parked at the side of the road, but, although we are using the normal procedure (turning the engine over with the starter), the engine will not start. It is obvious that the successful performance of step 2 (statement of the problem) requires some insight into the possible problems and their physical aspects.

This, we noted, is typical of step 2. In performing step 2, in the case being discussed, we would not divide the car (in our thinking) into four geographical quarters and make a hypothesis concerning each. Rather, we would assume (make a hypothesis) that the problem is in the ignition system, or the gasoline system, and so forth, using any clues connected with the situation as guides, provided we know enough about this type of situation to make such a division and have enough insight to appreciate clues. Of course, we will, in effect, use the type of units used in step 3 (analysis) to give specificity to step 2. Certainly they are related. Really complete performance of step 2 requires a knowledge of what is possible in step 3.

To continue with step 2 of our simple illustrative case, we have pre-knowledge that the starter turns the motor over so we can rule out the possibility of either a bad battery or starter. We may proceed with our analysis with the assumption that the defect is in the ignition system. When subsequently we seek the facts in a systematic fashion (analysis), we may find not only that we have a good spark but that the plugs do not appear to be fouled and that the gap is relatively correct. We must discard our hypothesis and return to step 2. Next, perhaps, we may assume that the problem is in the fuel system. Again we seek facts. We may find that we have gas in the tank but none in the carburetor. In both analyses, dividing the problem into parts appropriate to the problem, we "did" as well as "thought." We physically checked the spark; we disconnected the incoming gasoline line from the carburetor.

Let us continue. Let us assume we find gasoline available at the intake of the fuel pump but not at the carburetor.

The application of basic knowledge (step 4—evaluation or critique) should tell us that if the fuel pump is working in the correct manner, gasoline should be in both places. On the basis of this knowledge and on the facts from analysis, we would perform step 5, synthesis; we would synthesize the final hypothesis that the fuel pump is malfunctioning. But we might have a vapor lock! We may have to return to step 2 or to step 3. However, let us say the fuel pump is faulty. This may alter the importance of the limitations. We probably do not have spare parts for the fuel pump or a spare fuel pump. Hence, our objective and limitations may change. They may now become: "To locate a mechanic who has fuel pumps."

The mechanic will, if given our hypothesis, follow the remaining steps of the scientific method, although it would be a rare case indeed if he thought of it in that manner.

Likewise, the football quarterback who fades back to accomplish his assigned objective of passing but fails to find a receiver available and, consequently, elects to run with the ball, rapidly performs each step of the scientific method, recycling some of the steps as we did with our car situation but in a continuous, smooth, and rapid sequence of thought and action. In the case of both the trained mechanic and the football player, continual exposure to repetitions of a situation has reduced the response to an intuitive or automatic level, but careful study or questioning would show that the previously described scientific approach was followed with surprising exactness. The individuals, however, will usually have difficulty in verbalizing their procedure.

The foregoing examples highlight two important aspects of the scientific approach. First, there is usually a good deal of recycling of the initial steps. Second, we follow it in simple situations so regularly that we frequently forget the format or even fail to recognize it. Instead, we focus our attention on the solutions involved; the simpler the situation, the more likely this is to be so. However, when the problem increases in complexity, magnitude, or importance, we must choose between two major types of behavior: (1) reestablish our understanding of the scientific method and within this guide to successful action constrain our approach to a situation or (2) lacking an intuitive behavior pattern to follow, let our emotions guide us at random into all sorts of unconstructive efforts such as attempting to apply a solution from another problem which was not the same. The more complex the problem or the newer the problem, the greater likelihood there is of facing this choice. We must learn to recognize this choice and avoid letting the situation drive us to blind copying or emotional reactions.

Scientific management, as the term is used in this book, refers to the application of this thinking pattern, used so successfully by the "pioneers of scientific management" to develop solutions to managerial problems.

However, problems of any kind do not take place in a vacuum. Problems usually relate to observable phenomena such as people or things. Unless one has an analytical basis for understanding these components, he may have trouble defining his objectives, criteria, limitations, problems, and so forth.

Hence, the group of chapters which follows relates to the four major groups of "things" referred to earlier in this chapter. Chapters 2 to 5 contain an analytical description and classification and an introduction to the methods of dimensioning (for design and control) the physical manifestations of these four groups of items, as well as a very brief treatment of the task of creating management designs in each of these areas. This is a preliminary to a real study of management activity.

Chapter 6 deals with *time* and *money,* two primary dimensions common to objectives, criteria, limitations, and problems involving the four groups of items discussed in Chapters 2 to 5.

Chapter 7 describes the origin of and the nature of the relationships between people in the present-day industrial organization (the social mechanics holding people together in integrated groups) so as to provide an introductory framework for the subsequent chapters which deal with things done by the people who perform managerial activity.

Chapters 8 to 11 deal with means of designing individual items in each of the four categories or designing configurations of these items.

Chapter 12 returns to a more detailed examination of the concept of control.

Chapters 13 to 20 deal with the design and operation of controls on the four groups of items and integrative activities affecting all of them.

Chapter 21 returns to a more detailed examination of decision making as fundamental to managerial activity and examines it in context rather than in abstract, as in Chapter 1.

This order has been chosen so that by starting with the physically observable things and their common dimensions, proceeding to a quick description of the actual industrial society, then controls, and finally back to the scientific method, one can see the reasons for the internal controls and management activities and thus more fully understand both the necessity and the implications of the scientific method. This order is suggested as a reasonable sequence of steps eventually leading to effective acquisition of sufficient knowledge to facilitate effective participation in the managerial activity.

REFERENCE TOPICS

The life and work of
   Frederick W. Taylor
   Henry L. Town
   H. K. Hathaway
   Henry L. Gantt
   Frank and Lillian Gilbreth
   Harrington Emerson
   Wallace Clark
   Eli Whitney

Industrial America
Industrial revolution
Scientific management
National economic growth
Industrial growth
Automation

SUGGESTED THEMES

1. Changes in one or more of the following as a function of industrial growth
   a. Gross national product
   b. Number of industrial plants
   c. Industrial employment
   d. Education patterns of society
   e. Use of electricity or other forms of energy
   f. The standard of living
2. The application of the scientific method to any specific problem

SUGGESTED CASES

Cruickshank, H. M., and K. Davis, *Cases in Management*, 3d ed. Homewood, Ill.: Richard D. Irwin, Inc., 1962. Cases beginning on pages 6, 45, 59, 160.

Greenwald, D. U., *Elementary Case Problems for Industrial Engineers.* New York: The Ronald Press, 1957. Case beginning on page 3.

Terry, G. R., *Case Problems in Business and Industrial Management*, 2d ed. Dubuque, Iowa: William C. Brown Company, Publishers, 1955. Cases beginning on pages 5, 7, 14, 70, 92, 155, 156, 161.

Ziegler, R. J., *Casebook in Production Management.* New York: John Wiley & Sons, Inc., 1962. Case beginning on page 1.

2 MEN AND JOBS

In order to apply the scientific method to a problem area such as industrial management, we must first have a classification of those things which appear in typical problems; this we set up, in a gross fashion, in the preceding chapter. The purpose of this chapter is a preliminary examination of the basic characteristics of men and their jobs in order to establish a more detailed classification and accompanying terminology and thus prepare an organized structure for relating known facts and various technologies.

Men and their jobs, or *man-jobs* as we shall call the combination, are the indivisible, discrete units of an industrial organization. Man-jobs are the basic ingredient of every managerial design. The use of these units in an industrial management design is complicated because (1) a man cannot be described by a limited set of characteristics such as are applicable to the inanimate materials used in mechanical designs, (2) the characteristics of any one man change with time, (3) the manner of change is not usually fully predictable, (4) the properties of a man are affected by his job as well as by his society (including the managers of his industrial organization), and (5) all of these factors interact.

Man-jobs cannot be studied fully from only one aspect, independent of the other factors. The emphasis at times may be on one factor, but we must never lose sight of the combination of factors and the complexity. It is this complexity that has given rise to the generally accepted statement that management is both a science and an art: a science in that there are facts which may be organized into reasonably general propositions which indicate causal connections permitting reasonable certainty of prediction; an art in that frequently the complexities require us to follow skillful "hunches" to accommodate the not fully known factors, particularly when dealing with the man-job component.

Man may be viewed and described from the chemical, physical, medical, social, psychological, sociological, economic, and anthropological aspect. From some of these viewpoints the facts, in different countries, may be somewhat different. Many volumes exist in each of these fields of knowledge, but even they only partly complete the description of man from these points of view. Further, this is not a complete list. Also, to describe *a man* (a particular individual) is different from the problem of describing *man* (a general classification), and any actual organization consists of individuals. Our discussion of the vast field of man-jobs and related technologies must obviously be limited in a book of this type to only essential, basic features.

In the typical enterprise we are primarily concerned with the setting up of jobs; the selecting, training, and motivating of men; the providing of leadership for men; and the maintaining of various controls which affect man-jobs. Hence, the discussion which follows centers around these aspects and the terminology usually employed and does not attempt to furnish a complete treatise on man and his work.

The word *job* is used in this discussion to represent "an assignment of duties accepted as a condition of employment." (It should be noted that the word "accepted" may refer to a range of relationships varying from fully voluntary to economic or forceful coercion; the particular relationship in any specific example will interact with the specific characteristics of the individual to produce his response. This interaction will usually produce highly individual results, but the range of response can be reasonably predicted.)

In the typical integrated group, an assignment of duties will range from (1) a set of duties wherein both the work to be accomplished and the manner of accomplishing it are thoroughly defined and described to (2) a set of duties wherein the objective is only vaguely defined and practically nothing is said concerning how to achieve it. In some tasks, the hours of work, the use of the hours, the location of the work to be done, the exact procedure to be followed, and the amount of work to be done per unit of time are specifically stated. For other jobs most of these items may be left largely to the discretion of the man. Therefore, for ease of description and to continue our classification to the next level of detail, we should classify jobs, in respect to *duty factors,* as *repetitive, selective,* or *decisive,* with various intensities of each type as well as various combinations.

In the repetitive job, the pattern and sequence of actions may be specified in detail. If decisions are to be made, the exact basis for making them can be specified. Most industrial jobs are of this general type.

In the selective job, the objective is specified and the manner of performing is laid down in general terms, but the order and detail of work are left, for the most part, to the discretion of the job holder.

In the decisive job, only the objectives are specified and sometimes only in very general terms (if anything is specified), but the job holder must decide on the total course of action. Many managerial jobs are a combination of the last two mentioned types, although the frequency and difficulty of the required decisions may vary greatly from job to job. It should also be noted that the nature of a job may change as conditions and knowledge change; e.g., a previously decisive job, when assisted by a system for more complete fact collection and logical data reduction, may become primarily a selective job or even a repetitive job.

In general practice, jobs in industrial establishments are also classified as *direct* or *indirect;* those who hold these jobs as direct workers or indirect workers. This subclassification does not interfere with the one just given. Direct work is work expended directly on the product in a fashion such that the amount may be directly and conveniently attributed to specific units of the product. The direct worker is usually altering the form, condition, or nature of the product of the organization. The amount of accomplishment of such a worker is usually, within limits, almost a direct function of the amount of time worked.

Indirect work is work so expended that it cannot be conveniently, economically, or accurately attributed directly to specific units of product. The indirect worker is usually facilitating the work of the direct workers, attending to sales, or attending to a multiplicity of activities such as machine repair, materials handling, or any managerial activity. In managerial activity particularly, the accomplishment may have little relationship to the amount of time worked.

Hence, up to this point, we have broadly classified job characteristics into six possible categories related to duties:

1. Repetitive-direct
2. Repetitive-indirect
3. Selective-direct
4. Selective-indirect
5. Decisive-direct
6. Decisive-indirect

It should be obvious that many combinations of these are possible within any one job.

In addition to the above classifications, jobs may be further classified in a more detailed fashion in terms related to that which is required to perform the jobs, that is, *performance factors*—physical strength, manual skill, dexterity, education, cognitive skills, familiarity with techniques or technologies, experience needed, responsibilities involved, and so forth. It should be noted that to describe in a systematic, consistent fashion is a form of classification.

We can also classify a job by means of a detailed description of the motion pattern to be used for specific tasks within the job assignment, this last form of description being applicable primarily to work of a repetitive nature, either direct or indirect.

For jobs which are indirect and where the specific nature, amount, and manner of doing the work cannot be described in detail, the job may be described in terms of the relationship of the job holder and his responsibilities to other jobs in the integrated group. We may describe the source of assignments, who reviews the work, where the work goes, what authority and responsibility go with the job, and so forth.

The preceding factors related primarily to the work done and can be grouped under the heading *internal factors.*

In addition, to describe a job properly, one should also specify *external factors* such as the hours of work, the conditions and rules surrounding employment, the wages or salary, the tenure or job security, seniority privileges, and so forth. Many of these items are affected by legislation and custom since they relate the job to man and his society.

At this point it should be obvious that both man and jobs, individually, are multidimensional; the combination more so. No master classification has ever been attempted. Instead, a series of techniques and formalized procedures has been evolved to treat different aspects. In that the application of a technique or formalized procedure often requires considerable knowledge of details and of past practice, each technique or procedure has tended to become surrounded with specialized literature. This is as it should be; we build on past knowledge. However, in general books such as this one, there has been a tendency in the past to organize the book in terms of these specialisms and to lose sight of the relationship between them. In a managerial design, we seek to classify the job in order to fit it into the integrated-group activity. Its multidimensional aspect demands that we view it in different ways, depending upon which factor we are attempting to fit into the design at the time, but all factors must eventually be considered.

Let us examine some of the specialisms which have arisen from the problem of classifying jobs. In the typical organization one usually finds *job descriptions,* but they may be of various kinds. Repetitive work is usually described in terms of internal factors. Such descriptions are written to help select a man for the job whose characteristics match the requirements. Such job descriptions would be essentially the same, no matter what the structure of the society in which they exist. They relate to observable fact.

Job descriptions may also be written as a preparatory step to determining the pay for a job. Such descriptions will vary widely from country to country, depending upon social custom. The use of such descriptions to relate job factors to wages is called *job evaluation.*

A job description in terms of a motion pattern is related to a series of techniques usually called *motion study.* Here the technique is used not only on the descriptive level but also as a design technique because, within the framework of classification, a large body of knowledge has been evolved concerning efficient ways of performing work.

A job description can also be written in terms of responsibilities, authority, relationships to other jobs, and so forth. Such a job description is related to a specialism called variously by such titles as *organization, organization analysis,* or *organization planning.* In this specialism, a large number of formalized conventions have been created to assist in describing the complex facts involved and a large number of general facts have been established. This specialism concerns the problem of creating a pattern of functions and people to accomplish a specified objective, in other words, describing some aspects of the integration of the human group.

The problem of relating performance factors and the time-rate of applying them to obtain a specified amount of output has led to the development of an extensive series of measurement techniques called *work measurement.* By such means jobs are essentially classified in terms of how long a job-time is required to produce a unit of product or to perform a unit of some activity. In that time is irretrievable, i.e., is expended without possibility of recall, job-times are a very important factor in managerial designs.

In this book we cannot examine all of these subclassifications and their technologies in detail but we should examine some general facts. Let us return to the simplest classification, repetitive-direct man-jobs. Without workers on such jobs there would be few problems for managers and not much need for managers as we have defined them. Let us examine briefly the problem of selecting men for repetitive-direct jobs.

In the selection of a man for a direct repetitive job, our objective is to pick a person who has the ability to do the job. A man's *ability* to do a job is a function of his capacity, training, education, experience, and motivation, and includes both rational and emotional factors. (Note that we immediately encounter the multidimensional aspect of man.) The present state of the knowledge of man and his behavior does not permit us to describe his ability with a single value resulting from an equation with a multitude of terms expressed in a system of mathematically homogeneous variables. Even a short study of the literature of psychology and sociology will reveal the qualitative rather than the quantitative approach as still being the dominant method when considering a number of variables simultaneously. However, even if the factors affecting ability cannot be stated in precise mathematical terms, they can be intelligently discussed.

Man's *capacity* is usually defined as the limit of his ability when extended to the maximum. Capacity is an inherent condition of birth and, to some extent, environment. Man's ability is the current status of his development. His training and education are represented by those behavior patterns he acquired. In the formal sense, training usually refers to the teaching of specific responses to specific problems; education, to the teaching of ways of developing responses to achieve different objectives in different types of situations. Learning, however, is a continuous process of any living organism, and experience continuously adds to the behavior patterns of an individual. Experience is the total of all exposure to all external and internal stimuli. Of course, in the industrial situation, we are usually concerned with specific types of experience, although, to digress momentarily from our main interest, for people who are going to do selective or decisive jobs, we may delve deeply into many related experiences to determine suitability for a job. Employee selection, quite obviously, cannot really be separated from the job to be filled if one is to achieve the objective of matching the man and the job.

Motivation is a complex phenomenon. Motivation refers to those things which cause us to move or act toward a goal. Motivation may be furnished by providing a situation where it is feasible to achieve certain physical, economic, or social goals, although all the previously mentioned aspects of man may interact to determine the resultant motivation. Experience and success or the lack of it may produce varying results, depending upon the other characteristics of any specific individual. What motivates one to act may negatively motivate, or deter, another. Social habits typical of one society may operate to produce responses to a stimulus different from the responses we might obtain in another society.

One additional general characteristic of all man-jobs should be considered. When one designs some physical object consisting of a number of parts, one provides some mechanical means of keeping the parts together and some physical means for the parts to act upon each other. With a design for an integrated human-group activity, the holding together of the various parts and the acting of the parts upon one another in order to accomplish the desired goals are attained by a phenomenon called *communication*. To call this everyday occurrence a phenomenon may, at first thought, seem unreasonable but communication is one of the most complex aspects of our society.

The nature of communication is represented by the diagram of Figure 2.1. Note that the originator of the communication perceives some event or thing. He either sees or hears or feels or smells or tastes it. He compares it with past experience or knowledge to comprehend it. He then encodes it into symbols of some type such as written words or spoken sounds. These are transmitted to the receiver, although the method of transmission may take time or add noise or confusion to the message. The receiver decodes the

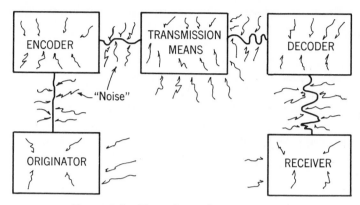

Figure 2.1   The nature of communication

symbols by comparing them with his encoding method and his past experience. The complexity of such a chain of events, the differences in experience backgrounds, the basic ambiguities of language, all make communication an extremely tenuous control, particularly when we consider the complexities of the typical integrated human-group activity in the industrial enterprise.

The problems of leadership and control, which are vital to the functioning of an integrated human-group activity, are deeply rooted in this phenomenon of communication. To define these problems briefly, we must first add an additional method of classifying jobs which is related to their place in the pattern of communications.

Managerial jobs may be divided into three main groups. We may define *top managers* as the group which determines the objectives of the organization in respect to the outside economic environment, the group which states the general policies or guidelines to follow in achieving these objectives. *Middle managers* may be described as the group which makes the detailed, time-phased action plans to achieve the objectives. *Supervisory managers* are the group which actually sees that these plans are carried out, the group which watches the actual doing of the work. In a large organization, of course, there will be in-between levels. In a small organization, one man may perform several of these functions.

But to return to leadership. *Leadership*, in the integrated human-group activity, means the providing of, by means of communications that will motivate men to act, the policies from the top managers to the middle managers, the action plans from the middle managers to the supervisory managers, and the detailed instructions from the supervisory managers to the workers. Leadership means providing, through communications, that which will cause those working to constrain their efforts into patterns favorable to the accomplishment of the desired objectives. Leadership implies the existence of a feedback system, by means of communication, describing what is happening so that the leadership may be realistic by responding to the real status.

From all of the foregoing we may see that a man-job, although it is the basic element in an integrated human-group activity, is not a simple thing. Further, those forces which hold the man-jobs together in a managerial design are of themselves of considerable complexity. The complex fashion in which all of these factors interact was superbly illustrated by a classic experiment performed at the Hawthorne Works of the Western Electric Co. in the late 1920s.[1] The experiment was originally conceived to obtain answers to the following questions:

1. Do employees actually get tired out?
2. Are rest pauses desirable?
3. Is a shorter working day desirable?
4. What is the attitude of employees toward their work and toward the Company?
5. What is the effect of changing the type of working equipment?
6. Why does production fall off in the afternoon?[2]

In this experiment, six girls (five assemblers and one materials handler) were selected from a group of one hundred girls assembling telephone relays. Previous to this, individual production records had not been kept, and the entire group of 100 was paid on the basis of the output of the group. For a period of two weeks a record of the individual production of the six selected girls was kept without their knowledge, in order to provide a base record.

The six girls were then told of the purposes of the experiment, asked to participate, and were moved into a test room, physically separated from the large group. They worked in this test room for five weeks, without any other changes in the conditions of work and with no change in the basis of computing their pay, in order to establish a base record for the new conditions.

For the next eight weeks they were paid on a new basis, a group rate based on the production of the five assemblers in the test room instead of on the previous basis of the whole group of 100. Production increased by about 4 percent.

For the next five weeks the test group was given two five-minute rest pauses, one at 10 A.M. and one at 2 P.M. Despite the decrease in working time, the daily and weekly output showed another definite rise.

For the next four weeks the group was given ten-minute rest pauses twice a day, and, again, daily and weekly output rose.

For the next four weeks the group was given six five-minute rest pauses per day, further reducing the working time. The girls expressed some dis-

---

[1] G. A. Pennock, "An Investigation of Rest Periods, Working Conditions, and Other Influences," *Personnel Journal*, vol. 8, no. 5, February, 1930.
[2] *Ibid.*

like of the constant interruption of the flow of work, and the output curves showed a small decrease.

For the next eleven weeks the group was given a fifteen-minute rest pause in the morning, with refreshments supplied by the company, and a ten-minute break in the afternoon. Despite the loss of production time, output returned to the highest level previously obtained in the experiment.

For the next seven weeks the group stopped a half-hour earlier each day. This was accompanied by a spectacular rise in both daily and weekly output. (At this point in the experiment, unforeseen circumstances necessitated replacing two of the operators.)

For the next four weeks the working day was shortened by an additional half-hour. The hourly output rose to such an extent that the daily and weekly output diminished only slightly.

For the next twelve weeks the group returned to working the full day but retained the fifteen-minute midmorning refreshment break and the ten-minute afternoon break. Daily and weekly output reached a new high.

For the next twelve weeks the half-day of work on Saturday was eliminated. Daily output increased. Weekly output fell somewhat but remained above all but two of the previous highs.

For the next twelve weeks the workers returned to all but one of the original conditions of work, viz., no rest pause, no refreshments, no shortened hours, but they were paid as a group of six. The daily and weekly outputs rose to new record highs and continued to rise throughout the entire twelve weeks.

For the next thirty-one weeks the group returned to rest pauses in the morning and afternoon, with the company supplying the morning-break beverage, and the girls their own food. The output rose again, establishing a new high.

It should be obvious to anyone that more was involved than the direct experimental changes. Mr. Pennock, in charge of the investigation, explained, "The results are mainly due to changes in the mental attitude."[3]

The investigators further stated, "The supervisor took a personal interest in each girl and her achievement; he showed pride in the record of the group. He helped the group to feel that its duty was to set its own conditions of work [oriented with the organization's objectives];[4] he helped the workers find the 'freedom' of which they so frequently spoke in the course of the experiment."[5]

Certainly this experiment demonstrated the interaction of the man-job characteristics, leadership, motivation, and communication.

Later, another test group was set up with mica splitters. One example

[3] Elton Mayo, *The Human Problems of an Industrial Civilization.* New York: The Macmillan Company, 1933, p. 70.
[4] The interpolation is mine. M. E. M.
[5] Mayo, *op. cit.,* p. 71.

from this second group is of special interest. One of the girls was bothered by stern parental control at home. Her output was extremely irregular. When she discovered, with the aid of counseling, that she had enough money to live away from home and moved into new quarters with another girl, her output showed a great improvement in quantity with no significant irregularity.[6] Note that the interactions extend to factors far removed from the direct integrated group.

In addition to the interactions just described, much could be written about people's resistance to change, even deep fear of changes which are not understood; their usual resentment of criticism; and how change and implied criticism are related. These are important factors in the industrial enterprise where constant change is a basic characteristic of an efficient plant. In situations involving change and criticism, it may be taken as axiomatic that people will frequently inject emotion rather than logic, even using emotional factors to replace facts within the framework of the scientific method described in Chapter 1. To the serious practitioner of management, this must come as no surprise. The phenomenon of resistance to change and the resentment of criticism must be considered in respect to the subject matter of later chapters which deal with constraints imposed by managers since constraint or control, as we have noted, involves comparison with plan (criticism) and adjustment (change).

Considering the subject of this chapter, it has indeed been brief. A thorough study of man would include a study of his societies and governments in all their forms and the forces that have given rise to his various religious and social customs. However, even if we thoroughly understood these items, we might know more about man, in general, but still have difficulty understanding or leading man in the specific. In the typical integrated human-group activity (and certainly in the typical industrial enterprise) it is the specific man and the specific job which concern us in our managerial design. However, our knowledge of the general and our realization of all the factors involved constitute a first step toward understanding an individual instance. Further, this becomes part of the framework for a rational organization of the additional knowledge involved in the use of man-jobs in creating a managerial design.

REFERENCE TOPICS

Industrial sociology	Job evaluation
Industrial psychology	Motion and time study
Applied anthropology	Work measurement
Job description	Organization planning
Employee recruitment	Employee training

[6] *Ibid.,* pp. 103–105.

SUGGESTED THEMES

1. Changes in hours of work since 1900
2. Changes in conditions of employment since 1900
3. Trends of wages for various occupations
4. Changing views on tenure and seniority
5. A discussion of the duties of various jobs

SUGGESTED CASES

Cruickshank, H. M., and K. Davis, *Cases in Management,* 3d ed. Homewood, Ill.: Richard D. Irwin, Inc., 1962. Cases beginning on pages 95, 100, 134, 157.

Terry, G. R., *Case Problems in Business and Industrial Management,* 2d ed. Dubuque, Iowa: William C. Brown Company, Publishers, 1955. Cases beginning on pages 36, 60, 138, 140.

3 PHYSICAL PLANT

In Chapter 1, in our definition of management, we referred to "the related physical facilities," viz., the industrial plant, and later listed, as one of the four groups of things concerned in managerial design, the item *physical plant*. The term physical plant is used to refer to the aggregate of land; buildings; production equipment; materials storage and handling equipment; maintenance equipment; clerical equipment and machinery; equipment for providing light, power, heat, and air; and the facilities which provide the amenities necessary for people to work.

This chapter, like the one preceding it, is primarily descriptive, (1) defining and classifying the various parts of the physical plant, (2) indicating a basis for evolving a structure for specific knowledge, and (3) indicating various special technologies which deal with certain reoccurring types of problems primarily related to physical plant.

Let us begin by considering the land on which the plant stands. Land, in respect to any specific plant, has both intrinsic and extrinsic value. Its *intrinsic value* is primarily its suitability as a platform to support the structure and provide adequate drainage and climate. Its intrinsic value is also related to the amount of site preparation necessary to make it suitable for the building. Natural water supply inherent in the land may be a factor in some types of industry. It should be obvious that different types of industry have different requirements for buildings and the intrinsic value of land may be different, depending upon the demands of the industry. It should be noted that civil engineering has exerted tremendous efforts to make it possible to erect structures on land of extremely low intrinsic value in order to gain extrinsic advantages. The extrinsic values usually outweigh the intrinsic values.

Extrinsic values are those created by the location of the land in respect to market, raw materials, labor supply, power, water, transportation facilities, local taxes, and other political conditions. In some cases, isolation from human habitation may be a requirement. I have classified as intrinsic those values related to the natural properties of the land itself; as extrinsic, those dependent upon man or society.

The importance of the two groups of factors and of subfactors within the two groups differs with different industries. Certain general observations may be made, although these change with time. Originally, perishable commodities were produced near their market; now preservation and shipping methods have greatly reduced the importance of this aspect. However, where the bulk of the item is large after manufacture and the value of a unit of volume is relatively low, there may still be advantages in being close to the market. Where the bulk is large prior to manufacture and the value of a unit of volume is relatively low, as, for instance, in the production of copper concentrates from copper ore, we find closeness to raw-material sources of great importance in terms of the extrinsic values of a location; hence, the copper-ore reduction plants in Utah and Nevada in the United States. Where bulk before and after manufacture is low with respect to value, we find location in terms of nearness to market and supply of little importance, as with the watch plants in Switzerland and the camera plants in Japan.

Originally, climate was an important factor but present temperature and humidity controls have made inside-plant conditions practically independent of external weather. However, in various industries such as aircraft construction, to cite only one example, the maintenance of huge weather-controlled areas can be an item of considerable expense and may merit careful consideration.

The factor of labor supply may be examined from a variety of viewpoints. In the case of a large organization, the amount of available labor may be a factor, or the question may be "Will the location be able to provide habitation for a sufficient number of people?" However, as the mobility of labor increases, we find the factor of labor supply of decreasing importance.

The cost of labor is another aspect. In general, as one might expect, the larger the percentage of final-product value represented by labor cost, the more important the cost of this labor usually becomes, although there are many exceptions. For example, where the profit margin is very small, labor costs may be important even though they represent only a small fraction of final-product value. For instance, in meat packing in the United States, even though raw-material costs represent about 90 percent of the final-product value, the profit margin has usually been so low that small differences in labor costs will shift the general location of the industry. With the growth, in most countries, of national unions, wage differentials in different sections of the country have tended to be reduced, although not eliminated. Of course, there are often considerable wage differentials between countries. The importance of these differentials is influenced by fluctuations in the rates of currency exchange, the limitations on currency convertibility, the tariff problems, the additional complexities of transportation, and so forth.

Cost of labor in dollars per hour (or in any currency) is not the only dimension of a labor supply. One must consider the available skills, the cost of maintaining these skills, the steadiness and the general reliability of the available labor, and the steadiness of its society and government.

The other factors of extrinsic value—power, water, transportation facilities, local taxes, and so forth—can also be analyzed with respect to present cost and anticipated future cost. Some of the factors can also be examined from the viewpoint of quality of present supply, future supply, and reliability, and quantity of supply or of maintenance of characteristics of supply. Of course, the various factors vary in importance, depending on the product and its manufacturing process (or the service rendered and the manner of performing the service).

It should be noted that plants are located in two general ways: (1) by relatively fortuitous growth in a location and (2) by specific choice of location based on an analysis of the intrinsic and extrinsic values of the location.

Plants have often started in a small way in a particular locality because the entrepreneur (or originator) lived there or because he was able to obtain credit there. The plant may have grown in this location even though in respect to some of the factors of the value of a location, the location was poor. Such a condition may place special demands on managers. Sometimes these demands are so overwhelming that the plant is forced to move.

A plant which is forced to move because of basic economic disadvantages of its location compared with its competitors or a large "going" concern building a new or additional plant will usually make an extensive study of all of the intrinsic and extrinsic factors of a variety of locations to determine a "best" location. It should be noted that such a study will include many factors which cannot be expressed in monetary terms; hence the problems may be of considerable complexity.

Continuing on with our description of physical plant, let us examine the category of buildings. Buildings may be divided into three major classifications: (1) where the building is an integral part of the production equipment such as is common with chemical plants and steel mills; (2) where the building is merely a general housing for the production facilities; and (3) where the building has certain special features to facilitate the production process, for example, a monitor-type building with a heavy-duty craneway down the middle or a windowless air-conditioned plant for the manufacture of transistors or piston rings.

Buildings may be classified further as single or multistory; window-wall or blind (with all sorts of in-between varieties in respect to this factor); by dimensional characteristics, such as length of span between supporting pillars, height of ceiling, or size of openings to the outside; or by internal climate controls, such as ventilation, heating, and cooling facilities. Each of these characteristics may be of great importance in respect to a particular product.

Production equipment may be classified into four major groupings, based on the function of the equipment, as follows:

1. To chemically convert; e.g., to refine oil
2. To physically alter
    a. To change shape; e.g., to forge, cast
    b. To remove selective parts; e.g., to machine metal
3. To combine; e.g., to pack meat, concentrate ores

(These classifications refer primarily to the equipment of manufacturing establishments. Other organizations, such as department stores, may have "production equipment" to display goods, and so forth, inasmuch as they render a time and place utility rather than a form utility.)

The vast technology which has arisen since the industrial revolution has given rise to an enormous variety of different types of equipment designed to work directly on the product to increase the product's functional usefulness. Production equipment, as defined, includes the jigs (devices for guiding cutting instruments), fixtures (devices for holding pieces being worked on), and tools (in the narrow sense, the actual cutting or shaping instruments), usually detachable from the mechanisms which provide the power for the action. In a later chapter we will discuss some of the effects of revolutionary changes in tools and the technology of their use.

Some idea of existing variety of production equipment may be gained from the following list of methods of metal working. This list is merely a further, material-oriented subdivision of part of the previously given category 2, "to physically alter." One must also recognize that a large variety of sizes, designs, and brands of equipment exists to perform the work of each of the methods.

To physically alter
1. To change shape
a. Metal-forming methods
     (1) Metal spinning
     (2) Brake forming
     (3) Roll forming
     (4) Section contour forming
     (5) Stamping
     (6) Deep drawing
     (7) Rotary swaging and
          hammering
     (8) Wire forming
b. Metal-working and forging methods
     (1) Die forging
     (2) Hot upsetting
     (3) Die rolling
     (4) Hot extrusion
     (5) Cold and impact extrusion
     (6) Cold drawing
     (7) Cold heading
     (8) Thread and form rolling
c. Casting methods
     (1) Sand casting
     (2) Permanent-mold casting
     (3) Centrifugal casting
     (4) Die casting
     (5) Plaster-mold casting
     (6) Investment casting

d. Molding methods
     Power metallurgy
e. Treating methods
     Heat treating
To physically alter
2. To remove selected parts
a. Metal-removal methods
     (1) Flame cutting
     (2) Contour sawing
     (3) Planing, shaping, and slotting
     (4) Automatic and shape turning
     (5) Turret lathe machining
     (6) Automatic screw machining
     (7) Swiss automatic machining
     (8) Production milling
     (9) Drilling and boring
    (10) Hobbing
    (11) Broaching
    (12) Gear shaper, generating
    (13) Abrasive belt grinding
    (14) Production grinding
    (15) Tumble barrel grinding
    (16) Honing
    (17) Lapping
    (18) Superfinishing[1]

It should be obvious that similar lists could be developed for each type of raw material used by a plant in each type of industrial activity and type of product. Suffice it to say that general familiarity with a wide variety of equipment is a necessary attribute of a manager if he is to create intelligently managerial designs involving equipment and people to operate the equipment. The knowledge of the equipment must include a knowledge of general alternatives, as well as the basic capabilities of each type of equipment.

What equipment will be used in a plant leads directly to another problem area. The specific location, in a plant, of each piece of production equipment is a matter of importance with respect to the ease and cost of supervision, the maintenance, the operation of other pieces of equipment, and the

[1] Adapted from R. W. Bolz, *Production Processes and Their Influence on Design.* Cleveland, Ohio: Penton Publishing Company, 1949, vol. 1, pp. vii–viii, vol. 2, pp. vii–viii.

bringing materials to and taking them from the equipment. It should also be noted that as the production process increases in sophistication there is frequently a marked reduction in the number of direct man-jobs and an increase in the relative number of indirect man-jobs. The location of a particular piece of machinery may greatly affect the ease and cost of the indirect work which may exceed the direct in importance or cost.

The specialism called *plant layout* deals not only with the determination of the specific location of each piece of production equipment but with the assignment of all space in the building. The layout of machines usually follows one of two basic patterns; different parts of a plant may use different patterns; occasionally there may be a mixture of the patterns in one area because of some special factor. The two basic patterns are called *process layout* and *product layout*.

In cases where the flow of product is variable, it may be more advantageous (1) from the supervisory standpoint, in order to reduce the variety of decisions and required knowledge, as well as (2) from the scheduling viewpoint, in order to simplify the task of assigning the time of the equipment to specific work, to group together like pieces of equipment or equipment which performs similar functions. This is called a process layout.

When the flow and nature of the product are well fixed, we may find the equipment arranged so as to minimize the movement of material, usually in the order of the steps performed on the product. Such an arrangement is called a product layout or line layout. In some cases, the handling from machine to machine may be built into the equipment, creating a sort of "super-machine." More recently, self-adjusting devices have been added to such assemblies to prevent automatically their producing defective work. Such an arrangement has been called "automation."

In almost all cases, materials handling or equipment designed to move the product is provided as part of what we are calling physical plant, often with a high degree of specialization, and such equipment should be considered a vital part of the modern plant. The variety of this type of equipment is exemplified even by early basic listings such as for the National Materials Handling Exhibition as follows:

1. Powered floor equipment
2. Yard and outdoor equipment
3. Containers, racks, and storage equipment
4. Packaging materials and equipment
5. Nonpowered floor equipment
6. Conveyors and conveying equipment
7. Cranes, hoists, and overhead equipment
8. Plant and communications equipment[2]

[2] "Equipment and Buyers' Guide," *Modern Materials Handling,* May, 1958, pp. 12–13.

Maintenance equipment (and the adjunct tools, etc.) or machines for repairing the production machines and facilities are usually set aside and located separately.

As the size of the plant grows and as the need increases for rapidly and accurately performing clerical services, we find the clerical equipment growing far beyond the desk-typewriter-chair concept. Drawings must be prepared and duplicated; production orders written and the information duplicated for simultaneous communication to various parts of the plant; data collected and processed for understanding by managers and for the issuance of paychecks, invoices, statements, and preparation of accounts; and so forth. Electronic data-processing equipment using magnetic tapes, punched tapes, and punched cards has become a commonplace part of physical plant.

Light, heat, power, sewerage, and auxiliary services such as compressed air, hydraulic force, and steam play a vital role in many actual production processes and are also a vital part of the physical plant. Their availability, dependability, and cost may be extrinsic values of a given location.

° The amenities—toilet, washroom, locker room, food services, parking space, light, heat, and ventilation—which permit people to work and make working conditions pleasant are also an integral part of the plant.

As will be noted from the foregoing discussion, we have two top-manager objectives in respect to location:

1. Where to locate the plant to optimize the combination of intrinsic and extrinsic values.
2. Given a location and plant, to evaluate continuously the extrinsic factors of location and adjust detailed objectives and policies to meet the new factors related to serving the overall objective of operation. (This overall objective is usually economic.)

The nature of the criterion for problems connected with the first objective was succinctly stated some considerable time ago by Alford as, "The most advantageous location for an industrial enterprise is the one where the sum of the manufacturing and distributive costs are at a minimum."[3]

However, it should be realized that some of these costs are hard to ascertain accurately, some of the factors such as labor availability and reliability are difficult if not impossible to put into cost terms, and, further, many of the factors are not constant with respect to time. Hence, even if objective 1 is achieved at any one point in time and a plant is built, objective 2 constantly remains with the managers.

Middle managers have an intimate relationship with all the parts of the plant we have been describing and classifying, because their essential duty

[3] L. P. Alford, *Principles of Industrial Management for Engineers.* New York: The Ronald Press, 1940, p. 124.

is as follows: To create a managerial design for the selection, use, and control of all the necessary aspects of the physical plant (and the working force) to meet most efficiently top managers' objectives and conform to their policies.

This middle-management design involves considering raw material, product, plant equipment, and man-jobs, as well as the layout, as changeable. The basic element of this middle-management design is usually referred to as production planning and control and consists of a systematic procedure for coordinating all elements of production. Methods and equipment to be used by labor, the time for each phase of each job, and the total time-use of man-jobs and equipment needed during each chronological period must be determined and a communications system set up to indicate how each part of the design is to act. Further, account must be kept of actual performance so as to permit corrective action as needed. We referred to these problems previously and will consider them in more detail later in this book. However, considering all the elements in physical plant, the ramifications of middle-managers' designs begin to appear.

Supervisory managers have the daily problems of seeing that all aspects of physical plant are maintained, prepared as necessary, used as planned, and properly integrated with man-jobs.

However, before discussing these managerial problems in any detail, we need to consider briefly two additional essential physical features of the industrial establishment, product and raw material.

REFERENCE TOPICS

Transportation costs and networks
Distribution of population and
   labor supply
Availability of electric power
Tax structures concerning building
   and land
Industrial buildings
Production equipment

Automation
Transfer machines
Plant layout
Materials handling
Automatic data-processing equipment
Plant amenities
Manufacturing equipment

SUGGESTED THEMES

1. Margin of profit, as a function of type of industry
2. Margin of profit, for selected industries, as a percentage of labor costs
3. Analysis of selected industrial buildings

SUGGESTED CASES

Cruickshank, H. M., and K. Davis, *Cases in Management,* 3d ed. Homewood, Ill.: Richard D. Irwin, Inc., 1962. Cases beginning on pages 49, 234.

Terry, G. R., *Case Problems in Business and Industrial Management,* 2d ed. Dubuque, Iowa: William C. Brown Company, Publishers, 1955. Cases beginning on pages 61, 69.

4 PRODUCT

The basic purpose of an industrial organization is to produce *something of value* for the society in which it exists in order to achieve some external objective. One of the most usual forms of this objective is "to make a profit." The privately owned plant in a free economy usually has little choice in this respect. The "something of value" may take many different basic forms. It may be a *physical object* such as a wrench, a *condition service* such as dry cleaning, a *place service* such as transportation, or a *time service* such as storage or warehousing. In this book we are, for convenience, centering on organizations which produce physical objects, although many features of management and managers are the same, no matter what type of value the organization produces. Further, a nonprofit organization such as a government installation in a free economy or a plant in a controlled economy usually has an assigned workload and an assigned budget, so that, in many respects, many of the managerial problems are similar to those of profit-seeking plants.

In general, with respect to product, all industrial organizations producing physical products (goods) may be divided into two groups: *producer goods* plants and *consumer goods* plants. Those items which are consumed or employed in manufacturing other goods in other factories are called producer goods. Those items consumed or used directly by society in the course of normal life are called consumer goods. Both producer goods and consumer goods may be further subdivided into three groups: *durable goods, semidurable goods,* and *nondurable goods.* For example, a machine tool and a home washing machine are both durable goods; they are both expected to last a considerable period of time. Nondurable goods are those which have their destruction inherent in their use, such as soap powders, industrial fuels, and other supplies which require continual replenishment. The category of semidurable includes the vast range in between, such as industrial lights, clothing, home radios, and so forth.

As we shall see later, there are many ways of classifying products, and each type of classification may serve a different purpose. For instance, the differentiation between producer goods and consumer goods is a vital one to top managers. Considering the job of top managers, as previously defined, the type of product produced by their plant determines which segment of the overall economy should receive their major attention in performing their functions. Marketing and sales problems are also different for the two types.

Similarly, an even simpler classification of goods as durable and nondurable has its uses. The U.S. Bureau of Labor Statistics, for some reports, classifies industries in terms of their products into durable and nondurable. A condensed listing of this type is as follows:

MANUFACTURING
Durable Goods
    Ordnance and accessories
    Lumber and wood products (except furniture)
    Furniture and fixtures
    Stone, clay, and glass products
    Primary metal industries
    Fabricated metal products (except ordnance, machinery,
       and transportation equipment)
    Machinery (except electrical)
    Electrical machinery
    Transportation equipment
    Instruments and related products
    Miscellaneous manufacturing industries
Nondurable Goods
    Food and kindred products
    Tobacco manufactures
    Textile-mill products
    Apparel and other finished textile products
    Paper and allied products
    Chemicals and allied products

Products of petroleum and coal
Rubber products
Leather and leather products[1]

Such a classification serves to indicate changes in an industrial economy when used as a reporting basis for monitoring trends. A knowledge of shifts in relative amounts of money spent in each of the categories serves top managers in making overall plans, as well as it serves governments by indicating imbalances or impending difficulties in the total economy.

Industries can also be classified by general product groups or services rendered. To give an idea of the variety possible, a shortened excerpt from a list developed by John Immer follows (note the decimal identification):

20. INDUSTRY

21. BASIC INDUSTRIES

21.1 Coal industry
    21.11 Mining and extractive
    21.12 Processing
    21.13 Storage and handling
    21.14 Retail distribution
    21.15 Power-plant operations
21.2 Other mining and extractive industries
    21.21 Iron ore
    21.22 Other ores
    21.23 Stone quarries
21.3 Primary reduction
    21.31 Iron and steel smelting and processing
    21.32 Other smelting and reduction
    21.33 Foundry and casting operations
    21.34 Oil refining and processing
    21.35 Rubber, natural and synthetic (except products)
    21.36 Chemicals
21.4 Wood products
    21.41 Logging and cutting (including timber and poles)
    21.42 Sawmill operations—lumber (all sizes and shapes)
    21.43 Plywood and wood bonding manufacture and fabrication
    21.44 Paper and pump mills
21.5 Sand and gravel plants

22. MANUFACTURED PRODUCTS

22.1 Transportation equipment
    22.11 Airplanes (including supplies, controls, and accessories)
    22.12 Automobiles (including passenger cars and trucks, tires, equipment, and accessories)

[1] U.S. Department of Labor, *BLS 59–1441 News,* Dec. 9, 1958.

22.13 Railroad equipment (including trains and locomotives)
22.14 Railway repair shops
22.15 Boat building (including lifeboats, motor boats and sail boats)
22.16 Ship building (except naval construction)
22.17 Barge construction (including tugs)
22.2 Machinery
22.21 Machine tools
22.22 Farm equipment
22.23 Hand tools and equipment
22.24 Office equipment
22.25 Special processing machinery
22.26 Material-handling equipment and supplies

In the original version from which this excerpt was taken, the list continued, with similar detail, through the following subheads and main heads:

22.3 Household appliances
22.4 Electrical products
22.5 Wood products
22.6 Nonferrous metal products
22.7 Toys
22.8 Stone, clay, and glass products (except construction materials)
22.9 Others not listed

23. FOOD AND CLOTHING GROUP

23.1 Agriculture
23.2 Food products
23.3 Dairy and poultry products
23.4 Clothing
23.5 Leather goods
23.6 Personal services
23.7 Food processing

24. BUILDING AND CONSTRUCTION

24.1 Residential construction
24.2 Other construction
24.3 Concrete and tile materials
24.4 Glass
24.5 Structural steel and steel products (building)
24.6 Other building materials

25. MILITARY (except aircraft and truck manufacturing)

25.1 Quartermaster
25.2 Ordnance
25.3 Air Corps
25.4 Navy

26. MERCHANDISING

26.1 Warehouses and distribution centers
26.2 Retail distribution

27. TRANSPORTATION

27.1 Railroads
27.2 Trucking
27.3 Ships
27.4 Air transportation
27.5 Terminals

28. PRINTING AND PUBLISHING

28.1 Lithoprinting
28.2 Newspapers
28.3 Magazine publishing
28.4 Book publishing

29. OTHER INDUSTRIES NOT CLASSIFIED

29.1 Postal service[2]

Such a classification would serve as an indexing system for books and articles on materials handling or other technological classifications and thus organize knowledge in a form related to the problems initiating its retrieval.

It should be noted that the variety of products in a modern industrial economy, when examined in detail, is enormous. For instance, the American Society of Mechanical Engineers *Mechanical Catalogue,* a very specialized annual listing, usually contains about 6,000 product listings, which become about 40,000 different items when brands are differentiated. The count of consumer items in a mail-order catalogue is monumental; even the small store or gas station displays a sizable number of different products. Of course, in many cases, variations in size and shape are capricious and detrimental to the overall economy, and *standardization* may be needed to reduce unnecessary variety.

It should be obvious that there are many useful ways of classifying products, depending upon the objectives of the classification. Inasmuch as this book deals with management, I have attempted to create or select classifications of aspects of products that affect the task of management.

For instance, aluminum and wood canoes may have similar marketing problems, but the production of aluminum canoes may be more like making cooking pots; the production of wood canoes more like making furniture. Some of the direct man-jobs in making aluminum canoes may be like air-

[2] John R. Immer, *Materials Handling.* New York: McGraw-Hill Book Company, 1953, pp. 533–536.

craft manufacturing, but many of the direct man-jobs of aircraft manufacturing will be quite different from making canoes. There are similarities and differences, and we must have a way to sort these out. It should further be noted that a classification which groups products with respect to similarity of top managers' problems may be different from a classification which groups products with respect to similarity of middle managers' or supervisory managers' problems. We may need several classifications, but each classification should help "pull" related information together so as to help build a body of general knowledge which can be used in formulating solutions to problems.

As was previously stated, the dichotomous classification of producer goods and consumer goods represents a major division that has great significance for top managers. Likewise, the degree of durability of the product and the typical cycle of replacement has a considerable effect upon top managers' decisions. It should be noted that this last-mentioned characteristic is not totally inherent in the product but is greatly affected by the attitude of the society in which the marketing is done. Further, this changes with time. An additional characteristic of product of interest to top managers is the existence of numerous peculiarities of marketing which are specific to the product or product group. Of course, such customs vary from country to country and change with time.

Middle managers and supervisory managers, who are more directly concerned with the day-to-day operation of the plant, are usually more affected by more detailed aspects of the product, such as the *continuity of manufacture*. For instance, some products are made continuously; some are made intermittently in lots or limited quantities; and some are made for unique orders, each item being different from its predecessors. The middle managers' tasks (preparation of time-phased plans for action) and supervisory managers' tasks (watching and guiding man-jobs) will be greatly affected by which of these three types of continuity of manufacturing is involved. There will be similarities between the problems and their solutions in any two plants engaged in the same type of continuity of manufacture, even if they manufacture totally different products. There will be basic differences in plants having different types of manufacture even if they make the same sort of product. These are the kinds of similarities and differences we must recognize and classify if we are to be able to discern the underlying philosophy and procedures of management without having them obscured by the innumerable small peculiarities of the huge variety of product. We must list those factors whose nature is such that when products are similar in respect to any of these factors there tend to be similarities in managerial problems, similarities in methods of finding solutions, as well as similarities in solutions.

Let us continue to examine other factors besides those we have listed thus far, such as *product homogeneity*. For instance, some products are *bulk products* in that individual lots or items are merely convenient quantities of a relatively homogeneous flow, e.g., cement, paint, gasoline, plastic resins, or wool top. Other products are *unit products* in that there is a natural unit such as a light bulb, an automobile, a radio, a lathe, a sewing machine, or a pair of pants; the flow of product is discrete rather than homogeneous.

It should be emphasized that, from the managerial point of view, much more than just the physical appearance of a product and its use are involved in the consideration of product. That which we are calling product is an object described by a *drawing* and a *specification*. The drawing gives the dimensional attributes; the specification, the other physical attributes of the product.[3] They are the net result of the product-design man-jobs in the plant.

However, these two items, drawing and specification, only define the final result of the *manufacturing process*. Thus we come to another group of characteristics of product that is of basic concern to a manager: the process or steps (equipment and activity) that are required to perform the work necessary to bring the material to the desired salable stage. The design of the manufacturing process is called *process design, production engineering,* or more properly, perhaps, should be included within the larger term *industrial engineering,* although in certain cases, the field of knowledge can sometimes more properly be more closely identified with other types of engineering or other fields of knowledge. This would be true, for example, of the design of a process for complex chemical synthesis, which is based on chemical engineering, or women's clothing, which is style-oriented.

If we think of the manufacturing process as a basis of product classification, various differentiating aspects of product begin to emerge, although many of them are not totally independent but interact with product characteristics.

For instance, some products have a relatively high *stability of design;* others are subject to continual and often radical changes. These changes may or may not radically affect the process. Certainly this aspect influences the tasks of middle and supervisory managers.

Some products have a high degree of *external technical complexity;* a great deal of knowledge of a large variety of production equipment is required to design (or select) the most economical (or even merely an effective) sequence to make the product. Also, the production equipment may be very complex. Other products may have a low degree of external technical complexity.

Some products are most effectively made in large quantities, others in small amounts; this tends, in some cases, to affect the process complexity.

---

[3] I have used the terms drawing and specification. In some cases they may take other forms or have special names.

Some products require large and complex production machines, as in making aircraft engines. Other products require simple machines but much labor, e.g., clothing.

External technical complexity can be broken down, therefore, into three subfactors:

1. The amount and variety of knowledge of production equipment required to design a process
2. The complexity of the equipment
3. The requisite size of the activity

Some products are composed of materials with a high *internal technical complexity;* much must be known about these materials and their peculiarities to design a process which reflects adequate consideration of the nature of the raw material. The newer the raw material, the more likely its internal technical complexity is high. Titanium is such a material; so is radioactive material for reactor cores. Other materials are relatively simple. It is safe to say, however, that those things we know the least about appear, therefore, as the most simple. For instance, cow leather sounds like a reasonably simple material, but The Albert Trostel Company, in Milwaukee, Wisconsin, tanners of side leather, ship to meet 14 million different possible specifications. Clerical controls, communications, and the number of managerial decisions per unit of time are all affected by the factor of internal technical complexity. A vast field of technology of process design has arisen to organize effectively and make use of the process "know-how" which has been developed by experience. This will be discussed in detail in a later chapter.

The accuracy of the product is another factor which differentiates product. However, here we must compare not only the absolute measure of the accuracy which must be obtained but also the difficulty of obtaining such accuracy with the basic material. Hence, accuracy is a subfactor of internal technical complexity. We may summarize internal technical complexity as consisting of the following subfactors:

1. Difficulty in obtaining enough knowledge of material behavior to design a process
2. Inherent variety in material and product
3. Accuracy required and its difficulty with respect to material characteristics

Further, managerial activity is affected by the *complexity of flow.* Some products are unit products with essentially a single line of flow. The leather just mentioned is of this type; the product is always a unit "side" of leather from very early in the manufacturing process. The same could be said of automobile piston rings or household china. Other products have a multiplicity of components, each of which has its own distinct line of flow. An automobile may have 15,000 or more separate parts and an airplane well over 20,000. These parts may vary greatly with respect to both internal and external technical complexity. From one point of view, the product is really many producer goods made first to achieve finally consumer goods. Management problems change with changes in the number of parts per unit of product.

Products also differ in their *ratio of bulk and weight to value*. A high-grade 16 mm motion picture camera is worth about $100 per pound. A small car, at this rate, would cost $200,000; a fine man's watch at this rate would be worth only $12.50. However, the value per final unit weight depends upon both the intrinsic value of the raw materials and the value of the man-job (and associated physical plant) time expended in making the product. These may vary independently. These subfactors affect the process-design problems, the materials-handling design problems, and the managerial control problems.

Products may vary greatly in their *scrap characteristics* such as the amount and value of scrap or waste created in making the product. For example, in meat packing, the scrap (material which will not support the cost of its own disposal) is relatively small in amount, but much supervisory management time must be spent in watching man-jobs to keep scrap from being produced. In the production of copper concentrates from ore, the tailings, or waste, create veritable mountains. Therefore, two additional dimensions of product are: (1) scrap inherent in production and (2) scrap readily possible from poor production.

Yield is still another aspect of product. Yield is the amount of primary product obtained from raw stock. For instance, in making castings, the final product may be, by weight, only 66.5 percent of the total amount of metal poured. However, the pouring part of the process may have a yield of only 70 percent, 30 percent by weight being the parts of the casting which are not intended to appear in the final product but are necessary adjuncts to successful casting. The subsequent machining steps may have a yield of 95 percent. The 30 percent loss in yield in pouring may be difficult to alter; the 5 percent loss in yield in machining may be more susceptible to change. The method of measuring yield and the resulting figures are both important to managers. Decisions must be made concerning where, when, and how to measure yield, and what actions to take on the basis of the figures. In most cases the figures must be anticipated in order to produce a desired amount of product. *Quality control* and *inspection* are terms used to describe some managerial activity related to yield and are the terms under which some of the applicable knowledge is classified.

Products may be characterized with respect to *volume change* during manufacture. Steel wool, for instance, increases something like fifty thousand times in volume during manufacture; cardboard and paper have less volume than their raw material. Location, layout of plant, materials handling, and controls are all affected by the volume change during manufacture.

Some products are either intrinsically hazardous, being toxic, or explosive, e.g., many solvents, loaded shell for ordnance, industrial explosives, acids, and so forth. Other products employ materials of various degrees of toxicity in the manufacturing process such as cyanides, detergents with dermatitis dangers, anemia-producing cleaners such as trichloroethylene, and so on. These characteristics of products or of nondurable goods employed in their manufacture affect man-jobs, plant, process, and, therefore, managerial activity.

In summary, the management of an enterprise is affected by the product characteristics. The important product characteristics are:

1. Product group: producer or consumer goods or services
2. Product durability: durable, semidurable, nondurable
3. Continuity of manufacture: continuous, lot, unique
4. Product homogeneity: bulk, natural unit
5. Design stability
6. Process stability
7. External technical complexity
   a. The amount and variety of knowledge of production equipment required to design a process
   b. The complexity of the equipment
   c. The requisite size of the activity
8. Internal technical complexity
   a. Difficulty in obtaining enough knowledge of material behavior to design a process
   b. Inherent variety in material and product
   c. Accuracy required and its difficulty with respect to material characteristics
9. Complexity of flow: single item, multiplicity of items
10. Ratio of bulk and weight to value
11. Scrap characteristics
    a. Scrap inherent in production
    b. Scrap readily possible from poor production
12. Yield
    a. Relatively inherent
    b. Because of a defect in the state of the art
13. Volume change during manufacture
14. Hazards
    a. In the product
    b. In the processing materials

At this point it should be obvious that managerial problems are related to the product and to the requirements of the product in respect to physical plant, process, and man-jobs. Effective management must take at least these aspects fully into account. Further, product must be identified, stored, shipped, and invoiced and billed, and both product peculiarities and trade customs affect plant layout, clerical procedures, man-job communications, and so forth. Even organization, the manner of integrating the group and the hierarchy of final authority, may be affected by the process-design problems created by high internal or external technical complexity being dominant over sales problems or vice versa.

It should be noted that the characteristics of any given product, in terms of the factors we have listed, may change in the course of time. It is important that we recognize this possibility. The managerial procedures, the plant, or the man-jobs created to meet one set of conditions may be inappropriate when the basic product conditions change. Hence, even for a given product, the problems of management are dynamic; they change with time and with changes in other fields of knowledge.

REFERENCE TOPICS

Product research	Engineering design
Product simplification	Department of Commerce
Style	Product catalogues
Product standardization	Classification of services

SUGGESTED THEMES

1. Classification and discussion of selected groups of products with respect to the factors affecting the management of enterprises producing such products
2. Trends in industrial production with respect to product
3. Marketing peculiarities of different countries

SUGGESTED CASES

Cruickshank, H. M., and K. Davis, *Cases in Management*, 3d ed. Homewood, Ill.: Richard D. Irwin, Inc., 1962. Cases beginning on pages 206, 233.

Terry, G. R., *Case Problems in Business and Industrial Management*, 2d ed. Dubuque, Iowa: William C. Brown Company, Publishers, 1955. Cases beginning on pages 62, 93.

5 MATERIALS

Materials, or those physical things obtained from outside of the enterprise, are the fourth group of things which enter into most management designs. Materials may be classified in many ways. For the purpose of grouping them in terms of similarity of management problems, the following four major categories are suggested:

1. *Raw materials,* the basic input to the industrial organization; substances to be altered in respect to form, shape, or condition or chemistry to produce a salable product
2. *Components,* or finished product from other organizations, having specific uses in the form obtained for adding to or with the product and becoming part of the salable product, including packaging
3. *Operating supplies,* nondurable goods whose consumption is inherent in their use but which do not become a part of the final product such as abrasives, taps, drills, oil, or office supplies
4. *Equipment and plant supplies* for the repair, maintenance, and modification of plant and equipment, such as jigs, fixtures, bearings, motors, building materials, or new machines

In order to describe any of these materials accurately, the organization must prepare adequate, intelligible, and descriptive records of the required characteristics. The description, at times, may involve any one or all of the following items, depending upon the difficulty of describing exactly what is required:

1. A *drawing:* basic features of the item which can be graphically represented and dimensioned.
2. A *specification:* a list of the attributes or performance characteristics which may be described by words, numbers, or graphs and is commonly a combination of these three methods of communication.
3. A *model or sample:* a prototype to facilitate the description which may be extremely difficult to put fully into words, such as a product label or the color and sheen to be produced on the surface of the material or object. Of course, there are color dictionaries, but it is not always possible to readily compare the colors on different types of surfaces. Likewise, the feel[1] of an object may be difficult to describe.

These are the devices for describing a material. In addition, a material must be thought of as having many varied, important dimensional characteristics, as, for instance, its price. The price of some materials fluctuates considerably over short periods of time; others are relatively stable. Some materials are relatively unique in that there are no common alternatives; other materials have many alternatives and price variations affect the desirability of the alternatives. The number of alternatives may be a function of the peculiarities of the product design. When the cost of the material is a sizable portion of the final value of the product, particularly when the profit margin is small, managerial activity is greatly influenced by the various aspects of price. Hence, it can be seen that not only does material have many dimensions but its dimensions are not necessarily independent.

Let us list some of the various important dimensions of the characteristics of material which have an influence on management activity.

1. Price
   a. Variation with quantity bought
   b. Variation with degree of conformance to specification
   c. Period of fluctuation
   d. Amount or percentage of fluctuation
2. Uniqueness
   a. Number of alternatives
   b. Difficulty of using alternatives
   c. Identifiability from similar materials
   d. Technical complexity of verification of characteristics

---

[1] With respect to cloth or leather this is called the *hand.*

3. Bulkiness
   a. Volume per unit quantity of use
   b. Volume per unit quantity of weight
   c. Difficulty of handling
4. Perishability
   a. Time it can be stored as a function of holding conditions
   b. Temperature requirements
   c. Humidity requirements
   d. Restrictions on exposure to light, sunlight, contamination, etc.
5. Protection needed
   a. In respect to the requirements of item 4
   b. Probability of pilferage
6. Inherent hazard
   a. To humans
   b. To plant
7. Valuableness
   a. Per unit weight or volume
   b. Stability of value over a period of time
   c. For other or general usage (see item 5b)
8. Rate of usage
   a. Pieces or weight, etc., per period of time
   b. Fluctuation range of rate of use
9. Continuity of usage
   a. Relative certainty of volume and fluctuation
   b. Loss of unused stock versus cost of out-of-stock
10. Availability
    a. Time needed to make replacement
    b. Predictability of cost of replacement

Most products have some alternatives with respect to their raw materials, even if it is only an alternative of some aspects of the specifications. However, most alternatives have different values with respect to at least some of the dimensional characteristics just listed. Hence, considerable coordination must exist among product-design man-jobs (whereby certain materials may be selected), process-design man-jobs (which may have to respond to alternatives), plant-operation man-jobs (which will actually handle and work the material), and the man-jobs concerned with getting materials (which will be continually confronted with changes in some of the dimensional characteristics of materials affecting their desirability). It should be obvious that, in some cases, a given material may be cheaper as a raw material but may lead to a greater total cost after processing; the reverse is also a possibility; the facts will not always be clear. Hence, with respect to materials, many communication problems exist, particularly when the variety and amount of the materials consumed by the plant are large.

Let us look at some more of the relationships among the activities of product design, process design, plant operation, and materials procurement. The nature of many of the relationships will be affected by the peculiarities of the materials with respect to the dimensional characteristics listed, so it would hardly be correct to set forth general rules concerning fixed relationships among the man-jobs related to these four activities. Certainly it is a strong possibility that the specific material to be used will be affected by and have an effect upon all of the activities mentioned. Also, overall organization plans concerning the amount of activity will be involved. Thus we have some additional reasons for classifying materials and recognizing all the different dimensions which are possible.

In general, the materials create the following tasks, which at times are acted upon jointly by one or more of the four groups. First, a specific material must be defined for each part of the product and the amount needed computed as a function of a unit of product and as a function of time. Also, alternatives must be identified. A source of supply must be located and a determination made of the reliability of the source. Some type of record must be set up so as to make this information permanently available, independent of the people who compiled it. The importance of formal records increases with increases in the variety of materials, the variety of sources, and with certain values of various other characteristics of materials.

Second, when a specific amount of material is wanted, a contractual relationship (purchase) must be entered into with the supplier, and, because there may be price fluctuation, some rather rapid communications concerning alternatives may take place within the enterprise that needs the material. The contractual relationship will concern the amount, specification, place of delivery, date of delivery, method of delivery, price, and the method and time of payment. In some cases, the complexity of the alternatives of delivery may give rise to a function of selecting the delivery method, a function called *traffic*. The contractual statement may also specify the remedies available to either party in case of a failure, in whole or in part, to meet one or more of the conditions of the contract.

Third, the receipt of materials must give rise to communications which inform related man-jobs concerning the conformance or nonconformance of the characteristics of the material and the amount of the material to specification, as well as to any other related aspects of the contractual relationships, so as to allow the payment procedure and the use of the materials to start. This and the associated activity is usually called *receiving*. It should be noted that because of the variability in various processes certain minor variations in the characteristics and amount of material may be normal to the product and well accepted by custom.

Fourth, the received materials, after inspection and acceptance, must be stored under appropriate conditions, as required by their dimensional characteristics, and accessible for issue to processing (*materials storage*).

Fifth, when an issue is made, records must be made to assist in determining when materials must be purchased again. This last function is part of an activity called *materials control* or *inventory control*.

It should be noted that the supply of materials is a complex control system replete with communications problems and subject to all the typical difficulties of such systems. Such control systems will be amplified in a later chapter.

Still another problem connected with materials is the problem of identification in storage. Two bars of steel may look alike but be of vastly different specifications, properties, uses, and value. Color coding, bin tags, piece tags, and all sorts of markings are employed to label material readily and accurately and to facilitate the task of drawing from stock to supply the specific needs of production, a function spoken of as *issuing*.

For example, the ends of pieces of steel bars may be painted with a color code as follows:[2]

COLOR CODE	SPECIFICATION
Green	SAE 1020; general forging and case hardening
Yellow	SAE 1040, 1045
Blue	SAE, auto parts
Red and blue	SAE 1040, auto parts
Black	SAE 1120, free cutting
Red	SAE 1112, accuracy stock
White	SAE 1112, Bessemer steel
Orange	Bessemer high-speed steel
Gold	SAE X1314, open hearth, Rycase
Aluminum	Ry-Ax heat-treated axle steel
Red and yellow	SAE 1095, spring steel
Red and green	Lewis iron; chains, hooks, U bolts, mine car parts
Red and white	Lewis special iron, locomotive parts, ground shaft stock, key stock
Red and purple	SAE 3135, chrome nickel, hot rolled, heat treated
Red and aluminum	Ry-Arm heat-treated armature steel
Pink and white	SAE 9255
Green and white	Inland Hi-steel structurals, hot-rolled strips, flats, sheets, plates
Green and aluminum	Nichrome M heat treated, hot-rolled alloy steel
Green and pink	SAE 2340, $3\frac{1}{2}\%$ nickel steels, hot rolled
Black and green	SAE 2315, 2320, $3\frac{1}{2}\%$ nickel steel, hot rolled
Aluminum and blue	SAE 2330, 2335, $3\frac{1}{2}\%$ nickel steels, hot rolled
Yellow and blue	SAE 2345, 2350, $3\frac{1}{2}\%$ nickel steels, hot rolled
Black and brown	SAE 1335 Cumsco ground and polished shafting; Accuracy stock
Black and yellow	SAE 3115, 3120, hot-rolled chrome nickel
Black and red	SAE 3135, 3140, X3140, hot rolled, hot annealed

[2] From the J. T. Ryerson & Son Company (steel warehousers) catalogue.

Black and pink	SAE 3150, hot-rolled chrome nickel
Black and white	SAE 4140, chrome molybdenum, heat treated; Rychrome heat-treated alloy
Black and gold	Rytense AA hot-rolled, machinery steel
Black and aluminum	Ryco heat-treated, machinery steel
White and gold	SAE X1335, cold finished, hi-carbon, hi-manganese
White and brown	SAE 3150, hot rolled, annealed
Aluminum and pink	SAE 3250, chrome nickel, hot rolled, annealed
Blue and gold	SAE 4140, chrome molybdenum, hot rolled, not annealed
Yellow and aluminum	SAE 4150, chrome molybdenum, hot rolled, annealed
Yellow and white	SAE 4615, 4620, nickel-molybdenum, hot rolled, not annealed
Yellow and pink	SAE 6145, chrome vanadium, hot rolled
Orange and purple	HTM alloy steel
Red, yellow, white	Octagon steel poker bars, hot rolled, forging quality

The list above has been quoted in full to give some idea of the magnitude of the task of material identification. As an organization grows in size, not only does the problem of materials identification increase but the physical problems of storing materials (and products) may also become enormous. In an organization as large and as complex as the U.S. Army Materiel Command, we find depots storing as many as 80,000 different kinds of items, all of which must be identified and *inventoried* (a record kept of the quantity on hand), and all inventories in all the different depots must be added together to give a continuously up-to-date overall stock condition. The problems of an organization like the Ford Motor Company are not very different. The communications problem created is only vaguely comprehensible to one who is still unfamiliar with the usual details of such procedures.

Further, as an organization grows, there may be changes in processes or additional requirements with respect to the attributes of materials. For instance, in the early days of automobile manufacture, it used to take thirty-seven days to complete the painting of a car. Use of a paint which required so much time was intolerable as production increased. A new material for painting had to be developed.

Problems of physical accessibility of materials have led to the development of all sorts of equipment (physical plant) in the form of bins, racks, stacking boxes, shelves, skids, and pallets. Problems of keeping records relating to the purchase, receipt, storage, and issue of material have led to the development of all kinds of data-processing equipment and to the development of the man-jobs of operating such equipment.

The various functions and areas of activity related to such things as purchasing, receipt, storage, or issue may be performed by one group within an organization (centralized); by many groups, each handling the material directly related to their work (decentralized); or by a combination of such procedures, depending on the material.

It should be obvious that the problems of harmoniously relating materials to product and plant needs and the maintenance of communications (including record keeping), storage, and materials handling are the major problems of materials. The objectives of obtaining materials may be different in different cases; e.g., price may be more critical than time or vice versa. It should be obvious that these major problems are sizable.

As will be seen in the next chapter, time and money, as dimensions or as criteria, play a vital role in the functions related to materials, as well as to the work connected with the three other groups of things: man-jobs, product, and physical plant, described in the preceding three chapters. Indeed, the four groups of things which have been the subject of these last four chapters all interact with each other in management designs. Understanding (recognizing and knowing) about the specific nature of embodiments of the four groups of things as they occur in a specific plant is a requisite for solving the problems encountered in achieving the objectives of an industrial enterprise.

REFERENCE TOPICS

Traffic

Receiving

Purchasing

Materials storage

Markets for materials

Materials control

Inventory control

Materials standards

Materials receiving

Data processing

Materials handling

Materials identification

Commodity markets

SUGGESTED THEMES

1. Customs of sales peculiar to specific materials
2. Variety of materials available
3. Variety of specifications of a given general type of material
4. Trends in the use of raw material
5. Per capita consumption of basic raw materials as a function of the standard of living
6. Changes in the variety of materials as a function of time
7. Price of materials as a function of quantity

No suggested cases.

6 TIME AND MONEY

The physical characteristics of the four groups of things discussed in the preceding chapters limit the number of feasible alternative methods for achieving the physical aspects of the outputs of an industrial organization. If these were the only limitations, managers would still have a multitude of possibilities of action and great freedom of choice. However, there are additional limitations. Besides the concept of feasibility, there is the aspect of desirability, i.e., how well does the activity serve the objective.

The usual means of selecting the most desirable plan of action is a comparison of the alternatives with respect to some economic criterion. Managers usually make their decisions so as to optimize monetary considerations, i.e., least cost or most profit. It should be noted that these two criteria are not the only possibilities and further that they are different from each other. The data-gathering and solution-devising procedures which are used range from the extremely simple to the very complex, depending upon the problem.

Money, however, is only an artificial value (or dimension) attached to things to provide a means for obtaining an equivalence between dissimilar objects. In managerial problems, many of the dissimilar objects or things, as we have been calling them, such as man-jobs, do not exist in a fixed, static state or physical quantity but can only be thought of in connection with the duration of their use, the duration of their availability, or the duration of their application. Hence, time almost invariably enters into the monetary calculations. Indeed, as will be shown, time is usually the independent variable or dimension about which many managerial designs are made, and money is the dependent variable used as a criterion, although in some cases it may be vice versa.

Money, of itself, does not enter into the productive process, but it is one of the dimensions of the inputs to the productive process. Figure 6.1 shows roughly where money and time, as dimensions or as dependent variables, enter into the manufacturing cycle and provides a framework for briefly listing and discussing some of the uses of these two dimensions in managerial designs.

The block on the money bar in Figure 6.1 labeled *physical plant* usually represents a long-term investment of money, although equipment (both buildings and machinery) may be rented. Whether it is more desirable to own or to rent will vary with the specific case. It should be noted, however, that the items in this category are subject to two economic forces: that (1) of depreciation and obsolescence and (2) of appreciation or increase of value as time goes by. This second characteristic seldom applies to machines

Figure 6.1   Money, time, and the manufacturing process

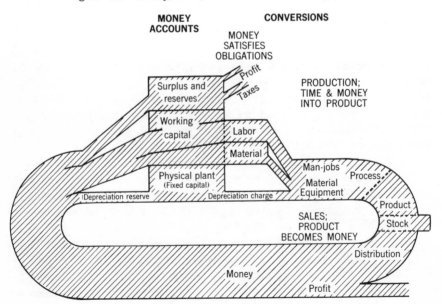

and buildings except over short spans of time, although it may well apply to land.[1]

It should be noted that physical plant is usually referred to as fixed capital inasmuch as it consists primarily of objects that will be used over a long period of time and the value represented will be maintained as a fixed or stable amount. The term *fixed* capital, or fixed assets, can be used to refer to either the objects themselves or their monetary value. Although these objects (physical plant) are not directly consumed in making a product, they are eventually either worn out, even though they are given continual care or maintenance, or made obsolete by changes in the economy, consumer demand, materials, processes, or newly available equipment. Therefore, some means must be developed for charging some fraction of their original cost and maintenance cost to the product being made, so that at the appropriate time, a sum of money equal to the objects' value is available to purchase their replacement.[2] Such a charge to the cost of a product is called a *depreciation charge,* and the money so accumulated is called *depreciation reserve.* Hence (in Figure 6.1), we have a small "stream" of physical plant shown entering the manufacturing process as the equipment is being used up, and we have part of the money obtained from sales shown as flowing back into the money bar representing physical plant.

An organization also maintains a certain amount of money for possible expansion, contingencies, and so forth; hence, the small money bar at the top of Figure 6.1 labeled *surplus and reserves.* Again note the small stream flowing out of this as dividends to stockholders (or profits to owners if there is no stock) and the small stream flowing in to replenish the reserves, *profit.*

Fixed capital and surplus and reserves are relatively stable values, usually changing only slowly over a period of time. Hence, on Figure 6.1, these have been distinctly separated from a value called *working capital,* the money used to purchase the consumed inputs which is continually expended and replaced by the sale of the product. It should be obvious that the shorter the time lag between (1) the purchase of raw materials and the purchase of labor to make these into product and (2) the sale of the product, the more often this money can be put through the productive cycle and the greater the volume of business which can be supported by a given amount of working capital. Purchase of materials on credit or *open account,* common in some industries, tends to increase the volume of business per unit of working capital, while selling on credit tends to reduce it. Working capital is, in general, *long-term capital,* in that a basic amount is needed almost continuously. However, to meet some temporary conditions, *short-term*

---

[1] And of course to certain products and raw materials, but these are not physical plant.

[2] In periods of rising prices, the discrepancy between original cost and replacement cost raises many problems connected with the objective of maintaining the fixed assets.

capital, or money borrowed for a period up to one year, may be used, although loans for longer periods are not to be regarded as unusual. Working capital can, in some ˜cases, be increased advantageously and effectively by selling *accounts receivable* (money due from customers) or by using them as collateral for bank borrowing.[3]

It should be noted that fixed capital, working capital, reserve for depreciation, as well as a number of physical factors, all come into consideration when making a decision concerning the selection of a piece of new equipment or when replacing an old piece of equipment.

The cheapest equipment, in terms of direct cost, is not always the best or most advantageous equipment when all types of money are considered. The true value of the equipment lies in such things as the net cost (depreciation charge and working capital costs) per unit of product from such equipment, the total profit on the product it can turn out, or the ability of the equipment to maintain its residual value until depreciation charges can be accumulated to restore the fixed capital in terms of money. Also, a more expensive machine may produce less scrap than a cheap machine, so that the net cost of the product may be less. Further, a more expensive machine which uses less labor or has a lower labor cost per unit, even though it takes a more expensive man-job to run it, may turn out product more cheaply than a cheap machine. Also, if the floor space is limited, a machine which increases the unit cost of a product may be the most desirable if in addition it turns out sufficiently more product so that the increase in total profit more than offsets the loss in unit profit. The problem does not hinge on a single variable; an understanding is needed of the relationships. Tax peculiarities may affect the desirability of any particular situation. Also factors such as rate of production (a time dimension), amount and quality of man-job time, depreciation charges, power and maintenance costs, availability of fixed capital, availability of working capital, and costs of short-term capital may all enter into the problem of equipment selection, as well as such indeterminate values as possibilities of obsolescence and so forth.

Let us turn our attention to raw material. (The remarks will apply equally to supplies.) As shown in Figure 6.1, in the usual plant, the entire value of material does not enter into each cycle of the manufacturing process. Although purchasing in large amounts may reduce the unit costs of the purchased material, it may also raise the amount of money needed for working capital and the costs of keeping this amount of money available may increase the total cost of operation more than the reduced costs obtained by the purchasing. In some cases it might be better to put the money into fixed equipment which might reduce the costs of operation, while in other cases,

---

[3] Of course, this discussion of capital of all kinds brings up the question "Who owns it?" This will be discussed briefly later, in Chap. 19, rather than now because the question, reflection will show, is not germane to this discussion.

too little material on hand may intermittently interfere with the continuous operation of the production process and thus raise overall costs. These are relatively simple relationships. As will be seen in a later chapter, the problem of the most economical raw material can grow quite complex when one is considering merely the alternative materials from the viewpoint of their physical dimensional characteristics. When the viewpoint of these alternative uses of money is added, the number of variables is greatly increased and the number of alternatives grows.

Raw material, as was noted in Chapter 5, has many dimensions which may influence managerial designs. In many cases, decreases in raw-material cost may interact with other dimensions in the manufacturing process. For instance, Figure 6.2 shows two alternative ways of making a part. Method A uses special specification steel strip, slit to a high degree of accuracy with rolled edges, and a simple punch-press die. Method B requires a more expensive die and an inspection operation, but the reduced cost of the commercial grade of steel strip usable with method B may more than offset both the cost of the additional step and of the additional scrap from the wider stock. Further, the steel strip used for method B may be usable for some other product, and this may lead to additional purchasing economies. On the other hand, this last factor might be in favor of method A, tending to create a reverse balancing effect. If the same material may be used for two parts, the total raw material kept on hand may be less in value, reducing the need for working capital. It should be obvious that more than one factor or dimension must be considered.

Even different time-phased action plans (process-time patterns) can have

Figure 6.2 Making the same part from raw material of two different specifications

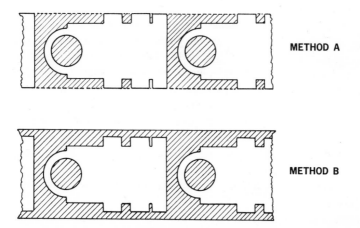

METHOD A

METHOD B

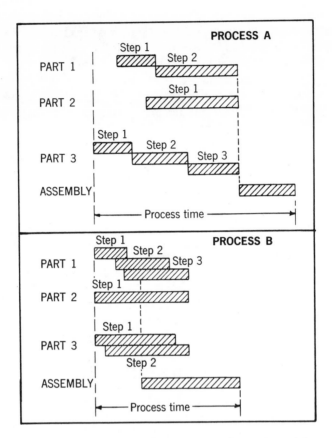

Figure 6.3 Two alternative processes, by parts and by steps, on a time scale

a variety of effects. For instance, Figure 6.3 shows in schematic fashion two simple, different, alternative action plans for a given product. Process A takes less man-job time, but process B takes less overall time for producing a batch of product. This fact, by itself, is not a sufficient basis for a decision concerning which process is most desirable, unless cost is immaterial. Questions concerning the specification of material required by each process, yield from each process, equipment required at the same time, direct unit costs of each step in each process, requirement for working capital and its availability, and rate at which product will be absorbed by the market, all must be taken into account, in most cases, in order to select the most desirable process; money, time, and the dimensions of materials, plant, product, and man-jobs all interact.

Money and time also enter into product decisions in other ways. Let us suppose we can make and sell any reasonable amount of any of six different products all of which are processed on the same set of machines, but each product requires a different amount of time per unit of product on each different machine. Let us further assume that each product has a different selling price and a different profit per unit of product. Of course, with a given amount of equipment, there is a limit on the amount of time available for production by each piece of equipment. A combination time-money problem arises when we attempt to determine how to achieve any of the following alternative objectives implicit in each of the following questions:

1. What is the most profitable mix of product to produce within the present working capital?
2. What is the most profitable type of equipment to buy if we are going to increase our capacity?
3. How much working capital is needed to handle the most profitable mix of product?
4. For a given limit of working capital, less than the amount from item 3 above and different from item 1, what is the most profitable mix we can produce and what additional profit will result?

Methods of handling the problems indicated by the above questions will be discussed in later chapters.

The category of man-jobs (as shown on Figure 6.1) is a continuous input into the manufacturing cycle and cannot be stored. Hence, the money bar, representing the man-job input, is shown as being of the exact width as the inflowing stream. Labor is different from materials in that it is bought as a function of time. The costs associated with labor are manifold. They may include:

1. Hiring costs
2. Salary or wages
3. Fringe benefit costs[4]
4. Insurance and tax costs
5. Supervisory costs
6. The cost of labor-relations activities
7. Paying costs, and other record-keeping function, including general administrative costs

Labor, once it has been expended, may be stored, in a sense, in the form of partly or fully completed product, produced well in advance of sale. Inasmuch as this increases the value of the inventory, this may create an excessive need for working capital. Also, this may produce storage and deterioration problems, depending on the dimensions of the product. There are compensatory factors, of course. If the product has a seasonal type of

---

[4] In some countries, notably Japan, the fringe benefits may exceed the direct wages and may cover housing, food, clothing, fuel, and so forth.

demand, labor, process, material, and equipment economies may be made possible by producing at a steady, or relatively steady, rate throughout the year and allowing the inventory to rise during periods of slack demand. In such a fashion, the need for fixed capital may be decreased; some of the costs which would be associated with the intermittent use of labor decreased; storage-space requirements increased (if plant building, this will be fixed capital; if rented space, working capital); working capital tied up in inventory increased; obsolescence risk with product increased; and so forth. This is the basic nature of the typical management problem: a time-phased problem involving the physical aspects of production with monetary considerations as additional criteria.

Most managerial design problems concern an order or sequence, a method, and a rate of putting the various inputs together to produce a product to achieve the objectives. The only dimension usable in producing such a design is time, i.e., a time-rate of use of each input and a time-place in the sequence for using it. Alternative designs, it is true, may be compared on a basis of money, but the actual design is a time-phased action plan.

Costs are affected not only by what equipment is used but by how long it will take to do the work; by when the equipment will be available; not only by what material is bought but when it will be bought and when it will arrive (supplies also); not only how much labor is available but how much, time-wise, will be used at each step and when it will be used. The pattern of the procurement and use of the physical things of the organization is a time problem.

We will find, as we proceed with our study of management, that time measurement is basic to managerial activity. Time and money are not things which enter directly into a managerial design but are dimensions or criteria for the layout of designs or for comparing alternative designs, whether in (1) *lead-time plans*—determining when the work on various parts of a complex item must start so as to be able to meet required completion dates, (2) *schedules*—setting forth the specific time and date when specific pieces of equipment will do specific jobs, (3) *work measurement*—appraising work in terms of time, (4) *process design*—determining how to make a product, or (5) *product-mix determination*—setting forth the production objectives in quantitative terms to achieve a given economic objective within various limitations.

REFERENCE TOPICS

Cost accounting	Equipment replacement
Balance sheet	Capital
Profit-and-loss statement	Taxes
Depreciation	Value analysis

Linear programming
Queuing
Wage policies
Union contracts
Wages

Lead-time planning
Scheduling
Work measurement
Process design

SUGGESTED THEMES

1. Economics of alternative materials for any product
2. Time and values in manufacturing situations
3. Delineation of inherent mixture problems for various situations
4. Changes in the tempo of industrial change

SUGGESTED CASES

Terry, G. R., *Case Problems in Business and Industrial Management*, 2d ed. Dubuque, Iowa: William C. Brown Company, Publishers, 1955. Cases beginning on pages 53, 57.

7 THE SOCIETY OF THE INDUSTRIAL PLANT

Up till this point, our discussion has centered around four groups of observable things or around the dimensions and variables related to these four groups. With the exception of some aspects of man-jobs, items in these four groups of things usually are easily identifiable wherever they occur. Furthermore, the characteristics of most of these things are essentially the same no matter in which plant, or for that matter which country, they occur. These things, of course, are continually changing, and changes in them affect the management problems. Also, the changes in recent years have been both extensive and rapid. If one looks through an old dictionary (even one from twenty years ago), the pictures of the machines and mechanical and electric devices are amusing. The tremendous changes that have taken place in our products, materials, equipment, and so forth are quite obvious.

However, management problems have other less tangible aspects. Implicit in the use of the words *management* or *manager* is the concept, as noted in Chapter 1, of an integrated human group. For the group to function in some purposive manner, there must be some type of authority structure, some accepted social relationship among the members of the group. At any given time, the social relationship reflects the group mores, the permissible, feasible, and acceptable forms of behavior. It also involves the value judgments of the group. It reflects the desirability the group and the individuals in it place on various things and on the various types of status to which value is attached, as well as on the symbols of status. It must be noted that most of these items vary from person to person within a social group, from place to place within a country, and from country to country, as well as changing with time. Even the meaning of words connected in any way with these aspects may be altered in different societies, and thus the differences are further obscured. For instance, the word "father" may have a meaning ranging from "an authoritative head of a household" to mere "biological male parent." The word "foreman," in different plants, may refer to widely different types of duties and a very different degree of authority, even within a limited geographical area. When one translates the word foreman into foreign languages, the similarity to that which is described by an equivalent word may become even fainter.

Even a simple word such as "employee" can have many meanings. I had considerable confusion in one foreign plant where I had counted roughly five hundred people at work. The management assured me that they had "only 250 employees." The confusion was occasioned by the local restriction on the use of the word employee to those who had life tenure at the plant; the remainder of the people engaged in productive activity were temporary workers (actually, in the language of the country, *subcontractors*) and hence were not counted as employees when I asked a question concerning their number. Also, of course, the concept of employee in different places will differ in privilege, status, and so on.

Of particular importance in working with problems in management is consideration of the type of gathering and exercising of authority (the right to make a decision and cause it to be followed) which is considered desirable, permissible, and feasible within a specific group of people. The political institutions of a country have a profound effect upon the nature of its industrial plants, although the converse is also true. The demands of an industry affect the social institutions of a plant, and this effect tends to change the nature of the external society.

The political history of man is primarily a story of changes in the pattern, hierarchy, and limits of authority. Many different patterns can be found and have worked in the sense that people have accepted them and lived successfully with them, although the words "accept" and "success" may have varying meanings. Western students of history studying the Tokugawa Shogunate in Japan (about 1500 to 1867) are always surprised and somewhat shocked to find that during the Shogunate, the people were governed by 100 laws, the last of which stated that these laws were not to be published or made known to the people. The laws were administered by the lords of each district. They alone had the authority to identify a crime and to assign a prestipulated punishment, resulting in many cases in maiming, death, and so on.[1]

No time of the courts was wasted in arguments over technicalities such as the admissibility of evidence, whether the crime was stealing or robbery, and so on. I am not trying to make a case for such a system but merely indicating that it did appear, at that time and in that society, to work. Of course, the main intent of the Shogunate was to arrest the progress and freeze the social system of Japan at the level of the 1500s. It succeeded in that, too. I have deliberately referred to this peculiar government (at least, at first glance, peculiar in Western terms) to permit its comparison later with the social structure of the American factory of the early 1900s.

The Tokugawa Shogunate is also interesting in that it represents the Oriental version of a government of people rather than of law and permissiveness; it represents a direct hierarchy of authority which, for such a long period, also characterized much of Western society. The Western concept of the king or emperor who ruled as absolute monarch was also a typical pattern dating from biblical times until relatively recent years. People and the hierarchical authority were organized in a straight vertical manner with the top man possessing ultimate authority; below him was a small group subject to his direct control but who exercised authority in his name; below them, a larger group who were under the control of the group above but who ruled a still larger group; this pattern was repeated with enough layers to control the total population of the society. Of course, the pattern of history also shows a progressive relaxation of the degree and extent of control, with expanding areas of activity in which individual actions were permissive within broader and broader boundaries; this was not a continuous change but a trend, subject to relatively short-term changes in either direction.

It would appear that changes in technology had an effect upon our patterns of authority and that changes in the size of the group likewise had effects. For instance, the change from a nomadic hunting existence to an agrarian type of civilization created a need for some additional areas of individual permissiveness; the growth of the Roman Empire produced some extensive delegation of authority; in a similar way, the introduction of industrial-type activities created the need for somewhat tightly controlled societies within looser societies, and an industrial plant must be thought of in these terms.

Technological changes place many stresses on society and even on basic customs, such as the form of language. For instance, take roman numerals. In a society in which financial transactions and mathematical computations played a minor role, this type of numeration was adequate, but imagine

---

[1] I have always wondered about but been unable to verify the possibility that the lords may have suspected the existence of still another set of laws, applicable but unknown to them and administered only by the shogun, or chief ruler.

attempting to perform complex computations with such a type of symbolic representation!

People usually are not aware of the rapid social changes taking place in their own society but much more readily perceive the material changes which either accompany or create such changes. The effect upon the industrial organizations is not really cognitively perceived, although within the past century these changes, in the American plant, have been profound. Many of the people who were instrumental in initiating these changes did not, it would seem, really understand that they were changing the very fabric of society. It should be noted that in societies where industry involves large segments of the population, as in the United States, changes made in the nature of relationships in industry may have a profound effect upon the external society; indeed, society at large may be responding primarily to changes initiated in the plant rather than vice versa. Such a viewpoint may be at slight variance with the viewpoint of the social anthropologist, to wit:

The recruitment, motivation, rewarding and punishing of individuals by other individuals comprise the basic task of organizing men into productive systems. From the work done by social scientists in the past century—from the work of such giants as Freud, Weber, Frazer, and Durkheim—we have come to know something of the nature of the forces that shape men's systems of motivation and of social relationship. We know for example, that a man's view of his world is profoundly and immutably shaped by his earliest experiences in his family. We know that the ways in which men think and feel are in large part different insofar as the society and culture in which they are reared differs. It is not necessary to detail these basic laws of human behavior; the literature of social science is their testimony.

Now factory relations are not separable from other relations. A man entering a company is not, by that fact, suddenly a different man than he was in school, or in his home. He has much the same feelings, problems, motives, intelligence and expectations in the company that he had earlier and that he has in other situations. We know too that societies differ in important ways from each other, and that the Indian in his office, school or home is in many respects different in his attitudes and beliefs than a German. A Japanese in the factory, school or home is in important ways different than an American. Not absolutely different, for we all share common experiences that enable us to communicate to some degree with each other, and often work usefully and successfully together. But the differences remain between cultures, and affect our behaviour wherever we are.

Given these facts, I am quite unable to see why anyone should be surprised to find that the relations between people in a Japanese industrial organization are in many ways different than the relations between people in an industrial organization in another society. Surely there would be agreement that Japanese and American family systems are not identical. Surely we would agree that the schools of our countries are not identical. Surely we would agree that the values held by Americans and Japanese differ in many ways. Therefore, surely in order to organize Japanese employees effectively it is not surprising that the methods of recruiting, training, paying and discharging people in Japanese industry are different in many ways from those used in industry in the United States.[2]

The differences between the viewpoint expressed in this book and the typical approach of the social anthropologist may be summed up as follows:

1. The similarities between industrial plants when they have relatively the same manufacturing technology, no matter what country they are in, outweigh the differences. If this were not so, one could not write a book on management that would have more than very limited local applicability.
2. The nature of the society in a plant may be, in many ways, different from the external society; it may lead the external society.
3. The nature of a plant may require certain patterns of authority for most effective pursuit of the objectives of the plant. Hence, if the objectives of the plant are agreeable to the mores of the external society, new patterns of authority may arise in the plant; these patterns may be surprisingly similar even in plants surrounded by different cultures.
4. Of particular interest and importance are not only the general aspects of recruitment, motivation, training, and remuneration but the details of the daily face-to-face relationships among people, the problems they are working on, and the social patterns created by such problems.
5. A man entering a plant and becoming a part of the society of the plant may, by that fact, become very different from what he was previously.

It should be recognized that, prior to the early 1900s, the American factory centered, in a small plant, around a boss; in a large plant, around a foreman. The foreman or boss ran the shop and in general made all of the decisions required, such as those related to hiring, firing, and hours of work and remuneration; but of particular importance he also made the decisions related to the technology of work, such as the manufacturing method, sequence, tooling, purchasing, scheduling, rate of output, machine settings, and tool and fixture designs. He was the center of all authority and had the right to make all decisions with only minor limitations on his freedom of action.[3] Authority was centered in the individual. Where large numbers of people were used, the hierarchy of authority (the right to make and enforce

[2] J. Abeglin (from the original English text), "The Japanese Factory Revisited," *Management* (The Japan Management Association), vol. 20, no. 10, October, 1961, pp. 43–49.
[3] It should be noted that in the early days of the factory system, particularly in the early spinning mills of England, authority over the hands was almost absolute.

decisions) made use of a small vertical organization that followed the historical patterns of control by direct authority.

In short, the foreman or boss was a powerful individual with a wide range of duties and broad authority and responsibility, but of course he was not necessarily an efficient individual. Nevertheless, we must recognize that he was assigned a set of duties to which industry (and society) were accustomed, and as a social institution, this arrangement was not normally subjected to very deep scrutiny or questioning. The rules by which he operated were usually unwritten and unknown to others except by inference from past events. The internal government of the plant closely resembled the previously described Tokugawa Shogunate.

It was this society that was shaken by the work of a man named Frederick W. Taylor, mentioned only briefly in Chapter 1 as a pioneer of modern patterns of management. However, Taylor did not seem to be really aware of the deep changes in society made by his proposals and activity. He appears to have thought of his innovations as merely logical techniques for effecting certain results of great economic value. With this in mind, many of the results of Taylor's proposals become really understandable, including the confusion about them which has carried down to the present time.

Taylor's background is also of great value in understanding his proposals. Taylor was a mechanical engineer. He was employed, at the time he began formulating his spectacular ideas, by the Midvale Steel Co., which later became a part of the Bethlehem Steel Co. One of Taylor's assignments was to reduce the cost of resurfacing the rolls used to make steel sheets and bars. These rolls are often as big as 3 to 5 feet in diameter and 6 to 12 feet long; hence the amount of metal which must be removed from such rolls, when resurfacing, is very sizable. Taylor, as a good engineer, brought a new approach to the problem. The problem, of course, had been researched before; it was well recognized as a problem, but the research had not been properly performed. Previous research had been done on separate aspects such as the turning feeds and speeds needed to give a satisfactory surface to the rolls, minimizing the consumption of power, or maximizing tool life between grinds, all of which were only partial approaches to the real problem. Taylor saw the problem from a much broader point of view. The problem was, as he saw it, How to return the rolls to the proper condition with a minimum total cost, considering all of the elements of cost such as machine time, labor time, the tie-up of capital in the rolls, the use of tools, the cost of regrinding, the use of power and so on? Taylor sought to find the most economical combination of all the factors affecting the product. However, in the course of this investigation, he and a coworker, Maunsel White, invented a new tool material called *high-speed steel* which so increased the capability of metal cutting machines that it must be thought of as a revolutionary innovation.

However, high-speed steel represented an innovation of tremendous import and tremendous potential utility only if used. Taylor appears to have recognized that his most important problem had become the problem of giving this innovation the broadest possible use to obtain the maximum potential economic benefit. Some generalization is worthwhile here to more fully understand Taylor, particularly as most previous texts have not seemed to recognize the basic problem. Taylor had an important technological innovation. He had a change in technology which, if properly used, could have important economic consequences for his plant. He was concerned with the problems of disseminating this information and of putting it into actual use. He knew only too well that an unused idea, no matter how good, produces neither utility nor profit. He was also aware of the fact that the normal course of acceptance of a new technology was extremely slow and that ideas can only be put to use through people; thus the organization of people in the plant and the arrangement of the hierarchy of authority became important in his thinking. He felt that when change is to be rapid and radical, a special form of organization is needed.

Another innovation also motivated Taylor to solve this basic problem. Prior to the formalization of the ideas created by his problem of introducing high-speed steel, Taylor also had made studies, correctly reported in almost every management text as a historical event, of the shoveling of raw materials and of the handling of pig iron in the mill. Taylor found that not only were the same size shovels being used to handle materials of radically different bulk-weight characteristics such as coke and iron ore, thus creating a basic inefficiency, but also that the method of handling the shovels varied from man to man. Further, he found that there was a particular way to use a shovel that made it possible to accomplish much more work with a given expenditure of effort. Taylor also found that varying the speed of work when working and varying the amount and occurrence of rest also had an enormous influence on the amount of output. It should be noted that Taylor's relationship with the workers while performing the necessary experimentation was, to put it mildly, highly authoritarian. Taylor was not, it would appear, sensitive to public relations and was apparently not fully aware that he was delving into more than just the mere method of work. Taylor was experimenting with a change in the form of society. His final proposals were radical and far reaching in their alteration of the authority hierarchy and regions of remaining permissiveness in the industrial plant of the 1900s.

Above all, Taylor did recognize that something would have to be done about the concept of foreman or boss. It appears as though he was aware that there were many problems similar to the problem of introducing high-speed steel and the details of the technology of using it and to the problems of changing hand tools and work methods such as shoveling. He seems to have realized that the normal method of organization current at that time was not economical in respect to the potential which could be attained by the better use of more advanced technology. Much later in the literature we find a reiteration of this exact point of view. As the late Dr. Harry Hopf wrote: "That a business cannot permanently occupy levels of effectiveness higher than those clearly determined by the capacity of its executives is self-evident, but it is not generally understood that the influence of superior organization upon the accomplishments of mediocre executives can raise the enterprise to heights not otherwise attainable."[4]

As a result, Taylor, in his presidential address to the American Society of Mechanical Engineers in New York City in 1903, enunciated a plan which he called "A Plan for Functional Foremanship." This proposal, to this very day, is probably the most misunderstood proposal in industrial management. I say "the most misunderstood proposal" because almost every text on industrial management states that Taylor's proposal was impractical and has never been used, despite the fact that his proposal forms the real foundation for the industrial organization of almost every modern industrial plant in the world today.

For instance, in a recent management text in the discussion of staff, we find a general theme found in almost all general texts on management. This theme, in my opinion, represents a gross error of understanding originated by some early author whom I have been unable to identify or by some early critic of Taylor (and he had some bitter ones) but which has been repeated parrot-like for decades. The authors say:

This tendency to explain the distinction between line and staff, in terms of managerial functions may possibly be traced to Frederick W. Taylor's attempt to separate planning from performance. It will be recalled that Taylor, in his quest for specialization of functions, enunciated a principle of functional foremanship, through which he advocated specializing the functions of foremen into eight groupings and these, in turn, into a planning and a performance level.

That this principle has never had wide application in industry and has not been regarded as workable is not surprising, for as will be noted presently, it involves the subdivision of managerial functions, the division of the indivisible.[5]

Taylor envisioned the division of the direct supervisory activity among eight people or groups whom he called *functional foremen,* although his choice of this title and the individual job titles was unfortunate because of the undesirable connotations of the terms he used. These eight activities were divided into two main groups, *planning* and *performance.* The eight people (or groups) were as follows (the terms are Taylor's):

[4] H. A. Hopf, "Organization," *Engineering Journal* (Canada), vol. 20, no. 12, December, 1937 (copyright by Dr. Harry A. Hopf).
[5] H. D. Koontz and C. J. O'Donnell, *Principles of Management,* 2d ed. New York: McGraw-Hill Book Company, 1959, p. 140. (The italics are mine, M. E. M.)

Planning   Performance
1. Instruction card clerk   5. Speed boss
2. Order of work or route clerk   6. Repair boss
3. Time and cost clerk   7. Inspector
4. Disciplinarian   8. Gang boss

In place of the previous direct line of command wherein one person always went to one specific individual for all of his orders concerning everything that had to be done, Taylor, in effect, was saying that there is no reason why one man cannot be directed in his activities by a group of individuals, provided the separation concerning what is to be referred to each individual is clear-cut and provided that such a change has advantages. Of course, one of the obvious advantages sought was the use of a specialist for every activity. Taylor was also seeking a more fluid type of organization which could react more rapidly to changes.

It was unfortunate that Taylor used the term functional foremen for the type of positions he had in mind because they were not similar to foremen with regard either to the previous usage of the word or to current usage. The confusion was compounded by calling some of the positions clerks, with all the connotations of that word. Particularly with people who were not willing to drop their old concepts of organization or with people who did not really want to understand and who therefore tended to misunderstand any proposal made, the use of the words foreman and clerk added fuel to the arguments over Taylor's proposal. Because the arguments were essentially illogical in nature during the meetings in Taylor's day, they often grew bitter and acrimonious.

Taylor was proposing to divide the concept of the foreman of the 1900s into eight different categories of people. He was not going to multiply the foremen by eight, as some have thought, but he wanted to divide the duties into eight different groups and to provide each group with different amounts of manpower, in accordance with the amount of work needed to perform that function adequately. Taylor, in effect, was dividing the authority over the working people by functions and assigning each of these functions to a different person.

Such a pattern of organization created three radical changes in the society of the plant. First, the worker received directions from eight people, each of whom exercised some type of authority over him. Thus, there was no longer the historical pattern of a single direct line of authority. Second, the eight people who exercised authority had no authoritative relationship among themselves, except that stemming from the problems of getting the work of the organization done. To function successfully, they had to regard their problems as the authority and cooperate with each other in a nonauthoritative relationship. This new pattern had to be learned because it was at considerable variance with previous social patterns. Third, under the previous type of organization, the foreman occasionally delegated certain decisions to the workers when the pressure of time, workload, and circumstances made it impossible for the foreman to make the decision. With highly skilled workers this was a reasonably frequent occurrence and probably produced decisions similar to those made by the foreman. Under the new pattern proposed by Taylor, this area of permissiveness was reduced since Taylor's plan amplified the decision making capability above the worker. A reduction of an area of permissiveness usually creates emotional stresses within the society unless substitute areas of permissiveness are created or unless the group places a higher value judgment on the results obtained by reducing the area of permissiveness as opposed to the value of exercising individuality of action. In Taylor's time, he appears never to have understood this and was saddened and puzzled by the fact that the workers who he felt would eventually benefit by sharing the results of the greater productivity seemed to hate him bitterly. (It should be noted that some of their opposition was caused by related activities which were neither a part of nor fundamental to Taylor's basic concept, but hate is seldom rational.)

Let us examine the duties Taylor had in mind for each of his eight functional specialists in order to understand better the nature of the required relationships among them. The job of the instruction card clerk was to issue, for each piece of work to be done in the shop, when the work was supposed to be done, a form stating the specifics of how the job was to be done. For example, tool angles, speeds, feeds, motions, times, and other details of "the science of work" as developed by Taylor reached the shop via an instruction card. It should be noted, in passing, that it was this area of activity to which Frank B. Gilbreth, with his more analytical study of work, brought even greater effectiveness. Also, Allan H. Mogensen, with his concept of *work simplification,* wherein the worker participated in working out the most effective methods, attempted to restore some of the area of permissive action and thereby ease the social strain.

The job of the route clerk was to issue a formal statement concerning the order in which the work was to be done, the detailed route or sequence of the operations, and the date and time of day for (each major step of) the work.

The job of the time and cost clerk was to make certain that accurate records originated in the shop concerning performance, such as the actual time taken to do the work and the actual cost, so that managers would have actual, accurate facts on which to base decisions.

The naming of the fourth job in the planning group as disciplinarian is perhaps a good example of how badly Taylor chose some of his terms. The word disciplinarian almost inevitably implies a person who applies punishment to individuals who misbehave. Taylor had in mind only an individual who brought some sort of order and thereby created more disciplined relationships with the workers, as opposed to the disorganized and capricious relationships which frequently characterized the old-style foreman. Taylor had in mind the need for bringing such discipline into the hiring, into any firing, into the salary arrangements, into the discussing and arranging of the hours and conditions of work, into all of the relationships between managers and workers. The job of the disciplinarian included not only the enforcement of the requirements of the plant but also the protection of the rights of the workers and the introduction of equity into the relationship between managers and workers.

As speed boss Taylor envisioned an individual in the shop who would set up the machines and assure the managers that the speeds, the feeds, the tools, the tool angles, and all of the other features concerning the speed of the equipment (in Taylor's original case, primarily the speed of cutting metal) were as called for on the instruction card which recorded the known technology. The speed boss had nothing whatsoever to do with the speed of people, although there was frequently such a misunderstanding.

The concept of the inspector was to avoid leaving the determination of the quality to either the worker or a nonspecialist. Taylor planned to charge the inspector with the specific responsibility of making certain that the work turned out met the required specifications, thus making the responsibility for inspection independent of the responsibility for doing the work.

The repair boss had the task of maintaining the equipment so as to relieve the direct worker of the need for doing this, simultaneously reducing the amount of skill needed by the direct worker. Taylor anticipated that a specialist could do the repair work more effectively. Also, such a plan would tighten the controls on the productive worker because he would have less opportunity to pad his report of time usage by claiming to have spent time fixing his equipment.

The gang boss would retain the residual direct supervisory responsibility for the workers and would be concerned with seeing that they received the right kind of assistance from the appropriate specialist when they needed it, although the gang boss did not have any authority over the other seven types of man-jobs. The gang boss would also assist in keeping the daily flow of work going in accordance with the instructions issued by the planning group.

As we mentioned earlier, these organizational innovations (or slight modifications of them) have become the basis for the organization of practically every modern industrial plant in the world. The functions of the instruction card clerk and the route clerk have become centered in a group usually called *production planning and control*. We have a group with such functions in almost every plant today. The concept of the time and cost clerk has led to a *cost section* or cost group, apart from direct supervision but charged with the collecting and reporting of adequate, correct cost information concerning operations. Likewise, in practically every plant in the world today, the function which Taylor felt should be separated and which he called disciplinarian has been recognized as needing separation and is assigned to an *industrial-relations director* (or chief) or *personnel manager,* although in some cases we may have separate functionaries for salaried and hourly paid employees. The function of the speed boss in many American plants has remained separate and produced a job called a *set-up man.* In a similar manner, the functions of inspection and repair have been separated; specialized people are used; and the pattern is almost exactly as suggested by Taylor. The gang boss of Taylor's proposal has emerged as the present American concept of *foreman.* In short, the American plant and most of the plants in the world have, in effect, followed Taylor's recommendations and created an organization which responds more readily to innovation and change and which tends to exercise more effective control. However, the functional separation proposed by Taylor was not completely sufficient in itself. Taylor introduced, again without really appearing to recognize it, still one more change into the social structure of the plant. The use of the functional type of man-jobs that Taylor proposed in his plan for functional foremanship required an input of innovation, system, and procedure from still other individuals that would provide the technology needed to permit the men to do such functional work and to help create and maintain a routine relationship between them, without the introduction of an authority hierarchy. Taylor himself was the originator of the new technology, systems, and routines, and appears to have deprecated the importance of his own role. Hence, in the society of the industrial plant, besides the various services rendered in the nonauthoritative pattern, we usually find still other nonauthoritative groups performing the specialized functions of developing new technology, both of work and of the control of work.

These innovations have had some interesting effects. In a system within which there is only a direct hierarchy of authority, there is a tendency when a person is faced with a problem for which he does not have a certain answer to delay taking action to avoid making a mistake. He protects his reputation by doing nothing and this is regarded usually, in such circumstances, as a lesser fault than doing the wrong thing. Indeed, in some cases, only the person under whom the problem occurs is aware of it. Such circumstances are not the most conducive to progress.

In a system where a group of people must cooperate on developing a solution to a problem by each taking his portion of it, the emphasis is on achieving a solution, even if some error is involved, inasmuch as a default in providing an answer is readily perceptible. The lesser fault is to make a mistake; the larger fault, to do nothing. Frequent mistakes indicate needs for training or more adequate personnel, but this is likely to be a far better climate for change and progress.

The nonauthoritative relationships characteristic of organizations such as we have been describing place new social demands on people. These demands are not really new in sense but new in importance because more mutual respect must be observed and employed to replace the former authority. The typical modern industrial organization may be described as one wherein the demands of problems have, to some extent, greater authoritative power than that previously exercised by individuals. We need a behavior pattern wherein, among other things, there is:

1. An ability to agree on objectives and problems
2. A willingness to assign special types of problems to special individuals or special groups who have no other functions
3. A willingness to accept the answers from specialists in a functional area who may be inferior in age, other status aspects, or total knowledge; conversely, a willingness to accept responsibility for giving answers to others who will act on them
4. A faith in people who have no direct hierarchical relationship and an ability to achieve mutual trust
5. A genuine recognition that functional assistance does not diminish status

In short, the society inside the plant is, in many ways, somewhat different from the society outside the plant. The mutual acceptance of joint responsibility and the mutual regard for the demands of problems are seldom attained perfectly. However, these are the basic concepts running through the modern plant, in contrast to the historical hierarchy of authority. It is in this context that the task of management must be viewed.

REFERENCE TOPICS

Medieval social patterns
Feudal society
Early English factories
Labor movement
F. W. Taylor's experiments
Maunsel White
High-speed steel
Tungsten carbide
Harry A. Hopf
Functional foremanship
F. B. Gilbreth
Allen H. Mogensen

Work simplification
Authority
Industrial psychology
Industrial sociology
Applied anthropology
Motivation
Organization
Responsibility
Line organization
Staff organization
Supervision

SUGGESTED THEMES

1. Social changes in industry
2. Changes in laws affecting industrial employment
3. The current role of foremen or supervisors
4. The role of specialists in modern industry
5. Social patterns of selected plants

SUGGESTED CASES

Cruickshank, H. M., and K. Davis, *Cases in Management,* 3d ed. Homewood, Ill.: Richard D. Irwin, Inc., 1962. Cases beginning on pages 112, 117, 135, 149, 266.

Terry, G. R., *Case Problems in Business and Industrial Management,* 2d ed. Dubuque, Iowa: William C. Brown Company, Publishers, 1955. Cases beginning on pages 6, 22, 35, 143, 146, 147, 148, 154.

PART 2 DESIGNING
THE COMPONENTS
OF THE
INDUSTRIAL
ENTERPRISE

8 DESIGNING MAN-JOBS

In Chapter 2, a job was defined as "an assignment of duties accepted as a condition of employment." Also, jobs were classified in several ways. From the standpoint of designing jobs, the most important classification was the separation into the categories of *repetitive, selective,* and *decisive.* In all three types, the duties must be determined or, in other words, designed, but the procedures are somewhat different for each of the three types. The general pattern of thought as set forth in Chapter 1 will, of course, remain the same. This chapter will examine the design problems related to all three types of jobs.

In order to design, or to set forth, the details of a specific pattern of action (or duties) or to select a pattern from all possible alternatives, one must have an objective. In designing a job, the usual aim or objective is to assign duties so as most economically to achieve the organization's objectives. In industrial management, "the most economical" usually refers to monetary values, but the economy may be of time, material, energy, and so forth.

Of course, there always are limitations. The employment must be equitable, socially acceptable, and legally allowable, so that a person can and will accept the job, thus creating the basic unit, a man-job. Also, as was noted in Chapter 7, these limitations may change with time. Further, there are limitations connected with the capability and availability of people; there may be limitations imposed by organizations of workers with respect to the variety of crafts or skills which may be combined in one man-job. In addition, as was noted in Chapter 6, the most economical pattern, in terms of operating costs, may exceed the organization's capability with respect to fixed capital. There may also be limitations with respect to time, and expediency may rule. Further, the organization's total objectives may be difficult to describe in economic terms. Hence, in designing a job, there is usually some compromise between the objectives and the limitations. However, a conflict between the objectives and limitations is often the source of the impetus for change in customs or for changes in technology.

It should be noted that each job in an organization cannot be considered entirely by itself; it is part of an integrated human-group activity. The achieving of maximum economy, if limited to the consideration of one isolated job, may affect other jobs in a manner such as to increase the total costs. Such a narrow minimization of costs for one job (or for one section or group) is referred to as excessive *sub-optimization*. To obtain the *most economical* pattern for the whole organization would require the optimum condition for each man-job, taking all activities and related man-jobs into account. This would be *full optimization*. The usual design seeks to achieve full optimization, but it is seldom a perfect embodiment of this concept because of both the complexity of the working group and the necessary compromises between the objectives and the limitations. The introduction of new mathematical procedures, beginning about 1940, has provided managers with many new techniques to approach more closely full optimization in many managerial problems, including job design. More will be said about these techniques later, in this and other chapters, where appropriate. Nonetheless, in a large organization, the problems of full optimization of job design can be of staggering complexity. For instance, Fiat, of Turin, Italy, has 120,000 employees, 24 plants, 29 branches in other countries, 15 assembly plants, 150 concessionaires, and 4,000 dealers. Imagine the number of possible alternatives of job design which would have to be considered to have real full optimization! With the growth of computer capability, such a task may be possible but the economics may still be questionable.

An examination of any single man-job will bring the problem of full optimization into focus. In this examination the word *task* will be used to denote a separable step of work in the series of activities involved in producing a product or processing a fact. There are many ways of dividing the sequence of making a product into tasks. A man-job may contain one or more tasks; if more than one, they may be from the same or from different products. What constitutes a task and hence what is included in a man-job design is affected by equipment, product, and raw material. Full optimization requires a consideration of all of the alternatives within each of these categories, as well as the alternatives created by the interactions between all of the factors. It should be obvious in most cases but particularly in the start-up of man-jobs that much less than full optimization is all that can usually be achieved.

Let us begin our examination by listing the specific problems encountered in designing a man-job. An analysis will show that to define a set of duties and to state the conditions of employment for any of the three types of man-jobs originally listed, we need detailed statements concerning (1) the relationships between the work to be done and the total process, (2) the relationships between the man-job and other man-jobs to define the authority hierarchy, and (3) the dimensions of the job with respect to time, money, and the demands upon the worker, so as to permit costs and equity to be examined. Therefore, we must provide an answer to questions such as the following:

A. With respect to total process
   1. What is to be done?
   2. With what equipment will the work be done?
   3. How will the work be done?
   4. Where will the work be done?
B. In respect to other man-jobs
   5. From whom will the work for this job come?
   6. To whom will the work from this job go?
   7. Who will inspect, evaluate, or approve of the work done, and how will this be expressed?
C. In respect to the dimensions of the man-job
   8. When will the work be done?
   9. What will be the conditions under which the work will be done?
  10. What will the work require of the worker?
  11. How long will it take to do a unit of work?
  12. What will be the pay for the job?
  13. What will be the unit cost of doing the work?
  14. For how long a period will the job probably exist?

It should be realized that the answers to all of these questions will be formulated neither at one time nor, in the usual organization, by one person. The responsibility for providing each answer is usually assigned to a different person, depending on how much of such activity occurs, each person having responsibility for a different functional part of the problem of designing the job. The concept of Taylor, the separation of responsibility by function, is usually an operating reality, as was indicated in Chapter 7. In some cases, because of the nature of the functional division, several people may participate in finding an answer to any one question. Coordination of all of these people, keeping the objectives and limitations of job design in mind, may become a sizable problem in itself.

As the list of fourteen questions is examined in somewhat more detail, there will be suggestions concerning the sort of person who would normally supply the answer to each question, as well as suggestions concerning the sort of technique or field of knowledge which would be employed. These suggestions will be predicated upon the normal bases of functional separation which constitute the usual premises upon which various managerial jobs are themselves designed.

It seems appropriate to begin the discussion with an examination of the repetitive job; the discussion of the selective and decisive job will follow later in this chapter.

One should bear in mind that repetitive jobs can exist even with non-repetitive production. A variety of products made in lots or even for custom order may all have a similar or identical step on all or some of their components or a repetitive step in some support activity. Also, it is worth noting, the design of both product and process precedes the design of man-jobs, but the actual design of the production process is usually based on a knowledge of man-job feasibility. Hence, in this early section of this book, it seems appropriate to organize an effective understanding of the nature of man-jobs and of the manner of designing man-jobs before scrutinizing the problems connected with product and process. Also, processes are more alterable than people. When limitations of process and limitations of people confront each other, the process must give. Process design will be discussed in Chapter 10.

Let us take, as our first example of a repetitive task, the first task connected with the production of steel cylinder liners. These are to be tubular steel sections about 8 inches long, 6 inches in diameter, and with a wall thickness of about ⅛ inch.

It should be obvious that there can be many ways to make such a product. The process chosen will be a function of the quantity to be produced per period of time, the total quantity, the quality requirements, and so forth. Let us assume the quantity is considerable, the duration of production is anticipated as several years, and the raw material is to be tube stock. Let us assume that the first task is to cut the stock size of tube to the correct lengths. Hence, our job-design problem is "to provide an answer to the fourteen questions with respect to the task of cutting pieces to length from the tube stock."

(Of course, our job design could start with the ore-mining process, but even if we did this, we would eventually come to the section of the process selected for discussion here. It is worth noting that, in most actual cases, the starting point is usually fairly well defined by the usual variety of work considered economical within any given establishment.)

To design properly the job of cutting the steel tubes to length, we would first have to decide whether the tube stock will be sawed, milled, cut off in a lathe, cut off on an abrasive cut-off machine, or flame-cut. The job design would be, therefore, related to the equipment chosen. It would be related, because of the need for this choice, to the available equipment on hand in the plant, as well as purchasable equipment, and hence to the total money economics of the production problem unless, because of some unusual characteristic of the situation, some other criterion was to take precedence.

We would also have to consider the total process and the characteristics of the raw material to determine any limitations affecting the choice of the most desirable machine. For instance, the accuracy of length needed for the next production step would affect the method of performing the first step. Also, with some steels, flame cutting produces an undesirable hardening from the viewpoint of subsequent steps. Thus, we can see that there would be interactions between the design of the product and the specifications of the raw material and the process. In the background, there is always the possibility of purchasing more cheaply in the proper, short-length form, as compared with the cost of cutting from stock in the plant.

In short, the job of cutting the steel tube is related to the other three physical aspects of management problems, and we must have knowledge in all four areas, as well as full quantitative information concerning the product and its possible processes and economic data concerning all alternatives, if we are to approach full optimization or even reasonable sub-optimization.

Our discussion will return to the steel tubes, but in order to present a broader picture of the nature of all of the factors which may enter into the job-design problem, let us look at an additional example. Let us assume that the repetitive job being designed is the task of wrapping simple household aluminum measuring cups in crepe paper for bulk shipment. This job is far simpler than the task of cutting steel sleeves and may be treated somewhat more independently of the previous jobs in the process. One should note that the task of cutting the steel tubes physically modifies the actual final product; wrapping the cups does not. In general, jobs which modify the actual product are more closely integrated with the other three physical aspects of management; this integration tends to increase with increases in the internal or external technical complexity of the product.

To delineate more fully some of the problems connected with the design of a job, let us discuss, one by one, the fourteen questions previously listed, referring to the two jobs given as examples when necessary.

The first question was **What is to be done**. With the task of wrapping the cups, the wrapping is not an integral part of the product. The wrapping serves only the purpose of delivering the cup from the factory to either the point of sale or a repackager in a form sufficiently attractive to aid sales. The type of wrapping will depend upon the type and size of the outer container in which the cups will be packed and the manner in which this outer container will be handled. Hence, the details of what is to be done will be supplied by the person (or persons) who have the functional responsibility for the selection of the delivery container and for sales. They may request actions such as: "The cups are to be wrapped in a protective crepe paper (detailed specification), with the paper thoroughly wrapped around and tucked into the cup. The individual cups will be jumble-packed into a corrugated container (detailed size of box and strength of corrugated board), (quantity) to a box. The boxes will be imprinted (details) and sealed (manner of sealing detailed)."

From such information, we can deduce the work of the cup-wrapper. The job may require the job holder, or operator, to wrap cups in individual sheets of crepe paper, jumble-pack them in the correct quantity in a standard-size box, and seal these boxes. The word *may* is important. The work on the cups may be divided among several workers, one wrapping, one packing, one sealing, and so forth. Conversely, one worker may do more than wrap and pack cups. The job may include the work of getting the cups from the previous work station; the job may include the work of getting, from storage, the boxes in which to pack the cups; and the job may include the storing of the finished, packed boxes.

The work assigned to a worker can be one or more steps in the total production process, although the process will be designed in accord with a concept of the probable contents of individual man-jobs. However, it must be recognized that when we finally convert from a process step which has been described in a product-oriented fashion to a man-job which describes what an individual is to do, we must decide whether the man-job will be devoted to the one process step, to part of the process step, or to several process steps from this one process or from several processes. For instance, if the production of cups is large and the work continuous, the wrapper might wrap only cups. If the work of making cups is intermittent or if the volume is low, the worker may wrap a variety of products at different times. In general, the greater the volume of a given activity, the greater is the tendency to reduce the scope of each job. It should be apparent that reduction of scope can, if care is not exercised, be carried beyond the point of diminishing return; also, the potential for various psychological problems may exist. Job enlargement or an increase in the variety of work or in the depth of responsibility may, at times, more fully serve the concept of full optimization. This is certainly not a simple problem; it represents an area in which knowledge in the field of industrial psychology can be helpful.

Let us now consider the task of making steel sleeves. The work concerns a functional requirement of the product. The final process objective, the final characteristics of the sleeve and its dimensions, are given by the person (or persons) responsible for product design. Inasmuch as the product is to be sold, the sales group may have participated in some cooperative manner, particularly with respect to performance characteristics, but the design group would do the actual design work. The subsequent activity, the creation of a process to make the product, would be a function of the person (or persons) responsible for the process design, a task depending on different areas of knowledge and technology.

The process, as we have noted, may be broken down into steps in many different ways. In this example, let us assume that the first step, isolated from the remainder of the process, is as follows: "The pieces are to be cut from 16-foot long, stock-size tubes of (given) diameter, (specification) steel, to a length (dimension plus tolerance) reasonably free of burrs on at least one end, without heating the stock over (degree temperature), with the ends perpendicular to the axis of the stock (tolerances), and without distortion of the stock either about the longitudinal axis or in circularity exceeding (tolerances)."

As with the cups, we have the auxiliary problems of whether only one size of tube will be handled by the worker, the place from which he will take his actual work, where and how he will put the finished parts, and so on. The details of such problems will be considered under other questions, but the need for eventually determining an answer should be obvious at this point.

It is worth calling attention to the fact that our discussion, up to this point, is following the outline of the scientific method, as detailed in Chapter 1. The process requirements give the objective, viz., what is to be done,[1] but the conversion to man-jobs begins to delineate the limitations and problems. As we proceed through the rest of the fourteen questions we will steadily progress to the point where we have a full description of a man-job in sufficient detail to permit a person actually to do the job. We have then reached the end of the step previously described as innovation. We are then ready to proceed through test, trial, and so forth. Of course, the more similar a man-job design is to previous man-job designs, the more likely it is that the steps of test and trial will be so vestigial that it may appear as though we are moving directly to standardization, but we are following the scientific method. Recognition of this fact will assist in achieving a solution of the problem in a logical, orderly and efficient manner.

Let us proceed to the second question from the list, **With what equipment will the work be done.** Consider the job of wrapping the cups. Most of those who are familiar with such work will tend to identify this as an operation which, at the present time, is usually most economically performed by hand,

---

[1] This is a secondary or substantive objective, not to be confused with the main objective of the enterprise.

at a bench: a general-purpose bench if the quantity is low and a special bench if the quantity is sufficient to call for constant activity over a period of time. Of course, with changes in labor-hour costs, this situation may change. Insight, developed through familiarity with similar situations, plays a vital role in developing almost all such solutions. However, upon occasion, the real problem may be to rise above blinding familiarity and develop newer, more effective methods. There may also be a need to readjust one's sights to changes in the economic or social climate.

The operator, in the case of wrapping cups, will need a supply of cups, crepe paper, packing boxes, box sealing or closing materials and tools, and storage room for all of the materials used and for the packed cups waiting to be moved, depending on the decisions reached in reference to the first question concerning how many process steps will be done by this man-job.

As was mentioned earlier, the design of the packing bench would be affected by the volume and duration of production. The details of the work-place design may be decided upon by default, in that there may be a tendency to use existing benches; it may be decided upon by the supervisory manager of the area of the plant in which the job will be done, or, more commonly, this phase of the responsibility may be undertaken by a staff, or assisting group. Such a staff group may be referred to as a *methods group*. This methods function is usually contained within the complex of functions assigned to a group called an *industrial engineering group*. Wherever the function is, to perform the necessary economic analyses, there must be some cooperation from a *cost group*. In all cases, there must also be some recognition of the need for the input of methods information into the organization. Even if there is some routine staff service resembling Taylor's instruction card clerk, there must be some source for the information which such a person would distribute. (This was discussed in Chapter 7.) Also, as we shall see when we examine the next question, there is much interaction between questions 2 and 3.

With a job whose technical complexity is greater than work such as wrapping cups, the first step in answering question 2 is the determination of what equipment, if any, is already on hand that can do the work to the correct accuracy, in the correct volume, and at a tolerable cost. We may have general-purpose lathes, milling machines, saws, or special-purpose lathe-type cut-off machines already in the shop if the plant has previously been engaged in the making of any product similar to the steel sleeves under discussion. In such a case, there may be a considerable amount of past data, concerning labor costs, operation times, machine-hour costs, and so forth, available within a time and cost group, to use as a basis for computing the most economical equipment for the anticipated volume and rate of production. However, there may also be competing requirements for the use of the various types of machines; within a given capital structure, it may be desirable, in the interest of an approach to full optimization, to use some machines other than those which appear to be the most economical when viewed only from the viewpoint of sub-optimization of the economy of production of the sleeves.

In the case where a product like the sleeves is totally new to the plant, the process-design group will have to draw on their background knowledge rather than on the plant's experience in order to select suitable equipment. They would be aided in this activity by the purchasing group, who would make contact with manufacturers of potentially suitable machines. In either case, some specific machine will be selected to perform the activity.

It is worth noting that the separate functions such as process design, methods design, time and cost estimating, and purchasing, which have been mentioned, do not necessarily imply separate people. It is only when there is sufficient work in a particular function, or when the demands for knowledge exceed the capability of a single person, that we begin to find separate functional specialists.

The third question was **How will the work be done.** With both of the tasks we are discussing, the answer to this question requires the formulation and specification of the details of the repetitive cycle of the job. The repetitive cycle of the job is the series of physical acts which are repeated in a given sequence. If several process steps from different processes are combined intermittently in one man-job, each of these steps must have its own design. The technology of determining the most economical pattern for such a cycle is extensive and is part of a field of knowledge called *motion study*.

Motion study . . . is that branch of knowledge dealing with the scientific determination of preferable work methods . . . a procedure for scientific analysis of work methods considering (a) raw material, (b) the design of the product, (c) the process or order of work, (d) the tools, work-place and equipment for each individual step in the process, and (e) the hand and body motions used in each step, in order to determine (or design) a preferable work method. The criterion of preference is usually economy of money, but ease or economy of human effort, economy of time or economy of material—as well as other criteria . . . frequently may take precedence.[2]

The designing of the repetitive cycle may be left to the worker, who may be provided with the basic equipment for the task. Such a procedure seldom leads to really efficient ways of doing work. In other cases, the details may be designed by the supervisory manager who is responsible for seeing that the work is carried out, or he may be assisted by the methods or industrial

[2] M. E. Mundel, *Motion and Time Study,* 3d ed. Englewood Cliffs, N.J.: Prentice-Hall, Inc., 1960, p. 1.

engineering group referred to under the discussion of question 2. This latter arrangement is the one most commonly found in efficient plants today (other than small plants), although one frequently finds the supervisor initiating the method and the staff group improving and finalizing it. As was noted in Chapter 7, the use of a staff group reduces the area of permissive action of both the worker and his routine supervisor. The gain of better methods, higher productivity, and the accompanying benefits must be balanced against this loss. Cooperative understanding by all concerned is a fundamental requirement. It should also be noted that as technology advances more rapidly the need for understanding also increases.

Whoever designs the repetitive cycle, with the usual organization's objectives, the goal is to design a work method so as to most economically (money-wise) do the work such as packing the cup or cutting the sleeve. This usually implies employing the optimum combination of labor and equipment and further implies the design of a workplace compatible with this method; hence, the earlier reference to the interaction between questions 2 and 3.

The main body of knowledge in motion study consists of procedures for each of the steps in the scientific method as applied to the design of work methods. Among these procedures are many designed to assist in the ". . . analysis of the work method into subdivisions or steps, pertinent to the job, appropriate to its scope, possessing known characteristics, or concerning whose performance information is already available."[3] As indicated in Chapter 1, such analysis techniques play a vital role in the scientific method.

The various analysis techniques which are used to assist in designing the job vary in respect to the size of the steps into which they break jobs. The steps range in scope from single motions to gross groups of motions. The job designer must select an appropriate degree of detail to work with, considering both the nature of the task to be studied or designed and the economical use of his own time.[4]

The job designer will also bear in mind the dimensions of the human body and the related principles of effective work. If the job is important, he may even check a layout of the job with a scale model of a worker (as shown in Figure 8.1).

In one plant producing photographic film where many operators performed the same task, the chief industrial engineer estimated that each 0.001 minute of the repetitive work cycle cost the company $8,000 per year. In such a case, the job design would cover minute details.

In designing machining tasks where the feed and speed of the machine

---

[3] *Ibid.,* p. 27.
[4] This discussion centers on the design of the details of a job. As we will see in Chap. 13 when we look at industrial activities from a broader point of view, we may have recourse to techniques which use much grosser steps.

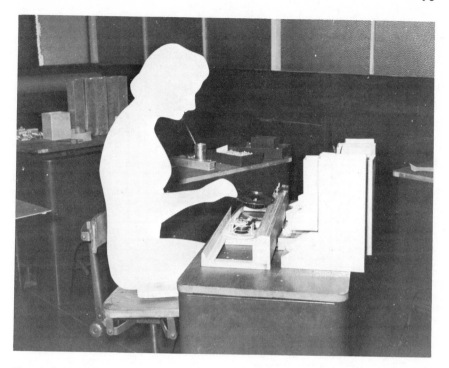

Figure 8.1 Checking dimensions on a mock-up of a workplace, Lucas Ltd., Great Britain. (From M. E. Mundel, *Motion and Time Study: Principles and Practice*, 3d ed. Englewood Cliffs, N.J.: Prentice-Hall, Inc., 1960, p. 213)

and the exact shape of the tools play an important role, the method designer's knowledge must either encompass this field or other specialists such as *tool designers* must appear. The importance of using this type of technology and having a formal means of seeing that it is put to use was one of the fundamental goals of Taylor's proposals (as described in Chapter 7).

The final result of the job designer's efforts will be an instruction sheet (including a workplace layout), an example of which is shown in Figure 8.2 for the job of "turn and thread tube." There are many different forms of instruction sheets in use.

The job designer will check the instruction sheet against the principles of effective work and thus complete step 5 of the scientific method.

Question 4 was **Where will the work be done.** This question concerns plant layout, materials-handling system design, and organization design. The job location will be affected by the scope of each supervisory manager. Because of the difference in the technology employed in finding an appropriate answer to each of these aspects of the main question, we may find three

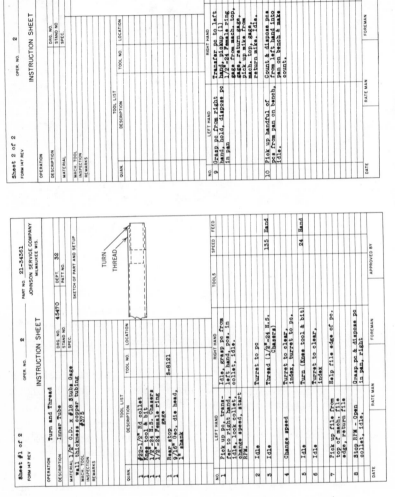

Figure 8.2 Instruction sheet from machine shop. [Courtesy L. Piel, Chief of Methods and Standards, Johnson Service Co., Milwaukee, Wis. (From M. E. Mundel, *Motion and Time Study: Principles and Practice*, 3d ed. Englewood Cliffs, N.J.: Prentice-Hall, Inc., 1960, p. 571)]

groups of specialists cooperating in producing an answer to question 4. However, because of the intermittency of the really unique problems of this type in a going organization, they may even be resolved by middle or supervisory managers on the basis of established guidelines. If the organization is sufficiently large so as to have a considerable number of people with functional jobs, subproblems may be assigned to the industrial engineering group or sometimes to what is called a plant engineering group. Certainly in a small organization, one person might answer this question as well as all other questions. The main item of importance is to recognize that the problem exists and must be solved.

Wherever the work is to be done, there must be space and conditions appropriate to the work with respect to cleanliness, temperature, humidity, and so forth. Further, the cost of moving materials does not add to their value; hence, each operation is often placed as near its preceding operation as is feasible, although there may be complicated conflicting factors. For instance, the Yanmar Diesel Engine Co., in Nagahama, Japan, made a critical contribution to the economy of several villages in that area by setting up small buildings in the village to house one or two machine tools to perform certain separable operations on some of the small parts of the engines. The *detachability* of the operation and the ease of separating the work machine-wise and time-wise from the main process were more important than the proximity of the next operation. In this case, the criterion of optimization was other than the direct cost of manufacture.

A decision must also be made as to whether all jobs on a product are to be performed in one area and under one supervisor or whether like jobs are to be grouped together in one area under one supervisor. Such a decision would be a middle-manager function. For instance, with respect to the cup-wrapping previously referred to, the question is: "Should all cup operations be kept in the same area, should the wrapping and packing of all products be in a separate area, or should there be a combination of these alternatives?"

In the particular plant from which the cup-wrapping example was taken, the space problems and the flow problems were such that all light wrapping and packing operations were grouped together. It should be noted that aluminum cups and similar products are extremely light and may be moved conveniently in large quantities at a reasonable cost. The decision to use such a solution would be influenced by studies which might be made by the plant-layout and materials-handling specialists, or these assisting groups may be part of a staff group already referred to as industrial engineering; or we may have a manufacturing-cost-analysis staff.

Questions 5 and 6 were **From whom will the work for this job come** and **To whom will the work from this job go**. The work being done by the repetitive worker is usually work directly related to the completion of a product. The place in the time sequence of manufacture must suit the needs of the product; what comes before and what comes after are also dictated by product requirements and the process chosen to make it. Hence, the answer to both of these questions is supplied by the process-design group, about which more will be said in Chapter 10. Also, the man-jobs of moving material may be independent from the man-jobs which modify the product. Additional man-jobs may be inserted to provide these services, and the relationship between these man-jobs and the direct man-jobs must be planned and controlled to achieve an effective, integrated group activity.

Who will inspect, evaluate, or approve of the work done, and how will this be expressed? This was the seventh question in the list given. With the cup-wrapping job being discussed, the task is sufficiently low in technical complexity so that inspection and supervision may be performed by the supervisory manager, previously referred to as foreman. In a large group, there may be an assistant foreman or lead worker who will perform this function for the foreman.

In cases of greater technical complexity, the inspection function may be assigned to a special group which will bring specialized training to bear in periodically (or continuously) inspecting the product, i.e., verifying the attributes of the product against a standard or specification. "In modern manufacturing, the inspection function is determining the acceptability of the manufactured article. Generally, the acceptability is defined by the specification."[5] The worker would have to be instructed concerning the time to seek inspection of his work. With jobs more complex than cup wrapping, he might be required to have the first several pieces checked by an inspector; he may also be required to check his own work at intervals and chart the results, so as to watch trends and stop before faulty product is produced. Statistical treatment of inspection data, usually called *statistical quality control,* seeks to prevent the production of faulty product rather than to sort it out by inspection. More will be said about the control of quality in Chapter 18. However, the inspection group may add to the job responsibilities and provide assistance in following the specific instructions.

When will the work be done? This was question 8, and it has two aspects, one concerning the problem of shifts or time of day, the other being *when during a shift.* By using plant facilities for the entire twenty-four hours, the investment in plant to achieve a given capacity may be greatly reduced and the obsolescence of machines made a smaller factor in the total economy of the plant. Each job must be examined in order to determine whether it is

[5] W. C. Ireson and E. L. Grant, *Handbook of Industrial Engineering and Management.* Englewood Cliffs, N.J.: Prentice-Hall, Inc., 1955, p. 962.

desirable to perform it during each shift or during some particular shifts. The availability of labor and equipment and the cost of second or third shifts must be determined. The acceptability of such employment must also be evaluated from the social point of view.

In the case of the cup wrapping, space in the wrapping department was not at a premium and the output of the two production shifts could be stored before being wrapped, without creating new costs. Hence, wrapping was only performed during the 8:00 A.M. to 5:00 P.M., or *day,* or *first shift,* as it is usually called.

With some tasks, such as those requiring the batching of work from several processes or the preheating of a furnace or those affected by the requirements of raw materials, as in vegetable canning, the time during a shift may be determined by process requirements and may be difficult to alter. With the wrapping job under discussion, this aspect of process is not of importance.

The ninth question was **What will be the conditions under which the work will be done.** The adaptability of the human organism is remarkably extensive. Men work in cold-storage areas at below 0°F and in furnace and forge areas in temperatures of over 100°F or perform complex tasks while weightless in space. The human eye can perceive objects in illuminations ranging from 1 to over 10,000 foot-candles. However, it should not be thought that a human worker is equally effective under all conditions.

Comfort affects mental attitude, as well as physiological capability, and, as discussed in Chapter 2, attitudes are also important in respect to their effect upon work. Among the basic physical factors that affect comfort are temperature, humidity, ventilation, and quality of air.[6]

In the early days of factory work, the working conditions were, from current points of view, intolerable. Now most factory work is done under reasonably normal environmental conditions, although there are still activities where conditions have not yet been ameliorated. Usually a section of a special department called either personnel, industrial relations, or safety will deal with this particular aspect of jobs. In addition, most supervisory managers are usually assigned the responsibility of attempting to assist in providing the best conditions economically obtainable. In most cases, this is also a subject for joint worker-manager negotiations.

The tenth question was **What will the work require of the worker.** This involves both the responses to the environment and the responses to the direct work of the job. In the case of wrapping cups, the environment was normal and the direct work required relatively little specialized skill, knowledge,

---

[6] For a more complete discussion, see *Handbook of Human Engineering Data,* Tufts College Institute of Applied Experimental Psychology. Washington, D.C.: The Special Devices Center, Office of Naval Research, 1951, part 7, chap. 2, sec. 2, pp. 1–13.

training, or education. Various other tasks may require varying amounts of ability to withstand unusual conditions of heat, cold, noise, dust, or vibration; unusual strength; special knowledge or experience; special training; or a degree of responsibility for the safety of equipment, product, or other workers. If quantitative scales are created to measure these factors in terms of a common unit, jobs may be not only qualitatively described but quantitatively *evaluated* and placed in a hierarchy in terms of their total requirements. However, from the job designer's basic point of view, in most cases, the fewer of these requirements in a job, the more effective the design, provided the desired work is performed. Such an objective must, at times, be tempered to avoid dividing jobs so finely that they become socially unacceptable to real men.

A job may involve a variety of different tasks over a period of time rather than a continuous repetition of one task. On such a job, the worker may need broad skill to perform this variety as compared with narrow skill needed for the doing of only one task. The resultant *job enlargement* may be desirable from the morale point of view, as well as from the viewpoint of adding flexibility to the manufacturing capability; if carried too far, it may make the job difficult to fill.

Question 11 was **How long will it take to do a unit of work.** This important question has two aspects: (1) What is a *unit of work* and (2) How long will the unit take to perform? With the repetitive type of job being discussed here, the first aspect is simple. The unit of work is one performance of the repetitive cycle of the process step or steps assigned to the man-job. The time required to perform this step is an important item of data. In Chapter 1, the design aspect of management was stressed. To design or to make detailed plans for an activity requires a dimension with which to work. This dimension must be such as to permit the fitting together of diverse activities into an integrated human-group activity. The dimension must be a physical dimension so as to permit realistic control of activity. The only type of dimension which fulfills these requirements on a day-to-day basis is some function of time. This was already mentioned in Chapter 6. The importance of time measurement was recognized at the very inception of scientific management and was part of F. W. Taylor's historic paper, to which reference was made in Chapters 1 and 7. To supervise properly, supervisors must know how long a job should take, using a qualified operator and a specific method. Upper levels of management have similar problems, but they cannot deal with work units as small as those dealt with by supervisory managers. We will discuss the concept of larger units of work in Chapter 12. However, regardless of the size of the unit of work, the determination of the required time is called *time study* or *work measurement*.

At the man-job level appropriate to this section of this chapter, the measurement of how long a job should take requires more than just the measurement of any performance. Any time which may be observed or determined from past records is usually affected by how hard the worker worked. Figure 8.3 indicates some of the factors that affect this type of situation. It should be obvious to even the casual observer of industrial work that work is not performed at the maximum speed physiologically feasible. This would be a pace that would leave the worker only enough energy after work to get home, eat, wash, and sleep to recover from the effects of work. Conversely, factory work is not performed at the minimum speed with which people can work without expending undue effort because of the slowness; conscience usually does not permit this. There is a minimum sociologically acceptable pace, vague though this may be. On the other hand, there is also a maximum sociologically acceptable pace which workers will not willingly exceed, this pace being the one that allows sufficient energy, after work, for civic, family, and leisure time pursuits, as deemed appropriate by the social group. (In a way, the difference between the maximum sociologically acceptable and the maximum physiologically possible, if economically sustainable, is a measure of the economic strength of a society and its technology. The absence of a difference indicates an almost slave population ripe for demagoguery.)

Figure 8.3   Wages versus rate of work and the area in which the actual work-pace lies. (From M. E. Mundel, *Motion and Time Study: Principles and Practice*, 3d ed. Englewood Cliffs, N.J.: Prentice-Hall, Inc., 1960, p. 335)

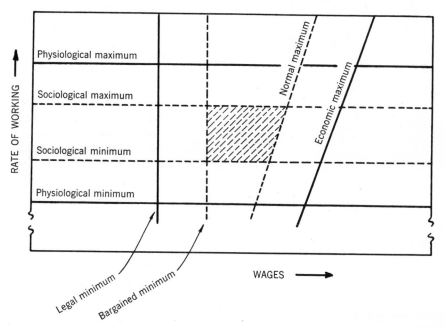

It is the function of the managing group to obtain worker acceptance of a pace economically acceptable to the industry and plant and to measure jobs, in terms of time, on the basis of a performance meeting this standard. Of course, there must be provision for an adequate amount of nonworking time during the day. Various aspects of this problem of design are participated in by the previously mentioned industrial-relations group, industrial engineering group, middle and supervisory management, and, frequently, representatives of the working group. This broad involvement emphasizes the basic nature of this aspect of the design. In all too many cases, the techniques employed to perform the actual measurement have the effect of passing the essential responsibility far too far down the managerial hierarchy or allowing past practices, representing many conflicting social pressures, to determine the time standards.

Methods of determining performance-time values for direct repetitive work include techniques of direct observation, the use of previously organized data, random sampling techniques, and manipulations of data of previous performances, as well as combinations of these. The job design is not complete until a time dimension has been determined. The details of determination are most commonly performed by a member of the industrial engineering group called a *time-study man, management analyst,* or *estimator,* depending on the type of work.

For a job such as cup wrapping, which we have been discussing, the time may be determined in advance of the job inception by the use of existing standard data tables[7] and would thus have greater reliability than a mere estimate. However, estimates would be made in all cases where fully reliable data were not available because the time must be determined in some fashion in order to complete other aspects of the job design.

Question 12 was **What will be the pay for the job.** If the plant is in the U.S.A. and is engaged in interstate commerce or in producing articles for interstate commerce (and this includes most sizable industrial plants), then a minimum wage per hour is set by law. There may also be state legislation on this subject. In most cases, not only does the pay exceed this basic minimum but different jobs pay different amounts of money.

The difference in pay for different jobs is usually related to five major groups of variables:

1. The amount of each of the various factors governing the response required from the workers, which are in the work, such as those related to

---

[7] For examples of standard time data of this type, see M. E. Mundel, *Motion and Time Study,* 3d ed. Englewood Cliffs, N.J.: Prentice-Hall, Inc., 1960, pp. 518–530; see also H. B. Maynard (ed.), *Industrial Engineering Handbook,* 2d ed. New York: McGraw-Hill Book Company, 1963, sec. 4.

environmental conditions and required worker abilities, as well as the time of the shift.

Sociologically speaking, some of these factors are considered compensable, and differentiation between the pay for different jobs on the basis of these factors is expected by the working group. A formal procedure for quantifying these differences is called *job evaluation*. It should be noted that these procedures reflect social attitudes only, and the factors and procedures may be vastly different in different groups or in different countries.

2. The basic difficulty of getting and keeping people to do the work.

3. The length of time the person has been employed.

4. The amount or quality of production produced by the worker as compared with the typical worker. Pay is often varied with respect to quantity or quality by means of what are called *wage-incentive plans* or *plans for payment by results*.

5. The effect of various social groups, formally or informally organized.

All the items above interact to produce a rate of pay for a man-job. The solution to this part of the problem of job design is obviously bound up with rates of pay being paid in other plants in the community, price levels in the community, and in the group relations between owners, managers, and direct productive workers. The wage will also be affected by the basic economic condition of the industry and the country.

Wages are usually settled in joint negotiations between workers and managers and are part of an agreement usually referred to as a *labor contract*. The negotiation of such an agreement is usually considered part of the basic responsibility of the labor-relations group, although it is so vital to the typical industrial enterprise that many levels of management will usually participate. Indeed, in industry-wide negotiations, the public interest may elevate this problem to one of national concern.

In conclusion, one should note that the question of pay and the question of equitable employment are closely related, although it should be borne in mind that there are other remunerative aspects to jobs besides monetary pay.

What will be the unit cost of doing the work? This was question 13. As with the introductory materials of Chapters 2 to 5, after an examination of the problems of men, plant, product, materials, and process, we come to money. The unit cost is somewhat different from the previous design questions; it is either a derivative value or a goal rather than a directly manipulatable factor.

The unit cost of doing a job will consist of:

1. The cost of the unit of material, with allowance for yield
2. The cost of the labor needed to produce a unit of work, with allowance for scrap

3. The cost of using the machine time including power, depreciation, maintenance, and space
4. General charges for supervision, management, and services

It should be obvious that the computation of the unit cost based on a given set of answers to the questions of job design may produce either a satisfactory or an unsatisfactory value. Of course, if a target was set ahead of time when the design task began, the possibility of an unsatisfactory value at this point can be minimized. However, even when each group participating in the design of the job attempts to find a most economical answer or an answer within the economic limits set for it as a guide, there will be both overages and underages. Hence, the net result may still be unsatisfactory, particularly if the economic tolerance is small. Of course, from one point of view, costs are always unsatisfactory, and there is almost always pressure to reduce them. Hence, the problem of the improvement of job design is a constant problem. One area of change is the improvement of the design as related to one or more elements of job design. There is also the possibility of *value analysis,* a careful and systematic scrutiny of the raw materials, product parts, or total design to find and eliminate unnecessary attributes that contribute to cost but not to function or salability.

The fourteenth question was **For how long a period will the job probably exist.** This relates the man-job to the society of the plant and to the outside environment. It should be recognized that a man-job, as a component of an industrial enterprise, frequently changes with regard to the *job* aspect but the man usually stays with the integrated group longer than the specific task.

In order to employ a person, certainly one of the important job dimensions is the anticipated length of the job and of subsequent jobs. The life of one task, which may be in the design stage, is only one item in answering this question. The whole pattern of operation of the plant is involved.

In conclusion, in the computation of process economics, of which job design is a part, we are concerned with task life. Inasmuch as a process step must be converted to a man-job, a process step cannot be considered apart from the man-job in which it must eventually be embodied if we are to avoid highly undesirable sub-optimization.

So far we have discussed repetitive jobs. It should not be thought that all jobs in this category are as simple as the ones used as examples. Repetitive jobs can involve long, complex cycles of work, as well as involve doing a variety of similar things, or a combination of these. The essential features of a repetitive job are:

1. The existence of a prescribed method (with varying degrees of formalization) for the pattern and sequence of the activity
2. The repetition of this pattern of activity for some considerable period of time

3. The removal, from the discretion of the job holder, of any significant latitude concerning how much will be done, where it will be done, when it will be done, and with what it will be done

Repetitive jobs may require extensive degrees of skill and may have lengthy learning periods, but the end results, means, and order of achieving them are predetermined. This type of job is the major consumer of labor in the typical industrial plant, although automation is changing this and will continue to; it may produce fewer but more complex repetitive jobs. Likewise, many clerical jobs in large organizations may tend to fall into the repetitive category because of increasing computer usage.

Some clerical activities may be more properly classified as selective. With a selective job, only the general manner of performing the work is prescribed. The objective is usually specified in detail and relates to a physical object or condition, but the order and detail of doing the work are left more or less to the discretion of the job holder. Typical of such a classification is the usual work of a secretary, maintenance employee, supervisor, or tool maker.

Let us briefly examine the questions of job design with respect to the selective job in order to expand our understanding of the problems of designing man-jobs.

Let us once again look at the question **What is to be done.** The resultant physical end-product or the objective, for all of the examples of selective jobs mentioned in the preceding paragraph, is given in detail by a higher authority. What is to be done is well known. The means of designing what is to be done, for clerical jobs, comes from a *systems and procedures group* or from the direct supervisor; for a maintenance employee, from the *maintenance specifications* whose source will vary with the type of plant; and for the supervisor, from the *organization planning group*. (Chapters 12 to 20 will deal with the design of control systems from which the tasks for many selective and decisive man-jobs are extracted.)

With what equipment will the work be done is a question not always fully answered for the holder of a selective job. This is one of the characteristics differentiating selective from repetitive jobs. The worker must often select (with varying degrees of freedom of choice) the most appropriate means for doing the work from the means which are available. An essential design question is "Are the occurrences of work sufficiently different so that preplanning would be uneconomical?" If the answer to the above question is No, then it is worth planning the work and changing the job to something more closely resembling a repetitive job in order to (1) reduce the cost of planning how to do the work (assuming that staff planning is more economical than daily planning by the doer of work) and (2) reduce the demands the job makes upon the holder of the job and hence make a lower cost feasible from either a lower wage or a greater productivity standpoint. Also, as the amount of one type of activity within a selective job increases, there will be a tendency to reduce the area of discretion or we may find this activity being taken out of the duties of the selective man-job and assigned to a separate repetitive man-job. There will, of course, be combinations of selective and repetitive duties in many jobs.

How will the work be done? With the selective job, the amount of discretion allowed the worker will vary. In some cases, there may be procedure manuals of considerable detail, although the worker will have to select the appropriate procedure. In other cases, the starting point and goal will be indicated, but the in-between details will not be given.

Where will the work be done? As with the repetitive job, this part of the job design will be developed by the layout group working through the level of supervisor above the employee or will be determined by the requirements of a task. For instance, a maintenance employee's work is frequently done at the point needing repair.

Let us examine questions 5 and 6 together. These were **From whom will the work for this job come** and **To whom will the work from this job go.** In the case of the selective job, these questions are answered in a somewhat different fashion than with repetitive jobs. The selective job usually involves doing a number of things which are less alike than the variety of things done by the repetitive job holder. In most cases, the service is to a person, to an area of the plant, or to all things throughout the plant which have some similar aspect, such as all parts of the electrical system, rather than directly to or with the product. The output of the plant may alter but the work of the selective job be unaffected. In our discussion of the repetitive job, we indicated that the order of work was dictated by product requirements and by process requirements. The selective job usually differs because the answers to questions 5 and 6 come from a different group. The group usually responsible is either the systems design group or the organization planning group, although it is possible to have a selective job created by the process group, for example, production repairman, whose functions might be to repair defects in products coming through normal processing. This last example, however, is not the most typical of the selective job.

The seventh question is **Who will inspect, evaluate, or approve of the work done, and how will this be expressed.** This is another of the real areas of differentiation between selective and repetitive jobs. In the case of the selective job, a good deal of self-criticism or inspection is assigned the worker with general criteria rather than specific formalized criteria, as in the case of the repetitive job. The secretary, maintenance employee, supervisor, or tool maker must exercise a good deal of responsibility for the correctness of their own work, and they are expected to do this conscientiously. In many cases the job designer will note, in the job description, the responsibility and the nature of the self-check, but considerable discretion must be exercised by the job holder.

When will the work be done? This eighth question refers to an aspect of job design that is also a differentiating characteristic of the selective job. In most selective jobs, the higher authority may provide a list of what is to be done and even indicate an order of priority, but the worker is expected to exercise considerable initiative in changing the indicated order as conditions may require.

What will be the conditions under which the work will be done? This ninth question has unusual aspects with respect to the selective job. The working conditions, comfort-wise, of many selective jobs are superior to those provided for repetitive workers, although there is a chance of their being much worse, e.g., power-line repairmen working during a storm. However, in the case of maintenance employees who may work at times in difficult areas, the opportunity to clean up from their activity is usually greater than for the repetitive employee working in such an area. This seems to be a part of the nonmonetary value affecting the concept of equity of employment and may even be considered a reward denoting status. In our present society, those who have greater responsibility for their own work are, in general, regarded as being at a higher level of society. Inherent in the selective job, there are frequently some nonmonetary recognitions of this. It will be recalled that at one time clerical labor was referred to as *white-collar* in contrast to *hands,* this being the old term for direct man-jobs working on the product. The term hands is being supplanted by the term *blue-collar,* and in many modern plants, where process conditions permit, we may see direct-labor employees in white shirt, tie, and suit jacket, or female employees in street dress. The conditions under which selective jobs are performed are frequently influenced by the person to whom such workers report. In some cases, selective job holders may be given considerable opportunity to help design some of these conditions themselves, more so than repetitive workers. This could be discussed at great length, but the problems implicit for the job designer are obvious. Inasmuch as working conditions affect status and status affects attitude, which is essential to the self-discipline of the selective job, this particular aspect of job design merits careful consideration.

What will the work require of the worker? This tenth question brings up another aspect of job design which clearly separates the selective job from the repetitive. The selective job requires considerable initiative, some discrimination as to which task to do when, how to do it, and some ability to add to what is known and prescribed in order to serve the major objectives of the job. In many cases, the selective job will require more formal training or education than the repetitive job. The repetitive job may require considerable practice to achieve the requisite skill, but the requirements over a given period of time will seldom have the depth or variety characteristic of the selective job. Hence, the job designer will have to examine the details of the selective job and relate the requirements of the various tasks to the sources of such training so as to specify the requirements to be met by the employee to be assigned the man-job.

How long will it take to do a unit of work? This was the eleventh question. As was indicated earlier, to provide the correct amount of manpower for an organization, one needs to know how long the work is going to take. Stating how long the work is going to take for each repetition of a task requires stating how and with what the work will be done in detailed terms and how much of it there is. Hence, for the selective job, the problem of work measurement is different from that connected with the repetitive job. On the normal selective job, the time must be developed for a mix of activity, with the mix representing either the performance of similar tasks with slightly different characteristics or the performance of a variety of truly different tasks. Techniques for doing this, even in highly complicated work situations, exist within the field of technology called *work measurement.* The development of such information is vital to performing job design in a sufficiently detailed fashion to meet the guiding objectives.

The twelfth question was **What will be the pay for the job.** Factors similar to those considered for the repetitive job will be used. It is interesting to note that the additional amenities often provided and the greater leeway in "when to do what" often operate to produce a lower rate of pay than for a repetitive task. The equity of employment is equalized, it would appear, by some of the conditions and the status of the work.

What will be the unit cost of doing the work? This was the thirteenth question. As in the case of question 12, the very word unit raises special problems in the selective job. In the case of the repetitive job, the variety of what is worked on and what is done with it is either limited or directly related to discrete units of final output. In contrast, the selective job often involves many things. However, in order to provide goals and measures of the effectiveness of the activity, various unit costs on each of the activities should be developed, using the work-measurement information previously referred to and an appropriate array of units of work.

The final question is **For how long a period will the job probably exist.** It is handled in a manner identical with the procedure used with the repetitive job.

In summary, as with repetitive jobs, there are many gradations of selective jobs. The amount of responsibility and the amount of initiative may vary greatly. The area of discretion, though limited, is larger than in the case of the repetitive job. The objective of the job is usually described in detail and is usually readily checked by the job holder. Attainment of job objectives may be assessed by the supervisor.

Decisive jobs, like selective jobs, require initiative from the worker but differ in that they usually require much more. They also differ with respect to the nature of the job objective and its manner of being assigned. The decisive job usually has only a general objective covering a period of time, rather than specific acts. The job holder must interpret this objective for each specific assignment or piece of work that comes along. For instance, a quality-control specialist, mentioned earlier in this chapter, may well have a decisive job. His basic assignment may be "to develop an economical and effective quality-control procedure for each job assigned to his cognizance." These are broad terms. He must draw on his own knowledge to select from the many possible methods the one which, by his decision making criteria, best meets the needs of the problem. The actual attainment of the objectives in the case of the decisive job is somewhat more difficult to evaluate than in the case of the selective job.

Regarding questions 2 and 3, *With what equipment will the work be done* and *How will the work be done,* the details of the design of the decisive job must be supplied primarily by the employee.

The question *When will the work be done* is another area of differentiation between selective and decisive jobs. The decisive job holder may have many things to do. He is expected, in most cases, to exercise extensive judgment in giving priorities to certain assignments and to show some considerable flexibility in the amount of time he devotes to work. In the case of the decisive job holder it is much more likely that the job will be integrated with the totality of his life than is the case with the selective or repetitive job holder.

The fourth question was *Where will the work be done.* This question is usually answered quite differently from the way it is for the selective or repetitive job. The primary aim is to meet the internal needs of the work. The work of the decisive job holder is seldom tied physically to the requirements of the product or process.

As regards the fifth and sixth questions concerning *the source of assignment* and *to whom the work goes,* we have another area of differentiation for the decisive job. The output of the decisive worker usually has an extrinsic rather than an intrinsic value. Hence, rather than speaking of the flow of some physical work, we are talking about a hierarchy of authority and responsibility. Therefore, the answer to these questions, when designing the decisive job, draws on the field of knowledge called organization planning rather than on process design. The answer to this question will be greatly influenced by the duties required to serve the control concepts, which will be discussed in Chapters 13 to 20.

Who will inspect, evaluate, or approve of the work done, and how will this be expressed? This seventh question raises problems peculiar to the decisive job. In many cases, the method of evaluation is indirect and not immediate upon performance of the work. Again we must defer a discussion of this until later chapters in which we will examine the context in which decisions are made.

When will the work be done? In respect to this eighth question, the design of the decisive job is usually vague. The basic requirement is to perform the tasks when necessary. As we shall see later, such requirements are generated on an irregular basis. Because of their variety, the area of permissiveness is usually large, and effectiveness is the general criterion. Of course, the hours of work may be stated, but these vary and must be thought of as being flexible, depending upon job demands.

What will be the conditions under which the work will be done? This was question 9. Here again the design of this part of the typical decisive job is somewhat different from the other types. The main productive capability, in the decisive job, is the person himself. Hence, the amenities are designed around the person rather than around any requirements of product or process, although there will be cases, such as biological research, where all three must be considered. However, with the person as the main element, the person's comfort is generally given great consideration, although custom may play a large role regarding what is considered adequate. Also, the location is frequently not tied to any other aspect of the plant, and this eases the task of providing proper amenities.

The tenth question was *What will the work require of the worker.* We find the decisive worker usually needs much greater specialized education, training, and experience than the two preceding types of workers. The required education or training is usually in mental rather than in manual skills, although there are cases where both may be required. In most cases, it is also anticipated that the job holder will continue to obtain additional education and considerable permissiveness may be built into the job design to encourage the job holder to make decisions (or recommendations) in this respect, both for himself and for others.

How long will it take to do a unit of work? In designing the decisive job, this question may be answered in a variety of ways, depending upon the nature of the decisive job. If the decisive job is one of responding to the problems raised in the operation of one of the control systems (described later in Chapters 13 to 20), we can predict the mix of tasks that will arise and the probable frequency and develop a typical time for them. In this way, a time for doing work on which to base manpower may be developed. However, the problem of how long it will take to do a unit of work often becomes a reversed problem like the question of plant location; the reader will recall that the usual problem of location was, given a location, how to react continually to take advantage of it. In the case of the decisive man-job, a time for the achievement of a stated objective, *a project,* can be developed on the basis of professional estimates. Such data can be used to determine whether it is worth using the man-job on such objectives. In addition, if a long and involved series of projects is contemplated in order to achieve a complex, substantive objective, a series of techniques called *network planning* may be used as a basis for estimating the time for the performance of each separated phase of the work. The units into which work is divided are thus different again from those used in repetitive or selective work; but with a recognition of this difference in the meaning of the word unit, the question does permit a realistic and useful answer to be generated. In other cases, we may develop quantitative scales for such aspects as number of people supervised, area covered, number of decisions per week, difficulty of decisions, and diversity of fields of knowledge, and then develop index numbers for each such supervisory workload. By means of a man-hour value per unit of index number, we may develop an indirect measure for decisive work. While admittedly rough, such values may be of great help in designing such jobs.[8]

Question 12 concerned pay. As might be anticipated, the pay for decisive jobs is usually higher, on the average, than for the two preceding types of jobs. Many more factors are considered when determining a rate of pay, and, in addition, because the person is the unique factor in such a job, we frequently find rates of pay set for the individual rather than for the job or there may be greater differentiation because of the individual.

Question 13 referred to unit costs. With our different meaning of unit, this is a somewhat different question than in the case of repetitive or selective jobs. A unit cost is readily calculable in those cases where a major portion of the time of the decisive job is devoted to an isolatable project. Here, one should note, the problem is radically different from the problem with the repetitive or selective job. For a specific project, the anticipated time for performing it is often a matter determined by joint agreement between the decisive job holder and his superior. The man-job is in existence before this problem is undertaken. The required decision is whether to undertake the problem under discussion or some other problem. The unit cost answer is primarily helpful in deciding how to use the man-job, not in whether to establish it. If the problem is totally new to the organization and if the anticipated time is relatively short and they do not possess the capability,

---

[8] For an excellent example of such an approach, see C. W. Barkdull, "Span of Control: A Method of Evaluation," *Michigan Business Review,* vol. 15, no. 3, May, 1964, pp. 25–32.

they may hire a consultant for a short period rather than create a new man-job.

With a long series of activities, such as with an extensive project, costs might be developed for each subpart as well as for the whole. This is an appropriate part of job design, and as with repetitive jobs, will permit the job designers to determine whether they have reached their objectives or not.

In the case of decisive jobs, which serve one of the control systems to which we have frequently alluded, the cost can be developed in terms of serving the system in the manner indicated; the total service becomes the unit for which the cost is developed.

Hence, with decisive jobs as with repetitive jobs, we may say that appropriate work measurement together with rates of pay can be used to determine the cost of appropriately designated units of work.

This leads us to question 14, *For how long a period will the job probably exist.* In most cases, this question is related to the life of the organization. However, as we just noted, if the project is of short duration, a consultant may be sought rather than create a new man-job in order to minimize the cost of doing the work, particularly those costs associated with maintaining the decisive man-job after the initiating problem has been overcome. There are other peculiar aspects to this phase of the design of decisive jobs. In the U.S.A., it is typical that the holders of such jobs are somewhat mobile, particularly in their younger years. Hence, such jobs may be made into regular man-jobs, even if it is expected that the major reason for their existence may last only a few years.

In summary, concerning the designing of man-jobs, certain essentials should now be obvious. First, jobs are designed not as isolated problems, but in relation to each other, to the equipment, product, process, and raw material, and to the objectives of the enterprise. Second, the design of jobs may call on various fields of knowledge such as motion study, industrial physiology and psychology, sociology, economics, tool design, equipment selection, quality control, plant layout, job evaluation, wage incentive, safety, personnel administration, industrial relations, materials handling, organization, sales, product design, work measurement, and network planning, to mention some of the possibilities. (Of course, many of these fields overlap.) Third, the areas of freedom of design have social, as well as legal and physical limitations. Many of these fields of knowledge also serve other needs of the organization and, in addition, are usually part of the assignment made within the design of some job somewhere in the group. In the usual plant, assignment of duty is not usually made in terms of these fields of knowledge but in terms of objectives or responsibilities which may require the employment of one or more of these fields of knowledge to various degrees.

The concept of a job title, the name given to a job, and the name of an area of knowledge must not be confused. Many jobs in a plant may require similar or related knowledge but have different objectives as expressed in the job design, and these differences may or may not be reflected in the job title. There seems to be no fixed custom about this.

To create a man-job properly, men and tasks or duties must be brought together in a fashion which is conducive to the overall objectives of the organization, within the social and legal limitations. The task is not simple. The situation is not static.

REFERENCE TOPICS

Industrial psychology
Optimization of labor costs
Automation
Motion study
Time study
Work measurement
Job evaluation
Job enlargement
Job simplification
Motivation
Classification of industrial jobs
Value analysis
Industrial economy
Structural unemployment
Union contracts

Organization
Job duties, responsibilities, authority
Industrial equipment
Process charts
Work hours
Work conditions
Operation charts
Job training
Workplace design
Crew work
Tool design
Machine speeds
Conveyorized work places
Job description

SUGGESTED THEMES

1. Automation and employment trends
2. Gainful employment trends by industries and occupations
3. Industrial examples of "the law of diminishing returns"
4. Working conditions for repetitive jobs, selective jobs, and decisive jobs, in selected situations
5. Common decisions required in work situations
6. Mobility of labor
7. Collective bargaining and national interests

SUGGESTED CASES

Cruickshank, H. M., and K. Davis, *Cases in Management,* 3d ed. Home-wood, Ill.: Richard D. Irwin, Inc., 1962. Cases beginning on pages 242, 246, 253.

Greenwald, D. U., *Elementary Case Problems for Industrial Engineers.* New York: The Ronald Press, 1957. Cases beginning on pages 68, 75.

Terry, G. R., *Case Problems in Business and Industrial Management,* 2d ed. Dubuque, Iowa: William C. Brown Company, Publishers, 1955. Cases beginning on pages 34, 49, 107, 109, 110, 111, 113, 117, 118, 119, 166, 167.

Ziegler, R. J., *Casebook in Production Management.* New York: John Wiley & Sons, Inc., 1962. Cases beginning on pages 24, 33, 124.

9 DESIGNING PHYSICAL PLANT

In Chapter 3 we referred to physical plant as the totality of physical facilities of the industrial enterprise. The usual objective of plant design is to provide these facilities for the production of the required amount and variety of product in a manner that will minimize the total cost of production and distribution. This chapter concerns the problems encountered in achieving such an objective.

In a design problem initiated when there is no plant, the limitations are related to the requirements of the raw material, the product, the equipment, the people who will work in the plant, the community in which the plant will be located, and the economic factors affected by the location. For any given plant, such a problem occurs only once. However, as we have noted, many of these limitations change with time, creating new design problems.

In any of these subsequent design problems, additional limitations are introduced by the capital represented by the existing plant as well as by the physical configuration of the existing plant. The design problem may thus become one of achieving the originally stated plant-design objective for a new product or a new volume of product within the limitations of the old plant. With such problems, it is entirely possible that a solution which is economically acceptable may not readily be forthcoming. When this is the case, ways must be found for altering some of the limitations of the design problem. Typical of such solutions are changes in the product, radical redesign of process or equipment, acceptance of less desirable conditions by workers or communities, alteration of economic factors by governmental bodies, and so on. As was stated earlier, none of these factors are totally independent.

Certain aspects of physical plant are tautological. The land must support the building. The building must house the equipment and the man-jobs. The list of equipment and man-jobs which must be housed is the result of a selection of a product, a product volume, and a process. These aspects have not yet been discussed. One might ask why a discussion of product and process does not precede the discussion of plant. The reason is as follows. Problems concerning the making of changes in existing buildings to fit the requirements of product and process or vice versa are more frequently encountered than those concerned with totally new plants. If the limitations arising from the existing buildings and their location are understood, they may be considered when discussing product and process. In this way, product and process problems, the more common problems, can be more fully examined.

Physical plant was indicated in Chapter 3 as including:

1. Land
2. Buildings
3. Production and service equipment, including office equipment
4. Utility services, including any peculiar to the processes such as steam, air, and temperature controls
5. Amenities

The problem of plant location was discussed only briefly in Chapter 3. Now we may be more specific. Problems of plant location are of two basic types:

1. The selection of the best location for a new plant
2. The design of the best means of taking advantage of a location in the operation of an existing plant

Of course, selection and design are not completely different. Design involves synthesizing a number of alternatives and selecting one on some basis, or criterion, of preference. However, the word "selection" has been used to describe the first type of problem because the number and the nature of the alternatives are outside of the control of the selector; this is not true of the second type of problem. But in most other respects these two types of problems are the same. Hence, a discussion of the first type will also cover most of the problems associated with the second type.

The selection of the best location for a plant is essentially a problem subject to decision by a top manager, as this group was defined in Chapter 1. However, because of the considerable amount of detailed information which must be gathered, the preliminary work is often done by a staff group, such as the previously mentioned industrial engineering group; at times economic consultant groups will be used; at times the problem may contain heavy political implications and governmental bodies may be involved.

The first step, as indicated in Chapter 1, is the setting forth of the objective.

The usual objective is to select a location that insofar as it is possible to determine offers the most profitable place in which to operate for the life envisioned for the enterprise. If the essential criterion is other than profit, this will alter the weighting given to the various factors more than it will change the list of such factors.

An analysis of the general objective will indicate three general groups of limitations creating the problem of selecting a location:

1. Limitations connected with specific locations
2. Limitations connected with the organizers
3. Limitations connected with the purpose of organizing

When examining the first group of limitations with regard to the problem of locating a new plant, the usual procedure is to begin with a list of potential locations and compare them with respect to details of the general limitations listed above. With a problem associated with an existing plant, the site is predetermined; hence, the need is to compare the detailed limitations with respect to alternatives of product, product volume, or process.

The first group of limitations connected with a specific location may be expanded to many subfactors, such as:

1. Markets
2. Raw materials
3. Power, fuel, water, and other utilities
4. Transportation
5. Labor
6. Laws and codes
7. Available buildings on the site
8. Community living conditions
9. Local financial aid available
10. Nearby industries
11. National security problems
12. National political objectives concerning the economy of a region

With a list of detailed limitations of this type, a more detailed procedure for selecting a plant location can be developed, including a more detailed statement of the objective. Most of the factors in the preceding list would have a relatively stable value for an area larger than a plant site; they are more applicable to a region or general area. For instance, we can examine the potential cost and time to put the product into the customer's hands from different regions, the cost of moving raw materials to each region, the time required to move raw materials, and the dependability of the route. In such a manner, we could narrow our choice down to one or more regions and then make a detailed comparison of the available sites in these selected regions.

In performing such an analysis, we would list, next to each item, the sub-factors to be considered and the evaluation of each subfactor with respect to the region or site. To perform this effectively, we would have to differentiate between those factors or aspects of factors which have only a one-time cost, and those which have an annual cost. Further, we would have to differentiate between those factors for which an annual cost may be predicted with reasonable accuracy and those which are difficult to assess directly or accurately or which may be difficult to project for any considerable period of time. In addition, we would have to take into account the long-range growth plans for the plant.

Many of the factors will conflict. For instance, a region may be somewhat more expensive with respect to the cost of obtaining raw materials but preferable for attracting the desired types of employees. If the man-jobs in the plant are of a type likely to remain difficult to fill, an area of the country affording advantages for living may have some hard-to-calculate values. The situation may be complicated, though, because that which is considered an advantage for living may vary from person to person.

It should be obvious that the selection of a plant site, even from the viewpoint of region, is not a fully mechanistic problem; many value judgments will be required. However, the more one employs objective facts and the more the areas of value judgment are made specific, the more successful can be the final judgment. An excellent list of factors to be considered in selecting a region prior to evaluating specific sites is given by Ireson and Grant:

MAIN FACTOR	SUBFACTORS TO PROVIDE A BASIS FOR COMPARISON
1. Raw-material supply	a. Length of haul from source to region.
	b. Freight rates on the commodity, both raw and finished.
	c. Ratios of weights and volumes of finished products to weights and volumes of raw materials.
	d. Labor supply and attractions of accommodations to induce migration of labor to source.

	e. Availability of water, fuel, power, etc., at source. f. Different sources of raw materials. (They may be widely separated.) g. Availability of adequate transportation facilities.
2. Labor supply in region	a. Adequacy of supply of desired type for an additional plant. b. Competition for the existing supply. c. Suitability of existing supply, by former work or training, for the intended type of work. d. Union organization and strength. e. Race relations. f. Dependability of the type of labor available, and aptitude for factory work, training, and upgrading.
3. Marketing	a. Market area to be served by the plant. b. Concentration of market and stability of demand. c. Extra warehousing and inventories required as a result of plant location. d. Freight rates to principal market areas. e. Transportation facilities available to market areas. f. Travel expense for salesmen and service personnel. g. Risks of delays and damage to goods in shipment (customer relations). h. Competition for the market and relative location of competitors' plants.
4. Factory services	a. Adequacy of supply of power, water, fuel, etc., for present and prospective plant size. b. Availability of external plant services; sewage disposal system, repair and replacement parts, fire protection, public transportation for personnel, etc. c. Available supply of trained management personnel. d. Attractions of region (cultural, climatic, etc.) for professional management personnel.
5. Climatic conditions	a. Cost of construction to withstand forces of nature; earthquakes, winds, snow, etc. b. Heating or air-conditioning costs for either personnel comfort or process control. c. Probability of absenteeism caused by weather. d. Probability of work stoppages or interruption of supply of raw materials by weather. e. Necessity for premium wages because of weather conditions.

    f. Cost of maintenance, deterioration of products or raw materials, and rapid depreciation resulting from climatic conditions.

6. Laws and codes	a. Laws limiting scope of work permitted.
	b. "Fair Employment Practices Acts."
	c. Extra costs for unemployment insurance, workman's compensation, retirement insurance, and similar benefits.
	d. Waste disposal, smoke abatement, and nuisance regulations.
	e. Local tax laws on real property, corporate income, money on deposit, etc.
	f. State, county, or city building codes, and safety and health regulations.
	g. Ruling of such bodies as the Interstate Commerce Commission, which may penalize certain types of industries in certain regions.[1]

Within the general region or regions selected, communities and specific locations therein may be examined by comparing the economic costs and values, as well as the nonfinancial values previously mentioned, for each of the available locations. In considering the specific sites, it is also necessary to consider the cost of the land and the cost of preparing it for the building.

Peculiar local conditions pertaining to specific sites, such as tax advantages, local political conditions, and labor supply, will have to be evaluated with great care because such factors change much more radically and more rapidly than natural phenomena. It should be noted that changes in transportation facilities from early-day water and canal to railroads and then to highway trucks have had a great effect in reducing area differences. The increased daily and total mobility of the work force caused by the use of automobiles and the accompanying changes in social customs concerning fixity of residence; the general wage leveling created by unions and legislation; and the increased potential for control of inside-plant climate because of changes in heating, ventilating, and air-conditioning technology have all tended to reduce the importance of many regional characteristics which formerly affected the choice of a plant location.

The second group of limitations, those connected with the organizers, often assume an importance equal to or exceeding the first group of limitations, except with large plants. An individual living in or near a community may find local advantages with respect to credit, assistance, and so forth, which may, in his case, outweigh the other factors. The predominance of these factors in a decision to locate the plant in a specific location may

[1] W. G. Ireson and E. L. Grant, *Handbook of Industrial Engineering and Management.* Englewood Cliffs, N.J.: Prentice-Hall, Inc., 1955, pp. 556–557.

result in a site ·possessing a basic economic disadvantage, particularly if the business grows beyond a certain size, but these aspects must be weighed one against the other. In the case of a large plant building an auxiliary plant, the ease and convenience of service to the main plant and the ease of managing both with the same managers may outweigh all other factors. We may find the new plant being built in the same community as the main plant, even though this location is not, otherwise, the most economical location.

In other cases, a community may so desire new industries that considerable inducement may be offered to an enterprise to locate a plant in the community. For example:

Dresser Industries' new Wellsboro (Pa.) Compression Fitting Plant is a tribute to teamwork. A team made up of community leaders, company officers, local contractors, and the citizens of Wellsboro, all 4,500 of them!

To make their town competitive among 30 others, the townspeople oversubscribed a $180,000 goal by $50,000 in 10 days. With this they bought land and provided power, water, rail and sewage facilities.[2]

Such arrangements, which are not uncommon, must be carefully evaluated and, as was noted earlier, one-time costs separated from annual costs.

Now for the third group of limitations. In general, the basic objective for most plants is to make a profit while preserving capital. However, plants are sometimes built without this objective or with this objective as a secondary consideration. The location of the plant may be a matter of national security; the plant may be designed to enhance the economy of a particular region; or the choice of location may be affected by intranational economics. Such factors may limit the regional choice and reduce the selection problem to one of choosing among alternative sites in a region. In such a case, the problem of choosing a location is essentially simplified rather than radically altered.

It should be obvious that a specific site, or piece of property, cannot be considered independently of the building. In many cases the reverse is also true. The degree of mutual dependence is a function of the basic nature of the building.

Building designs may be classified into three major categories:

1. The building is an integral part of the production process, e.g., petrochemical plants, steel mills.
2. The building embodies special features to facilitate the process, e.g., flour-milling plants, heavy-machinery-manufacturing plants, airplane plants.

---

[2] "The Year's Best Ideas in Buildings and Grounds," *Factory Management and Maintenance*, vol. 116, no. 5, May, 1958, p. B-5.

3. The building represents general housing which can accommodate a variety of products or processes, e.g., light manufacturing, printing, toy making, electronics assembly.

Buildings of the first two types represent a meeting of the requirements of somewhat inflexible product-process demands. Hence, buildings of the first two types tend to set the specifications for sites. The third type allows more flexibility in adapting the building to the site. However, even when the type of building restricts the possible sites, there are a variety of feasible alternatives of the design of the building, particularly with regard to details, so that a suitable building can be designed for different sites. The various alternative combinations of design and site for these three major types of buildings may be compared by determining, for each alternative, the total of all of the different types of costs. Of course, the values obtained must also be examined in the same fashion. It should be obvious that the most preferable alternative will not always be easy to identify. The four major types of costs are:

1. Cost of fulfilling product-process requirements
2. Cost of fulfilling man-job requirements
3. Cost of providing material storage
4. Cost of meeting area requirements such as building codes and restrictions or community beautification programs

The details associated with the design of an industrial building can be categorized in a fashion that will assist in generating alternative designs and in examining the costs and values associated with each alternative. The following is a list of categories:

1. Area of building
2. Number of floors
3. Size of each floor and clear area
4. Shape of each area
5. Relationship (geometrical) between areas
6. Foundation
7. Floor: surface, load-bearing, and vibration characteristics
8. Sidewall construction
9. Entrances and exits
10. Roof: shape and material
11. Separation of plant, office, service, and storage areas and size of each
12. Yard equipment: structures and access
13. Parking areas
14. Electrical services, including lighting
15. Air and hydraulic services
16. Communications

17. Water service
18. Sewage and waste disposal
19. Ventilation, heating, air conditioning
20. Employee facilities: lockers, dressing rooms, lavatories (and other cleaning facilities as needed), food service, first aid, and so forth
21. Plant protection, including fences
22. Sprinklers and special fire-protection systems
23. Maintenance shop areas
24. Materials handling: cranes, chutes, elevators, conveyor supports, and so forth

An examination of these items will reveal that many of the required characteristics will be a function of the equipment to be housed and served and the required relationship of each piece of equipment to each other piece of equipment to meet the needs of the processes to be used. Of course, the final details of design will reflect not only the meeting of the needs of the equipment but a modification of the solution so as to meet the needs of the man-jobs which will serve the equipment and plant, as well as other compromises, but the initiating objective is to house the equipment.

Hence, the first task in the designing of the details of a plant is to obtain the full specifications of the products to be made, their processes, and the volume of each product and to ascertain the equipment which will be used to produce it. The amount of each kind of equipment must then be determined.

With this information, it is possible to establish the design criteria for the details of the building. These criteria are obtained by first creating the layout which provides the best configuration of the necessary equipment, work areas, storage areas, office areas, and so forth. A *layout* is the detailed information concerning the placement of all of the items mentioned. However, deciding upon the criteria for establishing which of all possible configurations is best is the problem which must precede the layout. For instance, it may be desired to place the equipment relative to its use in the sequence of production; another alternative is to group equipment by function; still another alternative is by size. Which of the possible criteria should take precedence varies from situation to situation and will be the subject of a later discussion.

To return to the problem of layout, scale models in two or three dimensions may be used, depending on the complexity of perceiving the problems. Mathematical models of alternative layouts may also be created and used to help in evolving the design which best meets the selected criteria of preference. The field of technology employed is called plant layout.

The problem of designing the actual building is one of attempting to house the ideal layout within the limitations governing such designs. This phase of plant design is a task for a civil or an architectural engineer who designs the building details and configuration so as to conform to local laws and codes; to employ materials economically while providing support and shelter for the manufacturing complex; and to meet, insofar as possible, the requirements of the ideal layout as specified by the process group and managers. In many cases, there may be conflicting demands between the ideal layout of the plant and the ideal building and the sites which are available, and a compromise must usually be developed to obtain a solution which is optimum with respect to the totality of factors. The designers of process, layout, and building must all cooperate in making such compromises. The more the plant is an integral part of the manufacturing process, the more important it becomes for close cooperation to exist between the civil or building-design engineers and the process-design group.[3]

Now let us return to the second type of plant-design problem. Earlier in this chapter we noted that a problem more common than the locating of a new plant was the problem "design of the best means of taking advantage of a location in the operation of an existing plant." In problems of this latter type, the primary alternatives relate to the selection of product, process, and raw material to fit the location and building which already exist and to select and lay out equipment to fit into the existing limitations, although there may be some opportunity to modify the building. Hence, problems of this kind contain practically all the same factors as problems of new location, but the nature of the possible choices, as was mentioned earlier, is somewhat different. Also, the sales or marketing group will be more deeply involved.

A subvariety of the above type of problems is even more common. In the usual plant, there are small but frequent changes in the amount or type of equipment or changes in the product which would be facilitated by changes in the layout of the equipment in the plant. Thus, a constantly recurring task of plant design is to modify the layout to accommodate such changes. Much has been developed in the way of techniques to assist in performing such design work to achieve desired goals economically.

REFERENCE TOPICS

Land values   Economic geography
Types of industrial buildings   Raw-material sources
Regional economics   Labor supply, regional

---

[3] The process-design group will consist of different types of people, depending on the type of product. With plants devoted to chemical processes or nuclear processes, we tend to find chemical engineers or nuclear engineers designing the process. Industrial engineers are frequently employed in designing normal manufacturing processes. In plants where the internal and external technical complexity of the product is low, we may find process designers from different fields.

Transportation facilities
Plant layout and design
Materials handling
Plant site
Decentralization of industry
Industrial dispersion

Industrial centralization
Physical facilities of plants
Building codes and restrictions
Legal requirements for amenities
Smoke-abatement programs
Water pollution abatement

SUGGESTED THEMES

1. Economic evaluation of the location of selected plants
2. Reasons for the location of selected enterprises
3. Patterns of location for various industries
4. Evaluation of selected industrial buildings with respect to suitability for the enterprise

SUGGESTED CASES

Cruickshank, H. M., and K. Davis, *Cases in Management,* 3d ed. Homewood, Ill.: Richard D. Irwin, Inc., 1962. Cases beginning on pages 61, 69, 199, 216, 237, 238, 255.

Greenwald, D. U., *Elementary Case Problems for Industrial Engineers.* New York: The Ronald Press, 1957. Cases beginning on pages 21, 23, 78.

Terry, G. R., *Case Problems in Business and Industrial Management,* 2d ed. Dubuque, Iowa: William C. Brown Company, Publishers, 1955. Cases beginning on pages 16, 17, 38, 39, 41, 54, 55, 63, 65, 66, 68.

Ziegler, R. J., *Casebook in Production Management.* New York: John Wiley & Sons, Inc., 1962. Cases beginning on pages 57, 60.

10 DESIGNING PRODUCT AND PROCESS

This chapter deals with the task of decision making with regard to what to make and how to make it. The variety of product is almost infinite, as was noted in Chapter 4, particularly if we extend the word product to include any output of the enterprise, such as the rendering of services as well as form utilities. Even restricting the discussion to rendering of form utilities leaves an enormous range. The field of activity is also broad. "The enlightened concept of product design shows that the design process is one of adjusting the product to everything within its industry and to all the factors affecting its distribution and use. The product itself is a symbol of a grand integration of all these factors."[1]

The basic motivating force stimulating the need for the design of a product may be such as:

1. An existing plant which must be kept active and profitable to preserve the capital value

[1] H. B. Maynard (ed.), *Industrial Engineering Handbook*. New York: McGraw-Hill Book Company, 1956, pp. 7–143.

2. A surplus raw material which either affects the profitability of the main product or presents the possibility of its use as a low-cost material
3. A desire to engage in profitable activity

Whichever of these three forces or combination of them surrounds the decision making process, this aspect should be thought of as a limitation or constraint affecting the range of alternatives from which the product to be made will be selected.

Product design is the preparation of the detailed specifications of what will be made to satisfy the need of potential customers. The word "need" is being used in the broadest sense of want. Need is reflected in sales, and the continuation of need is affected by use or acceptance. Use and acceptance reflect both real and apparent desirability. Desirability is often the result of a complex series of value judgments and comparisons by the customer concerning convenience, function, reliability, and alternative possibilities of purchase. These value judgments are influenced by social and economic changes affecting real needs and purchasing power, mores, and attitudes and fads, all of which are continually changing and are affected by many subfactors. In addition, product design is affected by legal factors, such as patent limitations and use limitations imposed by society. Further, in most Western societies, product design is performed in a competitive economy.

From the foregoing, it should be obvious that the decision concerning what product to make, which is inextricably tied up with decisions about how to make it, requires the coordinated effort of practically all the managerial groups mentioned in all of the preceding chapters.

The three motivating factors, mentioned as limitations, tend to focus attention in different directions within the managerial group as follows:

1. **Existing plant.** An existing plant has a given complement of equipment and man-jobs with their inherent skills. If these are the main limitations, the attention is focused on modifications of existing product or on the creation of new product which will allow the preservation (or conservation) of these values. This still leaves a wide area of choice. For instance, a pot and pan manufacturer may expand to include automatic coffee makers, corn poppers, electric frying pans, coated ware, and so on. An airframe manufacturer may attempt to produce house trailers or missile bodies; a shipyard may build dam gates, bridges, cranes, or other steel structures. The initial emphasis may be on market research or actual design; the process skills would not need much change.

2. **A surplus raw material.** With a surplus raw material, the emphasis is somewhat different. We need knowledge as to the properties of the raw material, how it may be processed, what it can be made into, and what kind

of market exists for such outputs. As examples of such undertakings, we have building board presently being made from sugar cane waste and fertilizer from sewage. It is worth noting that the affected areas of management activity are wider from the very inception than in the preceding category.

3. A desire to engage in profitable activity. In such a case, the range of choice is limited only by the capital available and the legal restrictions. This third motivating factor possesses the smallest number of inherent limitations, but the largest number of areas of management activity will be involved in reaching a decision. Also, this category is really the least common one in an industrial society because all existing plants are continually seeking change in order to continue to exist in a competitive economy, and the existing plants greatly outnumber the new enterprises. In an emerging society, the reverse may be true.

From the foregoing, we can see that if we focus our discussion on the first motivating cause, we will include an approach to the other two, which are less limiting motivating factors.

Also, we must realize that product design is a cyclic task. Once a product is designed, the forces of competition and changes in needs operate to require changes in product. Hence, we must think of the steps given as required for product design as a series of steps which are continuously repeated during the life of an enterprise. The rapidity of the cycle will vary with the product, the rate of technological change, the rate of social change, the amount and kind of competition, and the type of need being serviced. As a simple example, the need for punch-card and computer equipment was originally served by a few companies whose products changed very slowly. As technology progressed and as the demands of business economy and science altered, more companies entered the field, products changed faster, and design objectives, in relation to price and function, became more restrictive.

The first step in designing a product is frequently that of determining the need which will be served. As mentioned in Chapter 4, there are many ways of classifying product. Which classification is preferable depends upon the purpose of the classification. For organizing an approach to the problem of selecting the need the designed product is to satisfy, a special classification would be helpful.

In terms of the type of need served, we may divide product into three main groups:

1. Serving a basic, acknowledged need, with an established market
2. Serving an anticipated need, without an established market, as is typical of a radically new product
3. Serving specific needs, as specified by individual customers

Such a classification may be superimposed upon all of the classifications given in Chapter 4. For instance, in category 1 above, we will find products such as food, basic clothing, basic appliances such as stoves and refrigerators (depending upon the society, of course), standard lumber sizes, furniture, or gasoline.

In category 2, we may find special foods for the growing outdoor activities (in America, at least), new types of protective clothing, new appliances (refrigerators were once in this category), new plastics, new petrochemicals, or tape-controlled machine tools.

In category 3, we may find food for army field rations or expeditions, specialized clothing for the armed forces or for space activities, special machine tools, special electrical switchgear built to customer specifications, or oil tankers.

One should note that the three categories may refer to products which employ similar raw materials and similar processes and that categories 1 and 2 may even reach the same customers.

The value of such a classification is in its relationship to the nature of problems encountered in designing product and process. In each of the categories there are differences in:

1. The relative importance and uniqueness of the substantive decisions required with regard to product and process
2. The source of the data used in developing alternatives
3. The weight to be given to various evaluative criteria used to compare alternatives

For instance, in category 1 (with an established need and market), we need some competitive advantage such as a lower price, greater reliability, better service, and better style appeal. The emphasis is on a better serving of an established need and hence on a fuller knowledge of needs and on an ability to reflect these in such factors as the close details of product and process design, materials, or service. Price usually needs close watching.

With items from category 2 (anticipated need), we need much new data concerning market and product function. Design, material, and process may likewise be areas requiring the development of new knowledge. Price is usually not as restraining as in category 1.

In the serving of specific needs of customers (category 3), we may have two basically different types of subcases. For instance, if the customer supplies the design, our sole areas of freedom of action are in the procurement of raw material or components, the process design including tooling, and the design of man-jobs. Price is usually a critical factor, although time of delivery and reliability of product may be important. On the other hand, if the customer specifies only the function of the required product, we may have a limited version of category 1, mixed with some of the new product aspects of category 2. Depending upon the newness of the technologies involved, the emphasis will vary. If the product and process design represent well-known technologies, the emphasis may well be on price or meeting a combination of economic criteria; we will discuss these later. If the design of the product and process requires the use of new or partially known technologies, the emphasis may be on developing a functioning product design and a feasible process, with price of relatively little concern. The major area of management concern, in such a case, may be feasibility in the substantive area, and the economic criteria might be unimportant.

The actual development of a design will involve five substantive areas of decision making:

1. Actual details of configuration of product design
2. Raw material, nature and specification
3. Process design
4. Tool design
5. Man-job design

As has been noted in earlier chapters, these factors also interact. Also, many trade-offs can usually be made among these factors. A *trade-off* refers to an enhancement of the characteristics or values of any one factor, at the expense of another, or to the selection of conditions for more than one factor which improves the whole result, even if it does not provide the optimum conditions for any one factor. If the substantive result of a trade-off is negligible, the economic criteria may come into full play. For preliminary examples, a trade-off may be obtained by the purchase of a more expensive raw material to obtain a cheaper process, more tooling to use less labor, more man-jobs to reduce investment, change of product design to reduce tooling cost, change in process to use a cheaper raw material, and so forth. In the usual sequence of product-process design, the initial design is only a rough approximation of the final answer; the subsequent and major effort involves an examination of all feasible trade-offs to approach an optimum product-process design from the viewpoint of the economic criteria or whatever criteria dominate.

The economic criteria so frequently mentioned in the preceding discussion are usually vital. The usual industrial plant exists to make a product which can be sold at a profit. Hence, the decisions of designing or selecting product and process are made with economic criteria as the basis for choosing between alternatives. When the decisions are carried out, the adequacy or inadequacy of the decisions is revealed, leading to a continuous cycle of decision, evaluation, redecision, and so on. We have referred to this concept of control previously and will reexamine it, in more detail, in subsequent chapters.

The five interacting major factors to consider in developing economic criteria are:

1. Direct unit costs
2. Indirect unit costs
3. Volume
4. Sales price
5. Profit

Whatever is to be made and sold must produce a satisfactory relationship among these five interacting factors. The number of interactions is large. For instance, indirect costs (representing charges not directly attributable to individual units of product), such as the cost of indirect man-jobs, general plant costs, and amortization of equipment, are affected by volume. One element of direct costs, particularly direct labor, may be high if plant capital investment is low, but this will reduce indirect costs; raising indirect costs by increasing mechanization may produce a more than offsetting reduction in direct-labor costs. This last course of action may be desirable or undesirable, to a varying degree, depending on volume. However, volume may be a function of sales price, which itself is directly related to profit at any given volume. The numerous interactions possible should be apparent.

The steps of the procedure for solving a product and a process-design problem may now be listed in more detailed terms. Although the usual sequence of events will be in the order in which the steps will appear, there are conditions which will change the order. Such conditions are not uncommon. With most products, the difficulty of making the decisions needed at each step of the procedure will vary from step to step. In any actual case, the order of steps employed will tend to reflect such differences.

The following general steps are usually required to design a product and a process:

1. Specification of the need to be filled and the desired cost, sales price, volume, and profit relationships and restrictions, in order to establish specific goals and criteria for subsequent steps
2. General specification of the required product with respect to function it must perform
   a. Basic
   b. Reliability
   c. Convenience
   d. Accuracy
   e. Cost (of performing function)
3. General design concept
   a. Configuration and size

    b. Material and cost
    c. Processing cost
4. Development of prototype
    a. Drawings or sketches
    b. Breadboard, mock-up, sample[2]
5. Pilot model
    a. Drawing
    b. Model
    c. Drawing modification
6. Technical testing
    a. Function factors
    b. Cost estimates
7. Consumer testing
    a. Use
    b. Price and market
8. Tentative process design
    a. Raw-material specification
    b. Sequence of processing
    c. Equipment and tooling design and layout
    d. Materials-handling adjuncts
    e. Man-jobs
9. Process improvement (trade-offs among the subitems of steps 5 and 8 to approach optimum product-process combination with respect to function, process, and cost)
10. Cost estimate of final product-process design
11. Comparison with goals and recycling as necessary
12. Final detail of design of product and process and determination of anticipated costs
13. Decision to implement, recycle, change goals, or abandon in whole or in part

Even a cursory glance at these steps will suggest that the importance and difficulty of any one step will be a function of the type of need being serviced, the technologies involved, the motivating factor, the rate of change taking place in the industry, the internal and external technical complexity of the product, and so forth. With some products, some of these steps will be vestigial, while with other products, these steps may be extremely time consuming and critical and have many more substeps than indicated. For instance, with much women's clothing, the process-sequence design problem of steps 8*b* to *e* is almost negligible; with inertial guidance systems for sophisticated missiles, these same steps may be critical; with bread making, the cost (steps 10 and 11) and taste (5*b* and 7*a*) may be the main problems.

---

[2] There are a number of different terms, reflecting the custom of each industry.

For a fuller understanding, let us examine the manner of performing the thirteen steps, one by one, at the same time noting the interactions, the factors affecting the importance, and the feedbacks and the recycling which may be necessary. Even though we must look at the steps individually, it must be understood that the entire sequence is continuous; in much actual practice, it is being repeated even while the initial decisions are being implemented. Indeed, with complicated products and processes, several recyclings may be taking place simultaneously, with information moving through the steps like blocks of cars moving down a long avenue with empty spaces between the blocks of cars.

Step 1. Specification of the need to be filled and the desired cost, sales price, volume, and profit relationships and restrictions, in order to establish specific goals and criteria for subsequent steps. In an economy where goods are scarce, consumers are compelled to take what they can get. Where goods are plentiful, the consumer exerts pressure through selective purchasing on both product nature and price. Competition also affects the manufacturer. So do changes in custom or technology. Meeting consumer needs requires a factual quantitative understanding of those needs. Depending on the nature of the product, information bearing on needs may exist in publications concerning purchasing habits of the consumer. Purchasing habits are frequently reported in government publications (such as those of the U.S. Department of Commerce), trade publications, national trade association publications, or market survey organization publications. Data may also exist within the sales organization of the company itself or be developed by a special market survey. Because of the dynamic nature of the factors affecting need, the situation requires continual appraisal and continual examination of the alternative courses of action. Consumer complaints may provide a useful source of information. In product lines where style is important, change is usually particularly rapid. Social changes may have a large effect; e.g., the widespread distribution of electricity achieved by the Rural Electrification Administration slowly put the gas and kerosene refrigerator out of date. Economic pressure for additional lines of product may be reported by the production engineering group who assess the unused capability of the plant. Pressure for reduction of the product line may come from warehouse managers who seek to reduce carrying costs. There are alternatives such as product simplification to reduce unit price, product standardization to reduce manufacturing and carrying cost, or new product design to meet new needs.

Obviously, decisions in this area are critical to the life of an enterprise and consequently are considered areas requiring the attention of top managers. Market facts, knowledge of factory capability, and knowledge of economic constraints are all needed to make good decisions.

Any decision reached will be tempered with projections of the stability of both the economy and the need being filled, so as to anticipate any effect upon the potential size of the enterprise; economic changes may suggest expansion, contraction, or holding the size constant. Each of these three alternatives will have special costs and special risks.

The basic market projections will be examined in view of the five major economic criteria mentioned earlier in this chapter. The relationships among these five factors are best understood with the aid of a graphic analysis, such as a *break-even chart*. A break-even chart is shown in Figure 10.1. The ordinate is money; the abscissa is volume. The lines charted show the fixed costs, the incremental costs per unit of product over and above the fixed costs, and the income from sales. A different line represents the income at each selling price. For any given volume, the difference between the sum of fixed and incremental costs on one hand and the income on the other hand represents profit or loss. With a chart of this type, various assumptions and necessary conditions of the dependent variables may be examined, in coordinated form, with respect to the feasible or probable consequences.

Step 2. **General specification of the required product with respect to function it must perform.** This step involves the preparation of a more refined statement of the needs to be met in terms related to the required characteristics of the

Figure 10.1   Break-even chart

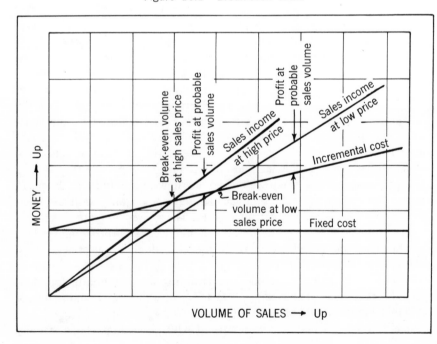

product. It is necessary to specify, with some exactitude, the way the product will be used, what the consumer will expect it to do for him, how reliable it will need to be, and what the cost of using the product will be. Comfortable beds that are too bulky to fit normal rooms, refrigerators too wide to move through normal doors, stoves which cook well but require awkward postures to use, bacon with excellent flavor but poor keeping qualities, TV sets with excellent pictures but needing much maintenance, air conditioners that cool well but use excessive amounts of power, clothes that look well but wash poorly, warm winter garments that wear well but make the wearer look like a tank or limit his movements, all must be avoided. Physiology, custom, social requirement, and aesthetics may all have a bearing. If the product is designed for export, the foreign customers' point of view must be determined. All relevant requirements must be examined.

In addition, the preceding factors must be studied against the cost-quality curves typical of the product involved to produce the first feedback to step 1. Such a cost-quality curve is shown in Figure 10.2. The ordinate is money; the abscissa is quality. One curve is drawn for cost of production, the other curve for value to the customer. The projected facts from such a curve must be examined from a viewpoint such as represented by the break-

Figure 10.2   Curves of money versus quality

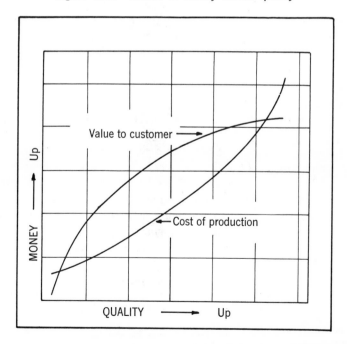

even chart previously mentioned because they will affect sales volume and costs. Additional market research may be necessary to draw such a curve because weightings for each of the product factors involved in value judgment will be required. Such a curve also reflects the state of the art related to the product.

It should be noted that the requirements of the product when given in detail may describe an article whose design problems with regard to both product and process fall within the known limits of knowledge. In such a case, the feasibility of production can be assumed and one may proceed to the next step. In other cases, much research may need to be performed to establish the basic information needed for the next step.

Step 3. General design concept. The creation of a general design concept requires an ability to draw on known facts to describe the nature and size of the object to be made to serve the intended use, considering the marketing method to be employed and the materials to be used. The general design concept indicates the general process, i.e., cast, form, machine, assemble, and the general sequence of these events which will be used to make the product, as well as the probable costs to process it. The general design concept is used to perform the first appraisal of the feasibility of meeting the general specifications within the known state of the art of the applicable fields of knowledge. When appropriate, the general design concept also establishes the means of meeting the aesthetic requirements.

The more complete the necessary fields of knowledge, the more specific the general concept of design becomes and the easier the task of converting the general design concept into final form for production; the more incomplete the requisite fields of knowledge, the more research implicit in the subsequent steps. The required research may concern the internal nature of the product itself, the marketing problems, the manner of use of the product, the materials to be used, or the processes required with the materials.

For a simple illustration, at one time a general design concept for a small portable radio with a 100-mile AM receiving range might have been: "A small black box[3] of plastic, about 2″ by 1″ by 6″, consisting of three subsystem black boxes; one, an electrical energy storage device, occupying not more than one-third of the total volume, with a use life of approximately 200 hours; two, a radio circuit, employing miniaturized components, with an audio frequency output sufficient to drive subsystem three; subsystem three is a black box transducer, converting electrical energy into sound of sufficient volume to be audible at 20 feet at full volume, with reasonable fidelity within the range of 60 to 4,000 cycles per second. The materials are to be hand-assembled at a cost not in excess of $5.00." Considerable

---

[3] The term *black box* is used to describe a device whose functions are known but whose design represents a problem to be solved.

research is indicated as necessary when the problem can only be stated in this form. However, the currently known state of the art permits the general design concept to describe the above subsystems in terms of standard components, purchasable, for the most part, on the open market, and permits the exact description of dimensions, style, and cost in complete and accurate terms.

The more complicated the object, whatever the state of the art, the greater the need for a general design concept to guide the designers of components or subsystems. The more complicated the process requirements, the more these are reflected in special features of the general design concept. The more that style or aesthetic appeal is inherently important in a product, the more likely it is that a sketch of the anticipated design will be prepared as part of this step. A good example of this is to be found in the architectural sketch of a building, long before the structural details are attempted, or the scale mock-ups of new automobile models.

Step 4. **Development of prototype.** The importance of this step and its place in the sequence will vary with the internal technical complexity and external technical complexity of the product. The position will also be affected by the use made of the product and the reliability required, as well as by the state of the art employed and the difficulty of employing the art. With complex objects, this step may be the first formally accomplished. For instance, a chemical firm may learn, via its research group, how to produce a new chemical whose use may be unknown but which appears to have peculiar properties. In such a case, step 1 will follow. With a new powered lawnmower, step 4 probably will be in its normal sequence, at which time the designer can create sufficiently detailed drawings so that the shop (usually a special section) can make up a sample model. In the case of a new electrical device, such as a radio or TV set, a so-called "breadboard" model will be made. The term refers to a model laid out to test the electrical and electronic features of the object, with no attempt to fit them into a particular size or package. With a new style of dress or pair of shoes, samples will be made. In wearing apparel, there is usually a customary size for such samples.

In cases where the state of the art is inadequate to permit the direct performance of this step, it will be performed, piece by piece, as the necessary facts are acquired. In cases where the state of the art is complete, steps 5 to 7 may be combined with or compressed into this step. The person or group performing this step will represent those who possess the knowledge of the substantive field of knowledge embodied in the product.

Step 5. **Pilot model.** The production of a pilot model, or one fully embodying all of the characteristics of the general design concept, may be separate from step 4 when the complexity of the object requires both a prototype to test the functional feasibility and a pilot model to fit this concept into the desired configuration. Further, in the production of the pilot model, the product designer must have some knowledge of the probable process and must modify the components to meet the requirements of economical processing. With objects whose processing is complex, there will tend to be a pilot model to adjust the prototype design to process requirements, unless the process is relatively fixed in pattern, as with automotive tires, radio tubes, or gasoline-engine piston rings.

Usually, the parts of the pilot model are made of the proposed materials while the preceding prototype is frequently made of materials which are economically convenient for making a model to serve the prime function of testing the concept embodied in the product. In the case of shoes or clothing mentioned in step 4, step 5 will probably be skipped.

In the pilot-model preparation, the product designer, representing the product state of the art, will be aided, usually by a group which represents marketing and production, in approaching as closely as possible to the original general design concept or in producing a better solution than originally conceived. Some recycling of steps 1 to 5 may occur.

Step 6. Technical testing. Technical testing is the evaluation of how well the product functions at its intended use. It serves to perfect the pilot model and to verify the assumptions made in the course of its design. Obviously, there will be considerable recycling between this step and steps 5 and 2 (pilot model and general specification), unless the designers are unusually fortunate or foresighted and have correctly anticipated all interactions among the product, its manner of use, and the environment in which it will be used.

The importance and complexity of technical testing will be affected by such factors as:

1. The type of need being met
2. The importance of a performance requirement
3. The allowable tolerance of performance
4. The internal complexity of the product and the state of the art employed in designing the product

With products designed to serve basic acknowledged needs, the criteria of product performance are usually well understood and the means of testing have usually been well established. This would be true of food products,[4] clothing, automobile fuels and lubricants, writing pens, and common electrical appliances. With products designed to meet anticipated needs, the technical testing may tend to become somewhat more difficult because of the need to anticipate the manner of use and to establish criteria to evaluate the product. For instance, there may be considerable discussion on the criteria

---

[4] Changes in legislation, reducing the allowable limits for residues, such as pesticides, may go beyond the state of the art of testing so these statements should be considered in such a light; changes may shift them into the more-difficult-to-test group.

of performance for a new type of automotive ignition system in terms of the importance of smoothness of response, repairability, economy, or cost. In the early stages of development of a product, there are usually continual changes in the criteria, as with automobile tires, typewriters, computers, and so forth. When products serve some specific need, as detailed by the customer, the criteria of performance may be set forth as "performance capabilities (with tolerance limits); a detailed description of test design and procedure; reliability and other endurance capability requirements; intended purpose and method of use; quality assurance provisions";[5] and so forth.

The importance of a performance requirement has, as might be anticipated, considerable bearing on the manner of technical testing. For instance, a disease vaccine will require a critical performance test, statistically controlled and extensive; a new airplane must meet a variety of detailed and rigorous static and flight tests. By comparison, a new low-priced ball-pen retraction mechanism may be given only cursory testing.

The allowable tolerance of performance affects the problem of technical testing. For instance, the size of pairs of shoes made of a new material and by a new process is a dimension allowing some considerable variation. On the other hand, bearings for high-speed motors must behave with precise characteristics; diesel-engine fuel pumps must function to precise limits for extended periods.

The state of the art has an even greater effect upon technical testing. In cases where the state of the art is well known, indirect tests may frequently be used because many relationships with other product characteristics which may be harder to measure directly may be well known; e.g., with subsonic aircraft, wind-tunnel tests of miniature models provide much useful information and will even precede steps 4 and 5. In contrast, the technical test of the first nuclear pile posed fearsome problems.

Technical testing frequently involves tests of performance under special conditions. Such testing is often classified under the following headings, although this classification is not a list of fully mutually exclusive approaches:

1. Environmental testing
2. Sample use
3. Accelerated aging
4. Mechanical, electrical, chemical, abrasive, or structural testing
5. Life testing

Environmental tests involve the evaluation of the functioning of the product under ambient conditions which it must be prepared, to varying degrees, to endure. The conditions of test may involve ranges of pressure, temperature, moisture, dust or other air contamination, salt spray, sunshine,

[5] R. R. Landers, *Reliability and Product Assurance.* Englewood Cliffs, N.J.: Prentice-Hall, Inc., 1963, p. 142.

and so forth. Such conditions may be simulated in test chambers or obtained in actual desert, mountain, or arctic areas.

Sample use is usually designed to obtain a knowledge of the effect of unanticipated conditions which may occur during use or the effects of varied combinations of such conditions. Use also provides a chance to expose the product to unanticipated conditions of abuse. Such tests are exemplified by such actions as putting a limited number of pilot models of turbine cars or trucks into regular use; statistically determining the effect of carefully controlled experimental groups with new types of shoes, clothing, and dentrifices; or exposing washing machines to the work habits of selected users (or abusers).

Accelerated aging is the term used to denote tests designed to compress long-term effects of use or environment into a short period. Such tests often pose challenging problems of test design. Care must be exercised to avoid creating artificial interactions. As a classic illustration, subjecting a fertile chicken egg to a warm, moist atmosphere for several weeks produces quite a different result from boiling in water for a short period.

Mechanical and electrical (and so forth) tests are usually made to determine the properties of a product. For instance, a car chassis may be subjected to torsional tests to determine not only how much torsion it can safely endure but also its failure point; a new design of condenser will be tested to determine not only whether it will safely handle its design voltage but also its breakdown point.

Life tests can be made by either accelerated aging or full-cycle aging. Banks of light bulbs may be burned continuously to determine their life, or they may be burned in periods simulating normal use to determine their working life. Motors may be run at normal loads until failure, paint exposed to natural elements until it fades, or shirts may be washed and rewashed until unwearable. Life testing of one form or another is common.

At this point, it should be obvious that adequate testing of a pilot model depends upon many factors and can take many forms. There is a clear-cut need for cooperation among those familiar with the need to be met by the product, the intended manner of use, and the market and the product designer, the test technician, and the production specialist. The purpose of this cooperation is not only to design adequate and realistic tests but also to interpret the results of these tests to help perfect the pilot model.

Step 7. **Consumer testing.** Consumer testing may refer to (*a*) a variation of technical testing; (*b*) a continuation of technical testing to perfect the design; or (*c*) a test of consumer reaction to price, features, and so forth, to correct the estimate of the anticipated volume of sales.

A new product, such as shoes made with a plastic substitute for leather, may be distributed, under controlled conditions, to evaluate acceptability to the customers. In another instance, a product may be sold in a given locality to evaluate price acceptance, attractiveness of packaging, and so forth. It should be obvious that this step, consumer testing, will not have a fixed place in the series of steps which have been listed; its position will tend to vary greatly with the type of information sought.

Step 8. **Tentative process design.** The performance of this step frequently interacts greatly with many of the preceding steps and, as a consequence, is often integral with them. The effective product designer, as mentioned earlier, must continually consider producibility. However, the newer the concept embodied in the product, the more likely it is that this step, tentative process design, will appear as a discrete event subsequent to the initial testing.

The end product of this step of tentative process design is a set of coordinated facts of five types:

1. The material specifications in a form suitable for use as a basis for procurement, giving the quantities required per unit of production
2. A list of operations in sequence, including the type and number of machines or equipment to be used for each step and the estimated production time per unit per operation
3. The tooling or adjunct equipment to be used at each step
4. The materials-handling equipment required to facilitate the flow of work within the process sequence
5. The man-jobs needed to operate at the desired rate of output

The materials specifications are a detailed description of the parts or raw material to be purchased, including the required physical characteristics such as size; mechanical, chemical, thermal, or optical properties; finish; or any other aspect pertinent to using the material to make the product by means of the contemplated process. The specifications are usually written to provide as much leeway as possible so as to allow economical procurement while still conforming to the product and process requirements. A knowledge of readily available materials and common specifications is needed to avoid requiring excessive special materials or parts.

The list of operations is influenced by the experience of the process designer, the general organization of the shop, the available state of the art required to make the product, the product requirements, the volume of product required, and the capital limitations. There are usually many alternative solutions to the problem of feasible process design. For instance, to make a hole to exceedingly fine tolerance in a piece of steel, one could (1) bore, ream, and grind or (2) bore, ream, hone, and grind. The final product would be the same. The economy of both methods would be affected by the assignment of tolerances and dimensional goals to each operation in the sequence. All of these details have a considerable bearing on the economy of manufacture.

A process sequence usually contains inspection points and, by inserting these at proper points, further economies can be obtained. Likewise, different machines have different capabilities with respect to range of variation of product. The process designer must select appropriately in terms of the requirements of the product.

The tooling list is a complete list of adjuncts to the machines and equipment. This list includes all forming or shaping tools, as well as any special jigs, fixtures, gauges, and so forth, required to perform each operation.

The materials-handling list represents the result of fitting the selected equipment into the physical plant. At this point, a *product-process chart* or other graphic aid is frequently employed to summarize graphically the process design. A product-process chart is a graphic representation of the separable steps required to transform a product from one stage of completion to another. The separable steps employed vary with the problem; in this context, the usual separated steps are *operations, moves, bankings, controlled storages, quantity-control points,* and *quality-control points.* These would be used to assist in plant layout, referred to in the previous chapter.

Finally, to complete the tentative design, a manning pattern is computed, giving the assignment of man-jobs needed to operate the equipment at the desired rate. Various means for describing man-jobs were given in Chapter 8.

All five sets of facts which have been described interact greatly with each other. There are usually many feasible solutions. The usual aim is to seek a solution which is optimum with regard to potential profit, although there frequently may be constraints, such as limitations of capital, process-design time, and equipment-procurement time. In plants making a variety of products, the design of the process for a new product often interacts with the processes used for other products. This situation can sometimes be usefully represented by a mathematical model which will be used to compute the pattern which is optimum, considering all products.

As a final step, from all the above data, the process designer will compute an approximate value, assuming a given volume of production, for each of the following items:

1. Capital required for equipment and tooling.
2. Fixed cost per unit.
3. Direct cost per unit.
4. Probable in-process time and value of in-process inventory. (A high in-process inventory increases the need for working capital.)

Step 9. **Process improvement.** The process designer will attempt to make trade-offs between and among the items of steps 8 and 5 to achieve an optimum solution within the constraints given. For instance, if the existing plant layout is by process, he will evaluate the cost effect of setting up product-oriented facilities for the new item. If the product is to be processed on existing equipment arranged in process layout, he can use linear programming or other mathematical models to assist in determining optimum volume, considering the needs of other products made by the plant. He can also test the probable effects of various capital expenditures. Queuing models may also be employed, depending on the nature of the problem.

The examination of trade-offs and alternatives can cause recycling to step 5 (pilot model) and create changes in design. For instance, stampings or forgings may be substituted for machine work. Various types of glue or fasteners may be compared. The range of possible change is usually very extensive.

The performance of this step is normally not only an initial problem but a continuing area of activity of tool designers, plant engineers, quality-control specialists, industrial engineers, line supervisors, product designers, and sales specialists, however the functions are divided and whatever the people are called. This step represents an area of activity in which each new development in material, equipment, tooling, or process know-how or product knowledge creates a possibility of improvement, and continual vigilance must be exercised to take economic advantage of these changes. It should be noted that excessive manpower and talent devoted to change may exceed the potential gain; to ignore change is to court competitive disaster; some in-between condition is desirable and usual but difficult to optimize. A continuous interchange of information among sales, finance, product design, and production people is needed to achieve an approach to full optimization rather than to an overenhancement of one factor at the expense of the whole.

Step 10. **Cost estimate of final product-process design.** After all the desirable trade-offs and changes have been made in the product-process design, the costs will be estimated as accurately as possible in order to compare the anticipated results with the goals developed in step 1. Cost estimates for new machines will be obtained from manufacturers, materials costs will be developed by those who do purchasing, tool costs will be computed, work measurement will be used to determine work time, and skill estimates will be made to determine probable labor-hour costs. Space charges and changes in overhead will be calculated. Investment, time to amortize out of profits, time to get into production, and so forth, all must be computed so as to provide a complete money-dimensioned picture of the proposed operation.

Step 11. **Comparison with goals and recycling as necessary.** This step, of course, could be considered as being integral with the preceding step, but it has been separated to indicate the need for a full consideration of all of the changes which may have taken place with respect to goals. The required price-volume relationship may have undergone changes since the inception of the project; the concept of need may have changed; the competitive position may have altered. Top management must make a decision to proceed and make a time-phased plan for implementation or decide to await the development of a more favorable plan.

Step 12. Final detail of design of product and process and determination of anticipated costs. This step and the step which follows will only occur with complex products or with processes so complex that step 10 was used only to produce an estimate. The reason for this is simple. If the cost of detailing the product and process in a form suitable for implementation is high, then a preliminary estimate is in order. The results of this step, in cases where it is applicable, are detailed drawings of product parts, subsystems, test procedures, equipment specifications, tooling, fixtures, jigs, and gauges; job instructions and standard times; and process- and production-control systems, all designed to be implemented in accordance with a schedule. Costs, investment, and profit are worked out as accurately as possible. The development of such plans will be discussed in Chapter 18.

Step 13. Decision to implement, recycle, change goals, or abandon in whole or in part. Management must consider all of the available facts and assumptions, the reliability of the facts and forecasts, and the uncertainties, in comparison with alternative uses of its money and facilities, and decide whether to proceed, wait, or abandon the project.

We have described, in this chapter, the general outlines of a management-information system designed to assist in making decisions. The details of procedure will vary with such factors as the type of product and the state of the art; this has been mentioned. However, a management-information system such as we have been describing or any other information or control system is, of itself, a process producing a product, the product being an internally consumed product and having extrinsic value rather than intrinsic value, as with a final product. The product-process-design determination sequence, for any internally consumed product, is almost an exact parallel of the sequence we have been describing, although the language used to describe the steps may be different. The sequence described is really just an amplification of the scientific approach described in Chapter 1.

REFERENCE TOPICS

Market research	Product testing
Price trends	Industrial standards of performance
Purchasing trends	Testing organizations
Consumer habits	Food and Drug Administration standards
Break-even charts	Linear programming

Production planning	Drafting
Queuing	Processing
Production equipment	Flow charts
Process charts	Pilot model
Man and machine charts	Prototype
Research and development	

SUGGESTED THEMES

1. Surplus raw materials
2. Analysis of diversification of existing plants
3. Changes in the computer industry
4. Classification of selected groups of products in terms of needs met
5. Development of a *black-box* statement of a product to serve a selected need
6. The Underwriters' Laboratory
7. Environmental tests for selected products
8. Analysis of failure of selected products
9. Life tests for selected products
10. Consumer tests for selected products
11. Differences in real and ostensible desires of consumers
12. Changes in anticipated product life with selected products
13. Changes in the society changing the "need" category of selected products

SUGGESTED CASES

Cruickshank, H. M., and K. Davis, *Cases in Management,* 3d ed. Homewood, Ill.: Richard D. Irwin, Inc., 1962. Cases beginning on pages 90, 203, 208, 257.

Greenwald, D. U., *Elementary Case Problems for Industrial Engineers.* New York: The Ronald Press, 1957. Cases beginning on pages 65, 81, 82, 98, 100.

Mantel, S. J., Jr., *Cases in Managerial Decisions.* Englewood Cliffs, N.J.: Prentice-Hall, Inc., 1964. Cases beginning on pages 39, 126, 190.

Terry, G. R., *Case Problems in Business and Industrial Management,* 2d ed. Dubuque, Iowa: William C. Brown Company, Publishers, 1955. Cases beginning on pages 18, 44, 47, 50, 58, 66, 77, 78, 79, 83, 84, 97, 122, 157.

11 SELECTING MATERIALS

In Chapter 5, which described *material,* some of the many managerial tasks relating to materials were mentioned. Some remarks were included describing only briefly the problems of performing these tasks. In the chapters which follow, it should have become increasingly obvious that the selection of materials was only one aspect of the many-faceted problem of designing an integrated system of man-jobs, physical plant, product-process design, and materials. Some of the interrelationships between materials and the other factors were pinpointed in Chapter 10 in the section dealing with the steps of the product-process-design problem. Particularly, in step 8, tentative process design, and step 9, process improvement, the inseparability of the consideration of material from the consideration of product and process should be clear and self-evident. The problem of selecting materials cannot be treated as an isolated subproblem. It is the purpose of this chapter to examine some of the interrelationships which affect the selection of materials, to examine a means of taking these interactions into account when making a decision concerning materials, and to examine a means of documenting such decisions.

A specific material is chosen for a given use because it possesses characteristics which give a desirable relationship between the costs associated with the material and the values it produces. The system of costs and values is essentially the same for all materials, but the relative importance of the subitems varies greatly from situation to situation.

The relative importance of the subitems of material cost and value is, in general, related to the four basic classifications of materials, *raw material, components, operating supplies,* and *equipment and plant supplies,* but other factors are often more important. Typical of such other factors are the scarcity of the material, the stability of its price, the effect of changes in material on the final product, the interrelationship with jobs and process, and the importance of material price to final cost.

The essential costs related to a material are:

1. Basic unit cost from the supplier
2. Cost of maintaining a contractual relationship
3. Cost of moving the material from source to plant
4. Cost of storing
5. Cost of verifying the characteristics of the material
6. Cost of internal handling
7. Cost of processing

The essential values are:

1. Suitability to satisfy the requirements of the product[1]
2. Availability of the requisite quality and quantity when desired
3. Compatibility with man-jobs

There are also intangible costs and values, such as the political friction created by using imported supplies, the advantages of using local or domestic material, the relationship between the supplier and user, and so forth.

An effective method of selecting a material requires a consideration of each element of cost and value on a factual basis, a proper weighting of each element, a consideration of the intangible costs and values, and, finally, the preparation of a specification describing the material which has been selected. In this chapter, some of the interactions encountered in assessing the facts concerning costs and values are examined first and are then followed by a discussion of the problems of preparing a specification.

Selecting a material is essentially a two-step problem. First, the required characteristics must be established and an actual material tentatively selected on the basis of available information. The costs and values of this material must be determined. Second, alternatives must be developed, evaluated, and compared, until the most desirable material is identified. These alternatives usually involve trade-offs related to the interactions among man-jobs, prod-

[1] The term *product* is used here in its broadest sense and includes both end products, or outputs, and those products which are consumed internally in the plant.

uct, plant, process, material, and market. The more important the costs of the material are to the economical operation of the plant, the more likely it is that the feasible trade-offs will need full evaluation.

The types of trade-offs connected with selecting a material can be classified usefully into a set of categories related to both the method of determining facts and the method of evaluation. These categories may be listed as:

1. Fixed material versus the mixture
2. Initial cost versus the processing cost
3. Initial cost versus the yield
4. Total cost versus product value
5. Cost versus the need
6. Cost versus special taxes or tax abatements
7. Cost and value of the product versus the nondangerous material
8. Certainty versus the new process
9. Part versus the whole
10. Cost versus the supplier reliability
11. Standard part versus the nonstandard part

Each of the types of trade-offs will be discussed in order to examine its nature and the type of information needed and to describe the coordination required in the organization to achieve desirable results.

1. Fixed material versus the mixture. There are many products which are commonly made from a fixed material or from a fixed mixture of materials, although they could be made to identical standards of quality from many different combinations of raw materials. Bologna, wool yarn, gasoline, steel ingots, and paper are usually of this type, to mention only a few.

For instance, bologna is made of beef, pork, and veal, together with certain spices, and it must contain a given percent of protein, fat, and moisture. It is permissible to use the meat from any part of the animals.[2] Each part, such as chuck, rib meat, shoulder meat, head meat, lip meat, and so forth, from beef, pork, or veal, contains a different percent of protein, fat, and moisture. Depending on which cuts of beef, pork, and veal are used to make the bologna, the requisite amount of each cut (material) will vary. A very large number of combinations is possible. The raw material represents the largest part of the total cost of the product. A problem arises because the price of each cut of beef, pork, and veal varies each day. A fixed combination of material will show a wide variation in price from day to day and, upon occasion, will exceed the normal selling price of the finished

[2] Meat is defined as the muscular tissue and the fat naturally attached thereunto; organs and glands are excluded. Also, the explanation is somewhat simplified here to reduce extraneous detail.

product. It is possible, however, to calculate the most profitable combination of cuts for any given day which meets the specifications for bologna and to change the mixture each day, thus taking advantage of the price changes while holding product characteristics constant. The processing costs are relatively independent of cuts chosen. The problem of making trade-off among the materials, viz., picking the optimum mixture, may be represented by a series of linear equations which can be solved to obtain the specifications of the mixture which will give the maximum profit, considering the particular prices at a given time. Such a use of mathematics often involves the use of a technique called linear programming.

A similar but more complicated problem exists with respect to wool yarn. Raw wool from different kinds of sheep and from different places contains different amounts of waste materials, such as dirt, plant matter, and oil. Some types of wool have larger amounts of short fibers, and some have larger amounts of long fibers. As a consequence, any different type of wool, for a given price, yields a different amount of long and short fibers. Of course, the various types of raw wool take different preliminary processing times and thus have different processing costs. These can be reflected in a "ready to spin" cost for each type of wool. Therefore, depending on the market price of each type and grade of raw wool, with adjustments for the preliminary processing cost, there will be variations in the mix of constituent wools making up the most economical mixture for a desired mix of fiber lengths. Despite the difference in the nature of the dimensions, this wool problem is similar to the bologna problem.

With wool, however, if the problem is pursued further, there is the possibility of additional factors to consider because, unlike the bologna, different types of wool require, as mentioned, different processing times on the preliminary equipment. Hence, the availability of equipment and its capacity must be considered in order to obtain full optimization with respect to profit. Also, total anticipated sales must be taken into account; if equipment capability is a limitation, a mixture other than the cheapest, from the first-cost aspect, may give the greatest profit. These additional constraints may be included in the mathematical equations used to represent the problem so that a mathematical model may still be used to assist in making a decision with respect to the trade-offs within the various types of wool.

Mixtures of raw materials for gasoline, steel ingots, and paper tend to resemble the wool problem. Much information must be gathered to construct the systems of equations, or *mathematical models,* as they are commonly called. Effort must often be expended on creating a means of solving these economically and in time to make a trade-off by reacting to market price changes. This reaction requires the cooperation both of the group who procure materials and of those who are controlling the process. Great care must be exercised to avoid undesirable changes in the product. Those in charge of product must be fully apprised of what is taking place so as to react properly to the change in material. Often considerable effort must be made to help them appreciate staff effort of this type, to assist in obtaining the value of the trade-off, as the method of computation may be hard to explain to non-mathematically oriented people.

2. **Initial cost versus the processing cost.** There are two subvarieties of this type of problem. The first is related to the higher cost of material resulting from a limiting of the variation permitted in the characteristics of supply; the second type is related to the natural mixture of desired and undesired materials in the supply, as with iron ore or copper ore.

As a simple example of a solution to the first type of problem, there are the variable condensers used in radio manufacture. Highly accurate condensers could be purchased, but they would be very expensive. Hence, considerable tolerance (with respect to capacitance) is allowed in the supply, and trimmer condensers or small separately adjustable condensers are added and adjusted during assembly to give the exact characteristics required by the radio circuit. The added cost of the trimmer and its adjustment is less than the additional cost of purchasing condensers with exact specifications.

In any such problem, one needs to obtain sufficient facts to evaluate the combined costs of purchasing and processing over a range of material specifications in order to make trade-offs between these two variables. The relationships, within the typical problem, are shown graphically in Figure 11.1. The ordinate is cost; the abscissa is variation permitted in the supply. One curve represents the cost of a unit of supply; one curve represents the cost of processing; one curve is the graphic sum, or total cost. It should be noted that these curves are idealized. There may be areas of discontinuity or odd shapes created by the standardization of certain quality specifications by the producing or supplying plant or industry.

The second type of problem, such as occurs with ores, in general, has an identical method of approach, although frequently it may be more appropriately identified as a mixture problem and an optimum solution sought from that aspect.

3. **Initial cost versus the yield.** Many materials, such as leather and lumber, are classified into relatively standard grades, and the price varies with the grade. For instance, leather for shoe uppers is classified into grades reflecting the number of defects in the surface. Shoes, however, require the cutting of many small pieces of leather, and these small pieces may be cut around the defects. The use of a lower grade of leather may reduce material costs by more than the sum of the cost of the additional scrap entailed and the additional labor time required to do the more careful cutting. The trade-off, in this case, involves a consideration of three variables, leather cost, yield,

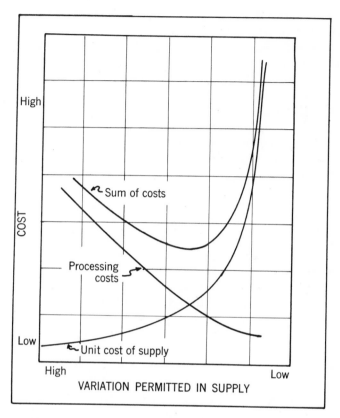

Figure 11.1   Cost of purchases and processing and
resultant final cost

and labor cost. Procurement and man-job designers must cooperate to solve
this sort of problem.

A similar problem may be encountered when comparing two alternative
sources of supply of unit-type items. The number of unusable pieces in the
material from one source may exceed the number in the material from the
other source, but the true comparison of cost is on the basis of the net cost
of a unit after sorting a batch to leave only units of acceptable quality.

4. **Total cost versus product value.** Product value is determined by customer
acceptance under the dynamic influences of competition. An automobile
paint which chalks may provide adequate protection to the vehicle and have
no effect upon its mechanical functioning but may not be as well accepted
as a more expensive paint which provides a longer-lasting, glossy finish. Pig
iron, formed by casting, may produce components strong enough, except

when unduly abused, but, because of this, they may not be as desirable as forgings made from a more expensive steel and by a more expensive process. The superior performance may enhance the long-run reputation and marketability of the product. As long as the cost of these changes can be recaptured in profit, considerable leeway may be exercised. The most leeway for a trade-off occurs when the increased cost of the alternative is small, the increase in value large, and the profit margin sizable. With products which have only a tiny margin between cost and sales price, even minor trade-offs between value and cost call for considerable scrutiny. Procurement, product design, process, man-jobs, and marketing are all affected by changes of this type, and considerable cooperation is required.

5. **Cost versus the need.** Failure to evaluate this type of trade-off properly often results in considerable difficulty. In Chapter 7 reference was made to the requirement of serving the needs of problems rather than of a hierarchy of people. Critical needs for materials frequently arise in a plant, such as for a repair part, components for the experimental laboratory, test equipment, or a minor item to complete a rush order. The value from prompt obtaining of these materials frequently completely overshadows the cost of the unit of material; anything meeting or exceeding the basic requirements is often economical, over a wide range of costs. However, the degree of importance of need and the magnitude of cost often approach borderline conditions. Hence, the cost of failure to supply a need in a given time should be subjected to a quick evaluation to define the problem. The making of this type of trade-off is often facilitated by giving certain groups permission to make direct purchases within certain values, or by maintaining a standing order with a selected supplier who will meet such rush needs at a reasonable price which may well be higher than the minimum which could be obtained by careful shopping; the trade-off enhances the speed of obtaining materials, at the expense of price.

6. **Cost versus special taxes or tax abatements.** The peculiar structure of excise and other taxes often creates peculiar possibilities of trade-offs. For instance, a cigarette lighter plated with silver may be classified as jewelry and subjected to a special tax; the same lighter plated with rhodium, another precious metal of similar hue, may be free of tax. Procurement, product and process design, and marketing are all concerned.

7. **Cost and value of the product versus the nondangerous material.** The phosphors used in fluorescent lamps, at one time, were carcinogenic.[3] In normal usage, of course, no danger was involved, but a hazard existed both in

[3] Cancer causing.

manufacture and in places of use from broken tubes. Substitute phosphors without this undesirable property were not as efficient or as cheap but were a desirable trade-off because of values not directly translatable into monetary terms. Similarly, lead paint has been eliminated from children's toys and inflammable material from cloth for clothing. Detergents, which could not be digested in sewage treatment, have been replaced with formulations that break down more readily. Carbon tetrachloride for cleaning may be replaced by a less toxic, though less efficient, material. Processes may be modified to reduce the output of fumes of air pollution. In general, the use of any unusually hazardous material suggests an opportunity for procurement, product, process, and marketing people to attempt to find a trade-off for the hazard.

8. **Certainty versus the new process.** An old process is usually well understood; its capabilities are defined. On the other hand, a new process always contains many unknown elements. For instance, forged crankshafts for automobile engines represented a well-understood process and product; the casting of crankshafts from new alloys had many unknown features. Product quality and real process costs cannot be known but can only be estimated prior to actual manufacture and performance testing. An additional cost of any radically new process, such as this example, is the usual need to run both the old and the new processes simultaneously, until certainty of the results of the new process is established, and the old may be eliminated. Evaluation of such trade-offs must include the changes in man-jobs, process, plant use, product, material, and development costs and the values of the altered product and process.

9. **Part versus the whole.** Often comparison of materials indicates one material as having many superior properties with respect to some aspect of the product and inferior properties with respect to others. Also, there may be a considerable difference between the prices of two alternative materials. There is usually a feasible trade-off, making part of the product of one material and part of the product of another. The brass inserts in plastic parts represents such a combination trade-off. Likewise, brass inserts cast in the die castings of carburetors to provide strong, tough screw threads, while taking advantage of the accurate and complex shapes possible with die-casting metals, represent a similar combination. Other examples are silver plating of switch contacts to obtain the superior contact of silver without the cost of making the whole part of this expensive metal, weaving fabric of a mixture of synthetic and natural fibers to achieve strength with some of the absorbency of the natural fiber, or making plywood whose face consists of selected veneers bonded to less attractive layers for strength. Part versus whole trade-offs are usually made to reduce material costs at the expense

of additional processing or to obtain characteristics which neither material possesses by itself. There must be cooperation among those responsible for procurement, product design, process, plant, and man-jobs, together with a thorough and continuous search for materials.

10. **Cost versus the supplier reliability.** There will always be suppliers who are more reliable than others with respect to delivery time and quality. Such suppliers may or may not constitute a more costly source of supply with respect to the first cost. If the first costs are equal, the additional values are a complete gain. If the first costs from the more reliable supplier are higher, then a careful study must be made to properly evaluate the additional values in order to make a decision. Sometimes the problem is more complicated. The less reliable supplier may be a sole source for a component; the reasonable but less preferable substitute may be considerably more expensive. In such a case, product and process values must also be taken into account to evaluate the trade-off fully.

11. **Standard versus the nonstandard part.** A standard is a model, example, or criterion established by authority, custom, or general consent. Some of the basic standards, such as units of length, volume, weight, and electrical current, are the subject of international agreement and are used to facilitate comparison and exchange.

Some small items have been completely standardized, such as small screws which are readily available in certain diameters with a given number of threads per inch. If other sizes are required, they must be made to order. There are, of course, a considerable number of standard sizes.

Electron tubes, in general, conform to certain standard types. The standards include a variety sufficient for almost all circuits. Steel and copper pipe are made in large quantities in certain standard sizes; there are standard sheet sizes for paper, steel, and plywood and relatively standard widths for woven cloth. Tires for automobiles are restricted to a given number of wheel diameters and shapes, although other characteristics of tires may show the results of individual plants exercising their individual decisions within the freedom of choice feasible within the standards. The same is true of the male plugs for 110-volt current in the United States. Although the plugs will fit into a standard receptacle, they are not at all identical. The standard size is a constraint which still allows uniqueness of design.

In general, when parts are ordered in small quantities, the standard parts are much cheaper than special unique parts. For instance, small brass gears of a standard size, with a standard number and shape of teeth, may be available at about 20 cents per gear; a nonstandard gear would cost more than $5 in nominal quantities. When quantities are sufficiently large, the price of special parts may be the same as for standard parts. Further, if the special part embodies some economy of material as compared with the standard it replaces, it may be cheaper.

In automobiles, most of the fasteners are standard sizes; replacements are easily obtained from any source. On the other hand, most of the important components, such as carburetors and distributors, are specific to the make and model. A similar combination is reflected in the cords for electric razors. The end used to plug into the main is a standard plug because the convenience of this is overwhelming as compared with needing a special outlet for shaving; the end which connects to the razor, however, is usually a special plug unique to the make or model. A complex philosophy, as well as consideration of the economy of the special versus the standard, is usually involved. For small parts whose replacement represents a problem of convenience to the user as opposed to an opportunity for profitable sale by the maker, standard sizes are almost always employed. In cases where the public has become thoroughly used to the standard and would resist the nonstandard, the standard is usually adhered to. Where the lot size is relatively small and the nonstandard would raise the price considerably, the standard is usually adhered to. Where the use of nonstandard items would create veritable chaos (such as each radio or television manufacturer employing different tubes), the standards are adhered to. However, where the quantity made and sold is large and where the part thus tends to set its own standard, the maker may employ nonstandard parts, particularly if replacement represents an area of useful (profitable) business.

Standards, however, cover much more than components. Items such as the basic steel alloys, cement, chemicals, and drugs are all usually standardized. Most of these items, produced in bulk, are enormously more economical when purchased to standard rather than to special specifications. In these categories, special materials are employed, in most cases, only when completely necessary to the functioning of the product but often large changes can be made in design to avoid these special materials at considerable savings. The trade-off is between design and material expense. People engaged in procurement must keep fully informed about standards and see that this information is in the hands of product designers. Both groups must work with those responsible for marketing to produce a salable, economical, and profitable product.

The basic concept of a desired material is usually developed during the design of the product and process. Most material trade-offs will be completed during this sequence, although additional trade-offs may be made later by those persons specializing in materials problems.[4] These later trade-offs may be feasible or necessary because of a variety of reasons. For instance, the newness of a product may have led to concentration on the problems of de-

---

[4] This activity is sometimes called "value analysis."

sign. There may have been inadequate coordination between those responsible for design and those responsible for materials. In other cases, there may be a need to obtain a larger measure of optimization of the costs of procurement and storage by using the same material for several products.

Whatever the procedure for selecting a material and whatever the trade-offs made, some material will finally be selected and will result in a specification. A specification is a formalized description of what is desired as a material. To avoid confusion between supplier and receiver, it should be as explicit as possible. A specification normally includes four major items:

1. Identification
2. Description of the material
3. Description of packing
4. Method of testing for acceptability

1. Identification. The identification may be a common or code name, number, or symbol in order to provide a quick means of referring to the material described in the body of the specification. The identification is for convenience in record keeping and will be related to the problem of material control described in Chapter 16.

2. Description of the material. The description is the essential body of the specification and includes both positive and negative statements, viz., what is wanted and what is not wanted. There are three basic ways of writing a description:

a. By describing how the material must perform, i.e., a performance specification
b. By describing the physical and chemical properties of the material or referring to the standards to which the product must adhere; a so-called quality specification
c. By combining *a* and *b* above

A performance specification is the least restrictive. This is both its value and its defect. It is essentially a declaration that anything which will perform as required will be accepted. In many cases, a material may have an undesirable characteristic which may not have been excluded because it was not anticipated; e.g., a synthetic rubber for weather-stripping may have a terrible odor. However, a performance specification allows the procurement group a wide range of decision making and often enhances the economy of their operation.

A specification based on physical characteristics may be too restrictive and limit the economy of procurement. However, properly written, it conveys the concept resulting from the product-process-design sequence directly to the supplier and avoids mistakes and their inevitable expense. It is usually used where the material is completely identified by a standard.

The most common type of specification, particularly with nonstandard items, gives both performance characteristics and some quality characteristics, with positive and negative statements under each category, viz., what the product will do and what it must not do and what properties it must have and what properties it must not have. Further, because the specification of any absolute value usually represents something either totally impossible or unnecessarily expensive, limits of conformance are usually given for each item of the specification. For instance, a length may be given as 8 inches ± 0.01 inch or a chemical may be described as 99 ± 0.1 percent pure with not more than 1 ± 0.1 percent, in total, of a given list of admissible adulterants. The specification must avoid including unnecessary performance or quality characteristics because these normally increase the cost of the material.

3. Description of packing. The term *packing* is used to include both the concept of the individual container and the combination of these into larger containers or groups. Packing serves to protect the product in transit and in storage so that, when ready for use, it possesses the desired properties. The package should also facilitate the handling because this usually represents a sizable cost. Containers themselves may be expensive and, hence, may be designed for reuse. This portion of the specification, like the description of the material itself, usually includes both performance characteristics and quality characteristics, positive and negative statements, and adequate detail.

4. Method of testing for acceptability. The method of ascertaining the conformance of the material and the package to the specifications should be stated in detail in order to facilitate conformance and to give reality to the specification. Test equipment to be used and its manner of use should usually be described in detail. The method of determining the percent conformance to allowable limits, if this is part of the specification, should also be given.

If sampling is to be used, that is, if instead of examining all the supply a portion will be taken as representative and examined, the method of obtaining the sample, the size of the sample, and so forth must be stated. If a standard sampling plan[5] is to be used, it should be identified.

Many parts of specifications tend to be identical; hence, some standardization of specifications themselves is possible and usually results in considerable economy in the use of man-jobs involved in their preparation.

A good specification represents the results of a joint effort by (1) those who determine the requisite properties of the material for most appropriately meeting all aspects of the product design and process and (2) those who undertake the work of procurement. The two fields of knowledge must be

---

[5] There are standards for these, just as with products.

employed in a coordinated fashion to achieve a maximum attainment of the objectives of the enterprise.

REFERENCE TOPICS

Materials	Materials handling
Commodity prices	Purchasing
Value analysis	Receiving
Sampling plans	Acceptance sampling
Testing	Specifications
Market research	Storage
Industrial packaging	Inventory

SUGGESTED THEMES

1. Grades of material and their effect upon price and value
2. Combinations of materials used in common products
3. Specification writing for selected uses
4. Market research to determine value of various materials for a product
5. Delineation of common mixture problems and the pertinent variables
6. Usual contract forms for material procurement
7. Seasonal factors in the purchase of various materials
8. Development of trade-off for selected materials to achieve assigned objectives

SUGGESTED CASES

Cruickshank, H. M., and K. Davis, *Cases in Management,* 3d ed. Homewood, Ill.: Richard D. Irwin, Inc., 1962. Case beginning on page 213.

Greenwald, D. U., *Elementary Case Problems for Industrial Engineers.* New York: The Ronald Press, 1957. Cases beginning on pages 32, 38.

PART 3 CONTROL

12

AN INTRODUCTION TO THE CONCEPT OF CONTROL

At this point a review is in order, to permit a fuller definition of the concept of control, which was introduced briefly in Chapter 1, as well as to relate the concept more fully to the activity of management.

The opening chapter of this book defined management as an activity. It also described the scientific method, emphasizing the importance of stating an objective and defining and analyzing problems. The four physical groups of things which entered into management designs were listed, and, in the chapters which followed, these were discussed in some detail. Various classifications were suggested for each type of thing to indicate, as an aid to logical thinking, the possibility of orderly groupings in terms of various similarities.

Following these chapters, time and money were discussed as dimensions. Also, the society of the industrial plant was examined. Subsequently, methods of designing man-jobs, plant, and product and process and of selecting material were examined, and the interrelationships among these activities were noted. Further, the use of different groups of people with various types of specialized knowledge was noted. The requisite coordination and cooperation among these groups were indicated.

Effective management uses the scientific method in performing the task of designing, predicting the performance of, and controlling the use of an integrated human-group activity and the related physical facilities for the purpose of producing selected outputs to achieve the desired objectives of the enterprise.

Man-jobs, plant, and product and process must be designed and material selected in a coordinated fashion; all of these must be procured and employed, and the outputs must be sold to achieve the objectives. Many different groups of people with specialized abilities or knowledge are used. The typical industrial enterprise embodies a complex set of activities wherein individuals and groups work together in a constantly shifting set of relationships under continually changing conditions. The plant itself changes as it is continually modified to meet the changing demands of product, process, material, and volume of business. The available technical knowledge changes, and this changes the activity in the plant. Obviously, there must be some overriding objectives and overriding constraints which effectively guide the continually shifting complex of activities toward the desired goals, while at the same time retaining them within the economic and legal limitations and allowing for the imperfections in men and equipment. Otherwise, chaos would result.

The systems of objectives and constraints are called *controls*. However, this definition often leads to misunderstanding. In reality, control is a concept. The manager seeks to exercise the concept of control. Any particular system only serves to assist him. The system itself is not control. If the concept of control is not fully understood, the systems which are designed usually have various inadequacies.

Control, briefly described, means the creating of a plan, the carrying out of this plan, the constant comparing of performance to plan, and the taking of corrective action, as needed, to constrain performance to match plan, with occasional changes in the plan as an alternative. Such a definition suggests a constant cyclic-type activity of plan-do-compare-correct and a continuous, concomitant system of communication or flow of information. For instance, there must be a constant flow of information on which to base plans so they are feasible of accomplishment, a constant flow of information concerning performance for comparison with plan, and a constant flow of information concerning differences between plan and performance to guide any corrective actions. Plans may be made for various spans of time; hence, we may have small relatively quick-acting control patterns within longer (time-wise) control patterns, i.e., control cycles within control cycles.

A truck operating between two cities with a time schedule provides a simple example. The truck is run at a certain general speed and its progress watched. This is the larger control cycle. The driver must also maneuver the truck as the road climbs or turns. This is a smaller control cycle. He must also observe, plan, and turn to adjust for holes, bumps, other vehicles, and so forth on the surface of the road. This is a smaller control cycle than the preceding two. The springs and the caster and camber of the front wheels continuously cause minor adjustments in the attitude of the truck; this is an even smaller control cycle which is more or less automatic within the equipment. The carburetor float is continuously adjusting the inlet of gasoline to the carburetor bowl to permit the motor to supply the power requested by the driver; this is an even smaller service control system contributing to the goal achievement of the driver, but it is not directly controlled by the driver. An industrial plant, likewise, has control cycles within control cycles, and service control cycles; the larger the enterprise, in general, the more natural is this type of layering of controls.

The task of management may now be defined in more detail than at the beginning of this book, with particular emphasis upon the concept of control or constraint within which most of the other activities take place. Management may be described as a task which can be represented by the following steps, which are continually repeated, essentially in a cyclic fashion, with a feedback (a flow of information) taking place between and among the various steps as well as between the first and final step:

1. Determine quantitative objectives for a given span of time in conformance with guiding principles or assigned criteria, considering known limitations and freedoms of action.
2. Plan a series of programs (time-phased plans) to produce the outputs required for achieving the desired objectives.
3. Determine the workload (necessary activities) which must be performed to accomplish the programs.
4. Determine the resources required to perform the workload, such as man-job time use, equipment time use, and material.
5. Acquire authority to employ these resources to perform the workload.
6. Use the resources to accomplish the workload, constantly constraining and improving the manner of use.
7. Determine the workload accomplished and the resources consumed, compare with the workload planned and the resources estimated as required, and take corrective action, as necessary, to cause performance to conform to plan.
8. Determine the amount of program accomplished, compare with the program planned, and take corrective action, as necessary, to cause conformance.
9. Determine the degree of accomplishment of objectives, compare with the original objectives, and take corrective action, as necessary.

The cycle of action is indicated graphically, in Figure 12.1, with only the major feedbacks indicated.

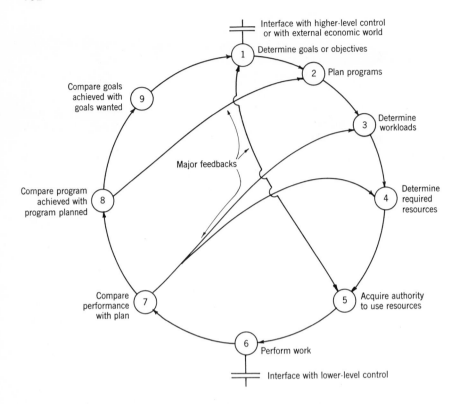

Figure 12.1   The cycle of control

The defining of the task of management in such mechanistic terms is neither to deny the importance of such problems as motivating or leading people nor to deny the need to give weight to human values. The mechanistic description is merely the definition of the matrix in which these problems occur. Also, it must be recognized that system and communication seldom operate perfectly. Further, people and equipment are usually far from perfect and, even when constrained by a system, frequently produce peculiar problems and situations. Hence, even though the scientific approach to management may produce an essentially mechanistic system, there is still much need for human and personal skill in performing the task of management; the mechanistic system and the human view do not inherently conflict.

The cycle of management, as just described, possesses some singular characteristics which are important to note. For one thing, the categories or units which will be used to develop a quantitative expression for each of the first five steps are all different. Further, if there are control cycles within control cycles, the usual point of attachment or point of mutual communication between the two or more control cycles will be from the sixth step of the higher level of control to the first step of the lower level of control. (For convenience, the two control systems may be described as being *interfaced* at this point.) In addition, the categories used to develop quantitative expressions for the first five steps of the lower control system will be different, in most cases, from those used in the upper control system. These singular characteristics should be examined in detail to properly amplify the concept of control.

For instance, in upper-level control cycles, such as top management controls, objectives are usually stated in net economic results or, in the case of a non-economically motivated organization, in social or appropriate substantive results. *Results* should not be confused with outputs. Results are stated in terms of what was achieved because of the outputs. The industrial top-manager's preoccupation with economically stated objectives is demonstrably obvious from the typical periodic report to stockholders made by any profit-oriented enterprise. This is as it should be because, as noted in Chapter 1, this is the objective for which the enterprise exists. To continue, in the case of the industrial enterprise, when stating objectives in advance of their attainment in quantitative terms, some considerable knowledge of economic conditions, enterprise capability, and the feasibility of sales is required.

Programs in upper-level control systems, on the other hand, are usually stated in terms of direct, substantive outputs of the enterprise. These must be stated quantitatively in units different from the objectives; hence, a different type of knowledge is required to select a set of outputs which maximizes the chances of achieving the objectives.

It is worth noting that in the performance of these two steps of the control cycle, stating objectives and planning programs, is found most of the real, basic differentiating characteristics between profit-motivated organizations and governmental organizations. The profit-motivated organization can state its objectives in monetary terms. Such goals are relatively easy for top managers to state and for managers to agree on. It is also easy to determine later whether they were achieved. In addition, a large number of alternative programs to accomplish these goals may be examined, and there usually are several alternatives which are equally desirable; any one of them will achieve the objectives. In the case of government organizations, in contrast, goals are somewhat harder to state because there is seldom a common denominator to use to compare alternative goals; value judgments intervene. Also, it is harder to measure the accomplishment of such goals. Further, the statement of a goal, or objective, in substantive or social results greatly reduces the real number of alternative programs that will permit the achievement of such goals, unless there is no limitation on the amount of resources which are available. Of course, the absence of such a limitation would be very unusual. In addition, although the number of alternative programs which will achieve the objective are fewer, the correct program is, in most cases, harder to define. Hence, in many government organizations, the delineation of objectives and programs in quantitative terms is seldom completely performed; that the subsequent steps of control, as a consequence, are performed in a more faulty manner is a natural concomitant.

After objectives have been converted to programs, programs must be converted to a statement of workloads. Workloads are described in terms of activities that must be performed. Activities are quantified in terms of units which are different from the units used to quantify programs. If the substantive outputs of the organization are simple, the conversion may be performed within the single-control system, although in the usual case, at least some intermediate steps of conversion may be needed to assist in a realistic conversion from program quantities to workload. In even more complex cases, wherein the programs, as stated in the upper-level control system, are so enormous and complex that they can only be stated in very gross, or general, terms, the conversion of program to workload cannot be completed within the single-control system alone. The conversion, in such cases, is finally completed within the subsequent interfaced lower systems of control, and the results are fed back to the upper-level control system to provide data for the upper-level system.

Whichever is the case, complex or simple substantive outputs (or service outputs), the eventual statement of workload must be converted into a statement of the amount of resources[1] needed to perform the workload in terms such as:

1. Time use of man-jobs.
2. Time use of equipment and plant.
3. Material.
4. Finished product or stock to be carried. (This category of resource may also be thought of as including product design or process design; these are a sort of resource, but they are not consumed directly; their resource value is the total of consumable resources required to produce them if they are not available at the time of planning and, consequently, will appear in the preceding three categories.)
5. Fixed capital and working capital (including plant and equipment).

The "authority" related to the fifth step of control must be stated in two types of quantitative terms, one related to the dimensions of the resources which are involved, and the other, to the extent of the authority granted.

It is important to recognize that in each of these required conversions, there are chances of errors being made. This multiplicity of chances for error

---

[1] If there is more than one kind of output, it is difficult to compare meaningfully the totality of these resources with objectives unless these resources are separately stated for each separable program.

gives rise to the need for the comparison steps building up in cumulative fashion in an order which is the reverse of the order of the conversion from objectives to authority acquisition. For instance, resources used and the workload accomplished might conform to plan but might not achieve the program desired; the conversion from program to workload may have been faulty. The programs performed may agree with the plan but might not achieve the objectives; the conversion from objectives to programs may be faulty, and consequently the substantive achievement of all programs does not accomplish the desired economic result. Separate comparisons are needed at each level in order to determine any necessary corrective action in definitive form.

It is important to note that the word *work* may be commonly used to refer to any of the first five steps of the typical industrial enterprise; this ambiguous use of the word work has undoubtedly contributed to the confusion over the concept of control. For instance, the objectives achieved are the results of the work of the enterprise; the outputs are the work of the enterprise; the programs are the work done; the workload is work; the resources are used to work; and the authority controls the work. Each of these uses of the word work employs a different meaning. From the preceding discussion, two significant conclusions can be drawn. First, there must be an equality between the overall content of the work in connection with objectives and the work as produced by the use of resources; otherwise it is hardly possible to talk about control as the term has been used. Second, the magnitude of the units of work used to describe work in quantitative terms or to give it dimensions when talking about objectives must be different from the magnitude of the units of work used for developing and expressing quantitative dimensions for the work involved in the subsequent steps of the control cycle.

Work, or human activity, or the results of human activity, in ordinary conversation, is usually referred to as an amorphous sort of thing with very loosely defined beginning and end points. To exercise control with true quantitative constraint, the work must be divided into well-defined, convenient pieces, convertible from bigger pieces to smaller ones and vice versa so that pieces of work of different sizes can be used for different steps in the cycle of control. Any amount of work separated and defined for such a purpose may be called a *work-unit*. A work-unit is, therefore, merely an amount of work which it is convenient to separate out for treating as an integer in order to develop meaningful quantitative ways of describing work to assist in obtaining realistic control of a situation.

The level of the control cycle, the complexity of the outputs of the enterprise, and the step of the control system will all have a bearing on the division of the work into work-units. For instance, a person designing an optimum method of performing a task may find it useful to recognize work in terms of individual human motions, but to describe the annual output of a plant in such terms would obviously be nonsense. It is less frequently recognized but equally nonsensical to talk about work at one level of control without knowing the method of converting to the work-units appropriate to the other steps or levels of control. Unfortunately, this kind of error is not at all uncommon.

Hence, to talk meaningfully about control requires the prior establishment of a set of terms for work-units of different magnitude, with agreed-upon meanings. These terms will help avoid confusion or ambiguity. These terms should facilitate communication within the actual operation of a control system, as well as assist in recognizing, defining, and approaching problems encountered in the operation of the system.

It seems most useful to have a set of classifications of work-units with descriptive names, numbers indicating their hierarchy, and general definitions. The following set of classifications has proved useful both for direct and indirect activity control systems:

NAME	NUMERICAL DESIGNATION	DEFINITION
Accomplishment of objectives	Eighth-order work-unit	The result of all of the activity required to achieve the stated goals of the enterprise.
Total output	Seventh-order work-unit	The result of all of the activity required to produce the substantive end products of the enterprise.
Program	Sixth-order work-unit	The result of all of the activity required to produce all of one type of substantive end product of the enterprise.
End product	Fifth-order work-unit	The result of all of the activity required to produce one unit of one type of substantive end product of the enterprise.
Intermediate product	Fourth-order work-unit	The result of all of the activity required to produce one unit of some intermediate product of the enterprise. (An intermediate product may be part of a final product, an incomplete final product, or something that assists in doing the desired work but never leaves the plant, such as a dispatch order, etc.)
Task	Third-order work-unit	All of the activity associated with and all of the things associated with the performance of a unit of assignment by either an individual or a crew, depending upon the method of assigning.

Element	Second-order work-unit	All of the activity associated with the performance of part of a task which it is convenient to separate to facilitate the design of the method of performing the task or the determination of some dimension of the task.
Motion	First-order work-unit	The performance of a human motion. This is the smallest work-unit usually encountered in industrial practice. It is used to facilitate job design or dimensioning and never appears in control systems above this level of use.

The list has been given starting from the eighth-order and going down to the first-order work-unit to conform to the sequence of work-units used in the steps of the control cycle, though the numbers assigned to the orders of the work-units do not conform to the numbers of the steps of the control systems. It seemed appropriate to use smaller numbers for smaller work-units. It should be noted that not all of these orders of work-units will be involved in every managerial control cycle. On the other hand, in complex situations, there may be a need for orders of work-units between the ones given here. The foregoing list is offered not as a strict exercise in the taxonomy of work, but as a guide, as facilitating nomenclature, and as a structure for generalizing with the knowledge at hand.

The steps of the management cycle may now be reexamined with the assistance of these terms to discern more clearly the basic problems involved.

For instance, a top manager concerned with the relationship of the enterprise to the external economic world may have several eighth-order work-units such as:

1. The obtaining of a given percent of the market.
2. The obtaining of a given percent of profit.
3. The obtaining of a given amount of profit.
4. Increasing the security of the investment represented by the enterprise. (There may be limitations concerning the size of the plant, with an ancillary objective, therefore, of increasing the size or holding it constant.)

These objectives may be stated in terms of one year, two years, five years, and so on.

To develop a seventh-order work-unit (or seventh-order work-units if there is a divisional structure), the top management must select from all conceivable feasible alternatives a total amount of substantive end product, or output, for each given time span, with the work-units for shorter time spans described or quantified in more precise terms than the longer time spans. As will be obvious later, the first time this conversion is performed, it can be done only in a tentative fashion because much feedback is needed from the subsequent steps before there can be any real indication of the real feasibility of this totality of all programs. The sum of the seventh-order work-units (if there is more than one) when converted from substantive dimensions to their economic equivalent will equal the eighth-order work-unit. The continuation of this step in the cycle of control will require the conversion of the statement of the totality of programs to a statement of the magnitude of each separable program. This would complete only step 2 of the cycle of control. (The total of the individual programs would be the equivalent of the seventh-order work-unit from which they were derived.)

Subsequently, the managers must convert the individual programs, sixth-order work-units, into quantities of fifth-order work-units; convert these into quantities of fourth-order work-units where necessary; and, finally, convert all of these into a list of quantities of third-order work-units or tasks.[2] Thus, a statement of the workload is set forth, a statement necessary to complete the third step of the cycle of control. As noted before, if the substantive outputs of the organization are complex, additional cycles of control may be needed to reach a level of detailed knowledge which will permit the next step of the control cycle to be performed in a realistic substantive fashion that is based on fact rather than wish or guess.

The next step in the cycle of control is to convert the statement of workload into a statement of the resources which will be necessary to perform the workload. These resources will be such as (1) man-job time use, (2) equipment time use, and (3) material as previously described. Unless this step is performed, there will not be a feedback to compare with the objectives to ascertain whether there is a feasible configuration of objectives and resources. If management does not know whether the configuration of objectives and resources is compatible, they are flying blind without instruments. The comparison steps of control will tell only a continual tale of trouble; corrective action will consist of continuous attempts to evade undesired results, or what is commonly called "brush-fire" management.

Control, as it has been described, is more frequently applied to the direct work of a plant than to the indirect work, although the control systems for direct work are often less than adequate. As the percentage of indirect work and the associated costs rise, the ill effects of this failure to apply the concept of control to the indirect activity of the plant become more pronounced and dangerous.

Earlier in this chapter, the statement appeared "For instance, a person designing an optimum method of performing a task may find it useful to

---

[2] This is the usual case. However, there are cases where the fifth- or fourth-order work-unit is sufficient for proceeding to the next step. However, it seemed inappropriate to consider such cases in this general discussion.

recognize work in terms of individual human motions, but to describe the annual output of a plant in such terms would obviously be nonsense. It is less frequently recognized but equally nonsensical to talk about work at one level of control without knowing the method of converting to the work-units appropriate to the other steps or levels of control." However, it is exactly typical of the managerial methods employed with most indirect activities and with all too many direct activities. The error is usually doubly compounded; not only is indirect work not subject to an adequate control system but this control system is not usually recognized as one that must interface with the control system of direct outputs if the total goal-resource structure of the enterprise is to have feasibility with respect to the attainment of objectives. The problem of controlling indirect work becomes increasingly important as the increasing sophistication of the industrial activity increases the percent of resources expended on indirect work.

Hence, if managers are going to manage, if they are to develop realistic configurations of objectives and resources, if they are to increase the effectiveness of the industrial enterprise by other than brush-fire methods, control systems must be employed which relate objectives to plans, plans to workloads, and workloads to required resources.

This last step, the conversion of workloads to required resources, requires the application of a series of techniques referred to as *work measurement*. Work measurement is the technology of developing coefficients of conversion from quantities of workload to quantities of resources needed to perform the workload.

Of course, it is possible to encounter situations wherein the sequential dividing of large or higher-order work units into small or lower-order work units finally produces tasks which have characteristics making the application of traditional work-measurement techniques difficult or impossible. Such a situation must be interpreted as one showing a need for the development of new or modified measurement techniques rather than as a situation which defies control.

The various technologies of management science are useful adjuncts to a performance of the various steps of a system of control. Those which relate to the development of objectives, to the conversion of objectives to programs, to the conversion of programs to workloads, or to the conversion of workloads to a statement of the required resources are all equally important in effectively controlling both direct and indirect work to achieve desired goals. However, with regard to direct work, these technologies have, for the most part, been partially employed, except in the step of converting workload to a statement of the required resources. The absence of the use of work measurement within the framework of the control cycle and in relation to indirect work (or direct work) leaves a missing step in the cycle of control; with one step missing, control is relatively ineffective. For the most efficient management, of course, all appropriate technologies should be employed to the limits of the economics of the situation. Work measurement is being singled out in this discussion because so many people seem to think that it is impossible to apply in the very rapidly increasing area of indirect work. If such an erroneous conclusion concerning the feasibility of work measurement for indirect work or service activities is accepted, it would be the acceptance of a basic challenge of the feasibility of real control for these activities. It seems appropriate to dispose fully of this challenge before examining the various control systems which are implicit in the concept of management being described.

To develop adequate factual work-measurement data for any work, including indirect work, suitable for use in a control system requires that a system of work-units be created which meets, above all, the following two criteria:

1. Suitable for use in a system of control
2. Brought to some level of detail that facilitates the use of some technique for developing coefficients for converting workload to a statement of required resources

This statement should not be viewed in the light of commonly known techniques. It refers to achieving an objective by overcoming the two problems implicit in meeting the two criteria. The statement, being objective-oriented, does not predicate the use of any particular technique.

Unfortunately, in many abortive applications of work measurement to indirect activities or to organizations producing a service,[3] one or the other criterion was used alone, and the resultant situation did nothing to aid control. This has often led to the erroneous conclusion that real control could not be obtained instead of to a recognition that the objective and problem had not been correctly identified. As a consequence, some work is commonly classified as unmeasurable and not really controllable. This appears to be a serious mistake.

A great deal of this confusion has been engendered by starting the development of work-measurement data with the identification of work-units at the task or third-order level. Such an approach allows too many undesirable alternatives. Indirect work, in the usual situation, can be divided into tasks in many ways, not all of which are suitable for use in a system of control. The usual purpose in dividing the work into tasks, in such approaches, is to facilitate work measurement but, as noted, this cannot be taken as the sole purpose. Much of such measurement will have no real use if the work-units measured cannot be related to the higher-order work-units,

---

[3] Including government activities, which, in America, account for about 25 percent of all gainful employment.

as required by the concept of control. It is usually much more effective to start with a work-unit, or order of work-unit, high enough to have obvious use in the system of control and to divide this work-unit into smaller and smaller or lower and lower orders of work-units, maintaining, at all times, conformance with the first criterion given but carrying the division to a point where the second criterion can be met. As noted earlier, some innovation may be required in the technology of converting workload to resources. Such innovation is obviously a preferable alternative to the relinquishment of control.

Of course, as noted, the effective use of a control system requires the use of other techniques from other areas of management science besides work measurement. Also, in the usual case of making a decision, i.e., in the course of using a control system, particularly with respect to the determination of objectives, programs, workloads, and corrective actions, many factors are involved. In such cases, it is also vital to use the scientific method because most such decision making situations have so many facets that informal analysis provides little chance of selecting a really desirable alternative.

In applying the scientific method, a large number of bits of information may be needed. The quantity may be such that they cannot be gathered in the time available for making a decision, or the quantity may exceed the human ability to handle data. Further, every problem cannot be approached as though it were unique. Every bit of necessary *intelligence* (facts concerning the current situation) cannot be obtained by some unique procedure that is initiated only when a problem is identified. The comparison steps of the control systems must continually operate to allow, indeed to force, an early routine identification of problems requiring a decision, and routinely provide a maximum of intelligence in a suitable form.

The effective use of any of the material discussed in this chapter hinges on the willingness of managers to make decisions. No control system is better than the people it serves. No system can substitute for people. It can only serve them. All of the discussion was predicated on the assumption that managers would use the control systems to assist them in managing.

In the first chapter that follows, attention will be given to the control cycle dealing with the basic purposive actions of the enterprise: the production-control cycle, which deals with the use of man-jobs; the use of physical plant; the use of product and process design; and the use of material to produce the outputs of the enterprise. The production of the product is the grand integration of all of the facilities of an enterprise, and the control cycle concerning production is at the very core of management activity. For this reason, the discussion of product precedes, rather than follows, the other things, as in previous sections. Subsequent chapters will deal with the control cycles of other things, followed by other specialized, related control cycles. These will be followed by a chapter on financial controls and one on sales control. The final chapter of the book will return to a discussion of the scientific method, under the title of "Decision Making," to review this concept in the light of the chapters dealing with controls which precede it.

REFERENCE TOPICS

Industrial control
Financial reports
Cybernetics
Planning
Long-range planning
Programming

Work-units
Work measurement
Industrial goals
Business cycles
Executive control

SUGGESTED THEMES

1. Financial resources of industrial organizations and the objectives of these organizations
2. Stated purpose of industrial organizations as it appears in charter of incorporation
3. Description of selected enterprises with respect to the pattern of control
4. Analysis of the budget process of the United States in terms of the concept of control, including the identification of various steps
5. Common concepts of control

SUGGESTED CASES

Cruickshank, H. M., and K. Davis, *Cases in Management,* 3d ed. Homewood, Ill.: Richard D. Irwin, Inc., 1962. Cases beginning on pages 8, 36.

Greenwald, D. U., *Elementary Case Problems for Industrial Engineers.* New York: The Ronald Press, 1957. Case beginning on page 93.

Mantel, S. J., Jr., *Cases in Managerial Decisions.* Englewood Cliffs, N.J.: Prentice-Hall, Inc., 1964. Cases beginning on pages 15, 61.

Terry, G. R., *Case Problems in Business and Industrial Management,* 2d ed. Dubuque, Iowa: William C. Brown Company, Publishers, 1955. Cases beginning on pages 26, 27, 28, 173, 182.

Ziegler, R. J., *Casebook in Production Management.* New York: John Wiley & Sons, Inc., 1962. Case beginning on page 145.

13 CONTROLLING PRODUCTION

This chapter is concerned with the quantitative aspects of production control. Production control is the management control system for coordinating the direct productive effort of the enterprise, and it contains all of the steps typical of a control cycle, as described in the preceding chapter. Production control may also be thought of as a lower-level cycle of control interfaced with step 6 of the top-management control cycle, "use the resources to accomplish the workload." As indicated earlier, this is the normal place of connection between two levels of control. This chapter will treat the quantitative aspects, leaving the qualitative aspects for a later chapter.

To design a control, one must design a procedure for carrying out each of the steps of the cycle of control. This design must include the methods of communicating the objectives which the system is to serve, the means of adding the additional detail to complete the first five planning steps, the means of communicating with the performance group, and the methods for reporting back concerning accomplishment. The design should also include the method of comparing performance with plan and the means of identifying significant variations from plan; it should also identify the variety of corrective actions which may be taken and the means of taking them.

The design of an effective system is based upon the understanding that the control cycle, by itself, does not produce anything of value. Its sole purpose is to facilitate the achievement of the objectives of the enterprise. Inadequate control, which permits chaos or misdirection to substitute for purposive action, is to be avoided, as well as overcontrol, which constrains performance beyond the point of economic return on the control effort.

The economics of any control system may be shown graphically (as in Figure 13.1). The ordinate is money; the abscissa is perfection of control. One line on the graph shows the value of performance; one line shows the cost of control; one line shows the net value, or the value of performance less the cost of control. The curves are idealized. Curves, on a purely theoretical basis, for any specific situation would be difficult to draw with any great accuracy. However, the relationship indicated is real and must be considered when designing a production-control system.

Different types of situations, if represented by curves such as those in Figure 13.1, would produce curves of different shapes, with the optimum in different places. As a result, there are a variety of patterns of production-control systems, reflecting the different control requirements of different types of situations.

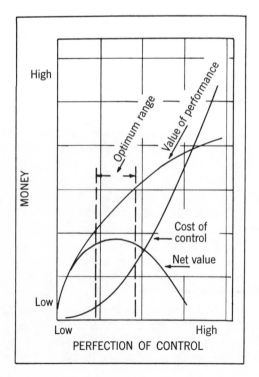

Figure 13.1 The economics of control

For instance, in Chapter 3, two types of plant layout were identified. These were product layout and process layout. This two-way division has an important effect upon the design of the production-control system. In Chapter 4, products were divided into categories in many ways. One way was a three-part division: continuous manufacture, lot manufacture, and unique manufacture. Still another division may be by nature of product, viz., bulk and unit product. These differentiating characteristics of product are significant with respect to the desirable and necessary form of production control.

Considering all of the basic variables related to the pattern of manufacturing which affect the nature of the production-control system, there are twelve basic patterns into which most situations may be categorized:

1. Product layout	continuous manufacture	bulk product
2. Product layout	continuous manufacture	unit product
3. Process layout	continuous manufacture	bulk product
4. Process layout	continuous manufacture	unit product
5. Product layout	lot manufacture	bulk product
6. Product layout	lot manufacture	unit product
7. Process layout	lot manufacture	bulk product
8. Process layout	lot manufacture	unit product
9. Product layout	unique manufacture	bulk product
10. Product layout	unique manufacture	unit product
11. Process layout	unique manufacture	bulk product
12. Process layout	unique manufacture	unit product

Naturally, some of the above patterns are more common than others, although as noted in Chapter 4 the particular configuration best suited to any particular enterprise depends upon a variety of other factors.

The pattern of production control is affected not only by the aforementioned patterns of manufacturing but also by the size of the plant. In this regard, as noted in Chapter 7, controls reduce the area of permissiveness, which creates additional problems, particularly in a large plant, wherein communications tend to become tenuous. Hence, the society of the plant and the society of the external community are also reflected in a production-control system.

In view of all these considerations, it seems appropriate to organize the discussion of production control in the following fashion:

1. A general discussion of the basic pattern of production control
2. A discussion of the nature of the significant changes introduced by the twelve patterns of manufacture, as well as by the size of the plant and its society
3. A summary discussion of the general procedure for designing a production-control system in any specific situation

The basic pattern of production control usually involves at least two levels of control. One level is the gross control, based on an annual or other similar time span of control, the particular time span being affected by the peculiarities of the industry. The gross control is embodied in the top-management control, which was examined in the preceding chapter. The second level of control in an ongoing, or daily, control, dealing with daily events. Both control systems must have a point of interchange of compatible data, or interface, which is typical of control systems, as previously noted. At times, there may be one or more intermediate levels of control between the gross and the ongoing, depending upon the complexity of translating from the gross data of the long time-span top-management control to the detail needed for the daily ongoing control.

The gross control, following the general concept of control described in Chapter 12, may have comparisons between plan and performance at weekly or monthly intervals or other appropriate time intervals natural to the plant and industry. The ongoing control will have comparisons between plan and performance at daily or other short intervals, as appropriate to the nature of the control requirements of the activity within the economic limitations discussed in relation to Figure 13.1.

The gross control operates in terms of gross information, as is appropriate to top managers. For instance, the gross-control plan for a shipyard may give the sequence of ships to be erected on each shipway and their "start" and "launch" dates. Control will be in terms of such gross events. The individual ship dates may involve six months or more on the shipways; the long-range plan may extend more than a year into the future, and it will be continually extended. A manufacturer of water valves may plan a monthly rate of output; a radio-tube manufacturer may plan the number of tubes to be produced per month. Neither of these top-management plans would be likely to specify types or sizes, except in gross groups, although this may not hold true in the small plant. These gross plans and gross controls depend, of course, upon a knowledge of the feasibility of making and selling the products.

Such controls, because of their grossness, are simple to communicate and simple to use in comparing plan with performance. However, corrective action, taken from a control of this level, may necessitate considerable additional fact gathering before the indicated action can be "pin-pointed." Also, when the gross-control system indicates a need for corrective action, this suggests either a failure to maintain control at the ongoing level or a mistake regarding the feasibility of making or selling the product. Obviously, inadequate methods of forecasting the probable amount of business, the seventh-order work-unit, will provoke considerable corrective action from the level of the gross-control cycle. The same will be true of any mistake made in the planning steps of the upper-control cycle.

However, in this chapter, we are more concerned with the detailed shorter time-span controls which, if effective and if based on a feasible configuration of objectives and resources, can obviate much corrective action from the larger, or gross, control system. An ongoing production-control system may be described in summary form in terms carefully chosen to fit all situations, as the following sequence of events: A bit of new information (intelligence), representing an objective, usually a sixth-order work-unit, is fed in from a gross-control system. This intelligence is compared with known facts (knowledge), and, as a result, the intelligence is amplified in respect to its implications and meaning for the productive facility. The process of amplification is repeated at several levels of increasing detail, such as the fifth and fourth order of work-units, until sufficiently detailed intelligence is accumulated to permit substantive action toward the objective to be taken, i.e., until third-order work-units are identified. These third-order work-units, or tasks, are matched to the available resources on a time-use basis; compatibility is obtained; and authority to do the work is issued. Subsequently, the actual performance of the production workers generates new intelligence, which is compared with plans so as to update the knowledge of the status of the production facility. The comparison should also indicate any necessary corrective actions with regard to either plans or events to make them conform to each other. The comparisons are made in the reverse order of planning in order to update the knowledge at each level, to take corrective action at the lowest possible level, or order of work-unit, and to provide a feedback to the upper-control system which furnished the original objective.

The complexity of any actual system and the difficulty of operating the system are affected by:

1. The number of independent bits of intelligence which are fed in per period of time, i.e., the number of sixth-order work-units
2. The difficulty of obtaining the necessary knowledge to add to the intelligence, i.e., the difficulty of converting from sixth-order work-units to third-order
3. The complexity of detailing the intelligence into form for action, i.e., the interrelations between units of product, steps of process, and third-order work-units
4. The number of bits of intelligence which are generated by the productive activity and which must be compared with plans to maintain control, i.e., the number of separate, discrete third-order work-units

A production-control system may be described by the same diagram used to illustrate the basic concept of control in Chapter 12. It differs from the top-management control only in the details of the manner of performing the steps and in the work-units used to aid in developing quantitative statements. However, a production-control system should not be thought of as a cycle through which a discrete batch of intelligence is cycled at discrete intervals. In most cases, new bits of intelligence will be entering the system on a continuous basis, and all of the steps of control are being performed all the time, with different bits of information at different steps of the cycle.

To continue with a discussion of the pattern of activity of production control, the determination of objectives, step 1 of control, for a detailed or ongoing system of control may consist of a statement of three sets of facts. Because these facts are quantitative values related to the desired accomplishment, they may be called *dimensions* of the objectives. These dimensions represent an input from the gross-control system at the interface between the two control cycles and would be developed within the upper-level control system from a knowledge of the market and the plant capability or from the actual orders on hand. These dimensions commonly are:

1. Allowable cost (a prime objective related to the profit)
2. Specifications and quantity of product
3. Date of delivery, or date for start of delivery, and rate of delivery of fifth-order work-units contained in each sixth-order work-unit

It will be noted that this gross information is typical of a gross-control system. Also, it can be made in a meaningful fashion only if there is prior knowledge, or feedback from the operating plant, concerning feasible performance.

The program planning, step 2 of control, involves taking the information from the interface between the two controls and, with more detailed knowledge of the capability of the operating plant, amplifying the intelligence by adding additional information, or dimensions, to the statement of the desired results in order to convert to fourth-order work-units. Thus, the typical program-planning step of the ongoing control requires the further dimensioning of the required results with regard to:

1. A compilation of a complete list of all of the discrete items, i.e., components, or fourth-order work-units, needed per period of time
2. An estimate of the cost of producing each item
3. An estimate of the cost of procuring each item from outside of the plant

From the above data, the completion of the program-planning step will result in the development of a list of components, the quantities to be made, and a list of those which will be bought. The knowledge which will be used as a basis for the "make or buy" decision may be a general knowledge of plant capability, particularly if the time allowable for planning is short and the planning work arduous and complex. In other cases, the ultimate decision to make or buy may be delayed until detailed data for item 2 above is available from subsequent steps of the control cycle. This feedback between and among the steps was described in Chapter 12.

The determination of the workload, step 3 of control, will require the examination of each of the components to be made and their respective quantities in order to determine the process and the tasks (third-order work-units) to be used to make the component, as well as the amount of material required for each unit of output. The output, at this level, is usually described in terms of fourth-order work-units. Many of the trade-offs among process, material, and product, described in Chapters 10 and 11, may originate at this point. There will also be a continual feedback of information to product-process knowledge.

The determination of the required resources, step 4 of control, will require a conversion of the statement of workload of both men and machines obtained from step 3 into a statement of the time of use of men and machines required to accomplish the workload. It will also require conversion of the unit requirements of material into a statement of the total amount of material which will be needed. The time-use data will also need to be converted into a statement of the number of men and the number of machines required during each period of time. The amounts of material for different components will have to be stated as the quantity of each type of material needed for each period of time.

For a successful performance of step 4, there are two basic requirements. The process information from step 3 must be complete, and there must be a realistic method for accurately predicting the use of man-time and machine-time required to perform each step of each process. This point was emphasized in Chapter 12; often, this requires very detailed, accurate work-measurement data.

In the subsequent performance of step 5, differences between requirements and capacity (available resources) may be detected. If the number of required hours of time-use of men and machines differs from the amount currently available, various alternative corrective actions are possible. For instance, the determination of the resources required may indicate the existence of one of the following general conditions:

1. An exact matching of capability and demand
2. A demand for the use of equipment or man-jobs in excess of the capability
   a. Under current work hours
   b. Regardless of work hours
3. Considerable idle time in various man-jobs or of various pieces of equipment
4. A combination of all three of these conditions, depending on the equipment group and man-job group

The most typical condition is number 4 above. This condition indicates a need for a variety of corrective actions. Number 1 would be very fortuitous; it indicates an exact attainment of the objectives.

There is considerable variety in the corrective actions which may be taken. For instance, if the demand upon a particular equipment group creates number 2a above, four alternative courses of action are possible. The first alternative is either to use overtime or to add a second shift of workers to operate some of the equipment. This is the simplest alternative, and some authority for taking limited action in this area may be given to the group operating the control system at step 5. This is in line with the general concept of permitting corrective action to take place with the least effort. However, such action may conflict with the objectives of the man-job control system described in the next chapter. Some interchange of information is usually necessary among the groups responding to these two control systems to maintain cooperative action toward the goals of both systems.

As an alternative approach, changes may be made in the process step details, i.e., corrective action at step 3, workload planning. For instance, gas-fired furnaces having idle time may be substituted for electric furnaces originally planned. Broaching may be substituted for jobs which have been planned for milling machines if broaching capability is idle and milling machines are overloaded. Hand-guided cutting of steel plates may be substituted for the use of a flame-cutting machine in order to reduce the workload on the machines. These alternatives, or trade-offs (feasibility is gained while most desirable process equipment is discarded), are limited only by the knowledge of technology and the peculiarities of product, process, and the particular equipment of the plant. Such trade-offs are usually made in cooperation with the process-planning group.

A third alternative is to change the capability of the plant by adding more equipment. The complexity of this alternative depends upon the amount of money involved. In line with the concept of allowing corrective action to be taken at the lowest level consistent with the attaining of the overall objectives of the plant, additional equipment up to a certain stipulated value may often be purchased upon the authority given, on a broad basis, to the middle managers of the plant. If the amount of money is in excess of these limits, the decision may be referred to the top managers who operate the gross-control system mentioned in Chapter 12. In such a case, this alternative is usually a long-range one, particularly in that such items as may be involved are usually neither quick to arrive at the plant nor quickly put into operation; hence, one of the other alternatives is needed as an interim solution.

As a fourth alternative, there may be a change in a program of the production-control system. A feedback to step 2 may take place, suggesting more purchase of semifinished parts or more purchase of components from outside and consequently less work to do in the plant. A higher order of feedback across the interface with the upper-level control system may lead to an alteration of the sales plans of the organization so as to obtain less work.

The existence of number 2b (a demand for the use of equipment in excess of the capability, regardless of the work hours) reduces the number of alternatives and forces the consideration of only the last three mentioned in relation to 2a.

The existence of number 3 (considerable idle time in various man-jobs or of various pieces of equipment) permits the same four general alternatives as described in relation to 2a, except that the actions indicated are reversed. For instance, reduced work hours, trade-offs in process steps to use more economical pieces of equipment, or increases in the "make" programs of the production-control system are suggested.

As mentioned earlier, the most typical condition was 4: a combination of all of the varieties, different for each group of machines. Hence, the real alternatives involve a shifting of labor within the range of the skills involved, some changes in hours, some process trade-offs, and some adjustments to the programs of the production-control system. Of course, the more regular the work of the plant (continuous manufacture), the more likely it is that a stable condition will be reached in which such corrective actions become few in number. The more the work of the plant becomes lot or unique manufacture, the more such corrective actions will be needed.

There are additional possibilities. For instance, the performance of step 5 for one period of time may indicate an excess of resources; the following period of time may indicate a shortage of resources. To relieve such a condition, it is possible with some types of products to alter the programs so as to manufacture for stock rather than directly for sales. When manufacturing for stock, the plant will build up an inventory, storing finished goods during the periods of excess productive resources and depleting this stock during the periods when resources are inadequate to meet the demands of the upper-level production-control system. In this manner, the inventory, produced during periods when productive resources are in excess, buffers or cushions the effect of the upper-level production-control system upon the lower-level production-control system. Thus, each system, for any given short period of time, becomes more independent. In general, such a buffer allows more flexibility in the form of corrective action taken to obtain the maximum output from the productive facility, although additional costs are associated with the use of the buffer or inventory of finished goods. Additional plant is required to house it, additional working capital is employed, and risks are taken with respect to deterioration, obsolescence, or excessive holding of inventory. However, mathematical models may be constructed, representing the costs and values of the inventory situation, and used to assist in examining the consequence of various alternatives with respect to the profit objective of the enterprise and to assist in selecting a desirable corrective action.

Other mathematical models may, at times, be usefully employed to assist in determining a desirable course of action when the demands on productive resources exceed the capability. (It should also be noted that the use of some of these models may also indicate some corrective action to the sixth-order work-units of the upper-level production-control system.)

For instance, suppose a plant makes a mixture of eight different products. Suppose also that the demands upon the plant, at times, exceed the productive capability. Several alternative courses of action should be apparent. These alternatives are:

1. Manufacture for direct sales but take, during periods of excess demand, only the most profitable mix of orders
2. Manufacture for stock, producing during periods of excess capability the most profitable mix of product
3. Purchase additional capability in a manner that will contribute in a maximum fashion to the profitability of the enterprise

To construct a model to assist in evaluating these alternatives, certain additional data are needed. Assume, in this example, that each of the eight different products is made by the same three-step process, but each product takes a different amount of time per unit for each step. The products may be designated as 1 through 8; the process steps as X, Y, Z.

To set up a model, the additional data needed are (1) information concerning the amount of time required to process a unit of product through each process step and (2) the profit obtained on a unit of each kind of product. The required information could be displayed in tabular form as follows:

PRODUCT	TIME IN HOURS TO PROCESS A UNIT OF PRODUCT			PROFIT IN DOLLARS PER UNIT OF PRODUCT
	Process Step X	Process Step Y	Process Step Z	
1	1	2	8	1
2	2	3	7	2
3	3	4	6	3
4	4	5	5	4
5	5	6	4	5
6	6	1	3	6
7	3	7	1	2
8	8	6	8	8

In addition to the above information, it is necessary to know the time available for using process steps X, Y, Z. For instance, if the plant operates forty hours a week, and has four machines for step X, four machines for step Y, and five machines for step Z, the gross available time is 160 hours per week for X, 160 hours per week for Y, and 200 hours a week for Z. (In actual practice, of course, these totals would need to be corrected to allow for breakdowns, and so forth.)

With the preceding data, a mathematical model could be constructed, consisting of a set of equations representing the operation of the plant with all possibilities of mix of product, indicating the profit from the mix. These equations can be solved to produce an answer to the following sorts of questions:

1. Under the current working schedule of 40 hours per week, what is the most profitable mix of the different products?
2. For a given amount of overtime, which is the most profitable process step, or steps, to which to apply the time, and what is the accompanying most profitable mix of product?
3. If the price of additional equipment is known, which process step, or steps, if any, will give the greatest return on an investment in additional equipment? What percent return on investment can be obtained?
4. Given a fixed amount of production for each of the eight different products, what mixture of which products will utilize the remaining capability in a manner that will produce the greatest profit?

It should be noted that when the problem is stated in this form, it is identical to the problems encountered in Chapter 11 in the discussion of the feasible and desirable trade-offs with regard to the constituent wools in a mixture and to the most economical mixture of meat cuts to make a sausage. This type of mathematics, like many other of the technologies employed to assist in management, may be used in a variety of situations.

It is important to note that corrective action can take place at various levels. Some can be instituted at the level of the men responding primarily to the operation of various steps of the control system; some must be referred to the process-control group; some must be referred to other control systems, such as man-job control; and some have an effect upon the gross-control system.

Step 5 therefore can suggest many important types of corrective actions. If requirements and resources do not match, some action must be taken. The earlier the comparison is made between objectives (or plan) and capability, the earlier will corrective action be indicated and the greater will be the probability that there is sufficient time to select and follow some desirable alternative plan or course of action.

The performance of step 5 therefore depends, first, upon successfully taking corrective action as indicated from step 4. Second, step 5 requires a determination of the exact starting time for each use of men and equipment and a determination of the required completion date so as to give the detailed statement of the "authority acquired." Third, this information must be communicated to the supervisors and to the materials groups, so that men and machines will be employed as planned and materials will be available when needed in order that step 6, "perform the work," may take place. The supervisors and the materials group must also have a communication channel so that any failures to provide any needed material can be anticipated and alternative uses made of the assigned man-job and equipment time.

The step of detailing the authority and the assigning of a date and time for each use of man-jobs and equipment is frequently referred to, in the literature, as *scheduling and dispatching* because it involves the determination of an actual "when-to-do-it time" and the sending, or "dispatching," of this information, together with specific instructions concerning what is to be done and when it is to be finished. (This is the performance of the functions of the route clerk and instruction card clerk as proposed by Taylor. In Chapter 7, note had been taken of the reality of this functional separation in every modern plant.)

Within the usual industrial establishment with large numbers of man-jobs and pieces of equipment, there are usually many possible alternative patterns of scheduling. Many techniques, including mathematical models, have been evolved to assist in selecting the preferred alternative from among the possibilities.

The problem of selecting a feasible pattern of scheduling was recognized as an important problem during the very early application of the scientific approach to the problems of management. More will be said about this later in this chapter.

One additional aspect of scheduling should be included. There are additional factors, related to internal-process details, which can complicate the task of scheduling. These are particularly important with regard to obtaining maximum use of equipment.

In the scheduling of the usage of equipment, there may be product-process-sequence interactions. For instance, a metal-smelting plant may have orders for pure copper billets, copper-zinc alloy billets, and copper-zinc-tin alloy billets. If a furnace is used to produce them in that order, there will be less time lost in cleaning up the facilities than if they are produced in reverse order. In a similar fashion, three parts, A, B, and C, may be scheduled to a large boring mill or lathe. The set-up for parts A and C may be the same. The set-up for B may be quite different, and it may take a considerable length of time to change from the set-up for A or C to B. Thus, if the parts are produced in A, C, B order, B, A, C order, or B, C, A order, this will take less time than A, B, C order. Also, A, B, and C may be made every week. If the bank, or quantity of parts kept on hand, is increased, it may be possible to change the set-up once in two weeks rather than once each week, resulting in more time of the machine expended on productive work. The amount of material kept on hand will be affected by the perishability of the product, the cost of storage space, the amount of capital tied up, and so forth. This aspect has been discussed.

In a really effective system of control, such factors are taken into account. Hence, in actual practice, the operation of the system may be somewhat more complex than appears from this preliminary outline of the general system; the amount of intelligence and knowledge which must be handled may be quite extensive. If the scheduling problem is sufficiently complex, additional levels of control may be necessary, leading to three or more interfaced production-control systems.

The use of the resources, step 6 of control, requires the supervisor to supervise, that is, to motivate, inform, aid, assist, and take corrective action within his permissible area of decision making or to seek advice when the problem exceeds his capability. Generally, the supervisor can change the schedule (the specific use planned for man-job and equipment time) within certain limits, order a limited amount of overtime, or take personal action to locate materials or tools. He may also correct some defects in the process design. The "do" step of control should be subject to continual improvement. He will also take corrective action on a smaller and more "local" control system with respect to keeping the equipment functioning. The actual use of resources is usually tied in with still another control system concerned with the quality and attributes of the product called a *quality-control system*. The supervisor must assist in coordination with this system. (More will be said about quality control in Chapter 18.) The supervisor must also see that information concerning actual accomplishment is communicated in a form suitable for comparison with the information developed in step 5 so that any residual need for corrective action may be determined and up-to-date knowledge will be available to determine the proper and appropriate form of the corrective action.

Step 7 of control requires the comparison of the information concerning the performance of third-order work-units with the information concerning the detailed plan for using the resources to perform the workload. To correct deviations from plan, there are usually a variety of alternative courses of action, involving either changes in the plan or changes in the factors affecting conformance with the plan, a duality of choice similar to that described with respect to step 4. Again, the more rapidly the necessary facts are assembled, the alternatives considered, and the corrective action taken, the less disturbance is usually incurred. Also, in this way, future plans may reflect real capability, or certain basic corrections may be indicated as necessary.

The most usual type of corrective action is to adjust for failure to perform as planned because of some nonrecurring event. The time lost on the equipment cannot be regained. The alternatives are to schedule overtime to catch up or to assign additional capability to the particular process step. However, the event may be of a recurring type, and a basic correction may be indicated. For instance, if the plant has been planning on eight hours of usage per shift for a given piece of equipment, the need for corrective action may be indicated by the experience of using it. The complexity and imperfection of the machine or its crew may result in only seven productive hours per shift. Future basic schedules may need correction to reduce the capability to seven hours per shift; requirements in excess of this may be treated as number 2a or b, as mentioned earlier in connection with step 5. Such a basic correction permanently applies corrective action earlier in the control system, in this case, shifting the corrective action from after the use of resources back to the adjustment of objectives and resources, giving more time for adequate response.

The determination of the program accomplishment, step 8 of control, requires a comparison of the performance with plans with respect to the number and cost of each component, fourth-order work-unit, produced. Again, corrective action may be indicated.

The determination of the degree of accomplishment of objectives, step 9 of control, is used to develop the information to supply the feedback across the interface with the gross-control system. It consists of a comparison of the total costs and quantities of products produced, fifth-order work-units, with regard to the cost and quantity objectives of each sixth-order work-unit. It should be noted that the required quantities could have been, in any particular case, produced with deviations from the time, cost, or quality goals, and so forth. Step 9 will provide a feedback to the larger control system and will influence future plans and future gross-control-system decisions.

Corrective actions at the upper level may take a wide variety of forms. Research into new products, processes, equipment, man-job technology, and so forth may be identified as the area in which alternative courses of action must be developed. Top-management decisions will be required to initiate such efforts. It is worth noting that any effort to develop an alternative course of action by developing new information in any of the areas just listed would create the need for a planned effort to achieve the desired result, together with its own one-time-use control system, a subject to be examined in Chapter 17.

The basic pattern of a production-control system, as described, is relatively simple. One of F. W. Taylor's close associates, Henry L. Gantt, while working with Taylor, devised a complete set of graphic methods for assisting in all of the steps of production control. Such charts are still in common use. Because they assist in all of the steps of the control system and use the same material for all of the steps, they tend to reduce system cost, although, of course, they have limitations with respect to the quantity of data which is economically handled. Gantt charts are designed to permit the plotting of plans against time and date to check feasibility, summarizing workload information, determining resource requirements, comparing these with available resources, determining alternatives, and comparing events with plans. They also permit updating knowledge to assist in correcting future plans. Such a combination of functions is made possible by a series of graphic conventions, designed by Gantt, which make it convenient to keep such charts continuously up to date without altering previously charted data. There are a variety of versions of such charts, and they may be adapted, in many ways, to reflect the individual characteristics of different situations.

Of course, the type of data drawn on Gantt charts, when the quantity of information is large, may be developed for use in punch-card or computer systems to perform the same functions with greater economy. However, it seems appropriate to examine a sample Gantt chart to obtain some insight into the method of carrying out the details of control, without introducing the extraneous problems of punch cards or computers. The actual techniques in use in any plant will depend upon the volume and complexity of the information which must be handled, but the functions performed will be essentially the same. Further, any technique is only an aid to those charged with the operation of the control system.

A Gantt chart for assisting in the operation of a production-control system is shown in Figure 13.2. The entire sheet, only part of which is shown here, represents the capability of a group of machines. Each row on this chart

Figure 13.2   The Gantt chart used for production planning and control

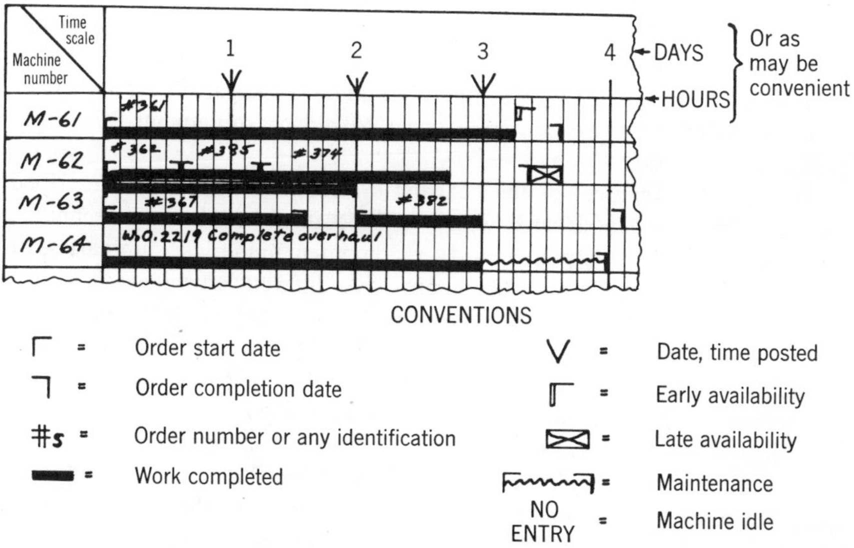

CONVENTIONS

⌐ =	Order start date		V =	Date, time posted
¬ =	Order completion date		⌐ =	Early availability
#s =	Order number or any identification		⋈ =	Late availability
▬ =	Work completed		∿∿∿ =	Maintenance
			NO ENTRY =	Machine idle

represents the capability of one machine; the horizontal scale, therefore, is time. Minutes, hours, days, weeks, or months may be used, as may be convenient. If the output of the machines can also be expressed as a constant amount per period of time, the horizontal scale may simultaneously represent both the amount of product and the time.

In Figure 13.2, the tasks are assumed to be expressed in "time anticipated as required for their performance"; hence, the tasks may be entered on the chart by means of the first three conventions, "start date," "completion date," and "order number" (or other identification). The last convention will key the posting to any more detailed information relating to the task, kept in file form. A posting of a sixth-order work-unit by means of the first three conventions automatically sets up a program, summarizes workload, and allows the required resources to be determined. More detailed charts may be used to show fourth- or third-order work-units. Note that in Figure 13.2, two shifts of work were assigned on order 367 on machine M-63 for the first and second day shown in order to complete this work before job 382 began. These are for fourth-order work-units.

A copy of such a chart, after any posting and made by any quick process, may form the basis of a "dispatch," or authorization to use resources, to the shop, or it may be used as a data source for individual man-job production orders.

The comparison of the workload completed with the workload planned is performed by posting the time equivalent of the work done by means of the heavy bar (convention 4) and indicating the date of the posting by the V mark of convention 5.

The need for corrective action is indicated by any failure of plan and performance to conform. The corrective action for the future is taken by means of convention 6 (early availability) and convention 7 (late availability) to permit future scheduling to be done in accord with feasibility. Of course, the reason for the deviation should be investigated to set up either better knowledge or procedures in order to reduce subsequent failures to perform as planned.

The essential features of the charting system which has been described represent the basic assistance which will be furnished by any technique employed, whether it is punch cards, a computer, numerical summaries, or any other method. Different techniques have different advantages and disadvantages under different circumstances. As with any control system, the system designer must have a broad capability in order to select a suitable technique and must train the plant personnel in its use. The task of operating the system is quite different from the task of designing it.

Although the basic pattern of a production-control system is simple, an examination of an actual production-control system in a large plant may suggest considerable complexity. The primary cause of the apparent complexity of an actual system is the large number of bits of intelligence which may need to be handled in a short period of time. With large-scale complex manufacturing activities, the number of details per short period of time may be enormous. For instance, in a plant employing process layout, lot manufacture, with unit products, and with 1,000 direct-labor man-jobs, there may be 2,000 process steps or third-order work-units per day, with each process step needing product information, process information, material information, machine assignment, tooling, and coordination with other process steps. The control system must be used to plan, communicate, compare performance with plan, and indicate corrective action, handling the large number of bits of information at least twice, once when authorizing and once when comparing performance with plan.

From the foregoing discussion of the nature of a production-control system, the effect of various types and sizes of plant and types of societies upon the complexity of the required control system can readily be anticipated. For instance, in general, a small plant producing one continuous bulk product would tend to need only a simple system. The number of new bits of intelligence entering the system would be nominal. The only really new bits would be caused by changes in process, equipment, or man-job technology. Of course, if the equipment and men were relatively unreliable or unpredictable, many corrective actions would be required, but even these would eventually tend to create a stable pattern.

On the other hand, a large plant producing a complex type of product by unique manufacture, e.g., shipbuilding or ship repair, would tend to have a large number of new bits of intelligence entering the system; the problem of amplifying these to actionable details would be large; the number of bits of information concerning performance would also be large. The control system would require much effort. In such a case, unless the lowest-level production-control system, through steps 3 and 4, generates better information than the supervisor would supply, or if it does not assist the supervisor to obtain better utilization of the resources of men and machines, or if it is not coordinated with the supply of material, then there is not much to be gained by detailed control.

It is interesting to note that if the shipyard changes its work to the continuous production of one type of ship or to the steady performance of a fixed type of repair or alteration, the number of new bits of intelligence entering the system will be much less than in the situation described in the preceding paragraph and the production-control system could be much simpler, even though it is still shipbuilding which is controlled. It is not the product alone which determines the type of control needed; the factors listed at the beginning of this chapter must also be taken into account.

For another illustration, with a continuous manufacture product-layout plant, the material moves steadily through a section of the plant. A control system which relates to the initial input and the final output of this section may be quite adequate; the in-between details are predicated by the process and layout and may be handled directly by the supervisor. However, with lot manufacture process layout, with a variety of products flowing in a mixed fashion through a section of productive equipment, a control system must give much more detail, except in those cases where the mix of product represents a steady repeat of a pattern.

The size of the plant can have a variety of effects upon the necessary complexity of the production-control system. With a steady state of manufacture and with only a nominal number of new bits of intelligence entering from the larger control system, the larger plant will tend to have more new bits of intelligence generated within the operating facility because it will be able to afford more specialized individuals to generate much innovation.

In a society in which the individual workers may be expected to take effective corrective action at the working level or if corrective action can be taken at the lower supervisory levels, the system can remain quite simple, even if the plant is large. If corrective actions cannot be initiated at lower levels, some type of procedure for facilitating the rapid flow of information to higher levels is needed to prevent a large deviation from plans needing large corrective actions to occur before the deviation is detected. An increase in the size of the plant tends to slow down the flow of information unless the control system is specifically designed to cope with the problem.

In a large plant with large numbers of new bits of intelligence entering from the upper-control system, the amount of control system activity can become enormous and require a highly mechanized system in order to feed the new intelligence to the working force and to feed intelligence concerning performance back in time to take really effective corrective action. Under such circumstances, mechanized data-processing equipment, commonly referred to as computers, may become almost a necessity if the comparison of performance with plan is not to be ancient history or if use of a veritable army of clerical workers is to be avoided.

In summary, product layout tends to reduce the amount of detailed information needed to carry out performance; process layout tends to increase the amount of detail needed. Continuous manufacture is usually accompanied by a relatively small input of new bits of information from the gross-control system; lot manufacture and unique manufacture both tend to increase the number of new bits of intelligence per period of time, with unique manufacture having the greatest number. Bulk product tends to have fewer new bits of information than unit product. Large plants tend to have more new bits than small. As noted, large numbers of new bits of intelligence entering from the gross-control system tend to complicate the production-control system. Also the more complex the amount of detail needed to constrain performance, the more complex the production-control system tends to become.

To design an actual production-control system, the systems designer not only needs to know the technology of systems design but must have insight into the production process. He must be familiar with the typical lead-times (advance notice) needed to obtain materials and the amount of detailing necessary to transform new bits of intelligence into actionable form. He must also have some knowledge of the increase in the value of the output which can be obtained by the amount of control and the cost of obtaining such control.

Such a system, when designed and put into use, may operate for a long time with little if any change in the structure of the system; the changes will be in the form of available knowledge for use within the system. Therefore, it is not infrequent to find a plant obtaining assistance from outside specialists for the design of such a system, particularly when the number of the bits of new information per period of time is large and the required system may be complex.

In general, the systems designer attempts to determine the amount of new information which will be entering the system per period of time and the amount of detail needed at the working level for effective action. Considering the various methods of amplifying the initial inputs of information into actionable form, he attempts to devise a suitable procedure, taking into consideration alternative approaches such as manual methods, mechanized procedures, and the necessary supporting forms. Once a tentative system is established, its use is usually simulated to determine if it will indeed perform the steps of control and produce the desired results. Subsequent to the preparation of the design of a system, all members of the organization who will be affected by it must be trained and assisted in using it. Because such a system will usually affect the workers, it is usually necessary to see that an adequate explanation is presented to them, as well as to managers. This general design procedure follows the outline of the scientific approach described in Chapter 1.

In many cases, new production-control systems will require the availability of knowledge, such as the detailed process-step time for men and machines that is essential to a realistic performance of step 4 (determine the required resources). If such data are not available when a system is designed, approximations may be developed to put the system to use. These approximations will be replaced by accurate data if such replacement is in conformance with the economics of control (as suggested by Figure 13.1). The system is usually designed before the development of accurate data because, as noted in Chapter 12, the requirements of the system will have a bearing on the manner in which third-order work-units, i.e., tasks, are defined.

In more definitive terms, the design of a production-control system will involve the following steps. The similarity to the steps given in Chapter 10 for designing a product should be noted, as well as the general conformance to the scientific method. The usual steps in the design of a production-control system are:

1. Specification of the need to be filled and the desired relationship between cost of control and contribution to value produced by the operating facility
2. General specification of the required plan with regard to the functions it must perform
   a. Number of new bits of intelligence entering from gross-control system
   b. Nature of the dimensions which must be added to make the intelligence actionable
   c. Complexity of detailing the intelligence
   d. Number of bits of intelligence which are generated by actions and which must be compared with plans to maintain control
   e. Degree of conformance of performance to plan which is desired and the costs associated with various amounts of deviation
   f. Incremental value to be added to performance by the exercise of control
   g. Operating costs of the control
3. General design concept
   a. General configuration; required additional details to the general pattern of control
   b. Tentative selection of manual, mechanical, or electronic methods for each major step of the general configuration
   c. Probable cost of each step of the control process and required manning
4. Development of prototype
   a. Systems diagram
   b. Samples of forms and working papers
5. Pilot model (improvements to the initial system)
   a. System diagram
   b. Explanatory material, as necessary, for presentations to those who will decide to use or not use
   c. Samples of forms and working papers
   d. List of required equipment
   e. List of required personnel
6. Technical testing (by simulation, viz., by subjecting hypothetical operations and situations to the system)
   a. Function
   b. Time and cost
7. Consumer testing
   a. Presentations to managers
   b. To present control staff, if any

8. Tentative process design
   a. Man-job details for control-system work
   b. Detailed form layouts
   c. Equipment specification
9. Process improvement, viz., trade-off among the subitems of steps 5 and 8 above to approach an optimum system with respect to function and cost
10. Estimate of cost of operating final system and additional value to be gained by the use of the control system
11. Comparison with goals and recycling as necessary
12. Final design of system; specification of system man-jobs and equipment, including forms and working papers, as well as a complete listing of any not yet available requisite information
13. Decision to implement, recycle, change goals, or abandon, in whole or in part

If management decides to implement a new production-control system, the final most critical task lies ahead. A production-control system affects many man-jobs. Old habits must often be changed. New knowledge must frequently be developed. Changes may be required in the system as new situations are encountered. Changes must be documented so that if the personnel of the plant changes, the information concerning systems is not lost.

REFERENCE TOPICS

Production planning and control
Scheduling
Dispatching
Systems design
Work measurement
Estimating
Information systems
Procedures design

Forms design
Data processing
Electronic or automatic data processing
Inventory control
Linear programming
Gantt charts
Network diagrams
Machine interference

SUGGESTED THEMES

1. Examples of plants, classified by type, with respect to factors affecting production-control system
2. Design of production-control systems for selected situations
3. Analysis of ongoing production-control system with respect to the means used to perform the various steps of control

4. Analysis of other methods of describing production planning and control with respect to the concept of control, with emphasis on the differences in terminology

5. Comparison of various control systems with respect to the probable location of the situation on the curve of Figure 13.1

SUGGESTED CASES

Cruickshank, H. M., and K. Davis, *Cases in Management,* 3d ed. Homewood, Ill.: Richard D. Irwin, Inc., 1962. Cases beginning on pages 15, 32, 88, 193, 223.

Greenwald, D. U., *Elementary Case Problems for Industrial Engineers.* New York: The Ronald Press, 1957. Cases beginning on pages 46, 49, 51, 54, 57, 60, 89.

Terry, G. R., *Case Problems in Business and Industrial Management,* 2d ed. Dubuque, Iowa: William C. Brown Company, Publishers, 1955. Cases beginning on pages 12, 28, 29, 50, 85, 100, 133, 134, 135, 136, 172, 174, 175.

Ziegler, R. J., *Casebook in Production Management.* New York: John Wiley & Sons, Inc., 1962. Cases beginning on pages 15, 48, 53, 78, 81, 93, 122, 143.

14 CONTROLLING MAN-JOBS

The objectives of man-job controls fall into two categories, as suggested by the use of the hyphenated title. Most of the primary controls in common use relate to the job aspects and are integrated into the major stream of the production-control system as described in Chapter 13. These primary job controls concern the performance of the job by the man; the job, or task accomplishment, is the primary goal. Job-accomplishment goals are, after all, related to the basic substantive goals of the enterprise; hence, it should not be surprising to see them, to some extent, tending to override the strictly human goals. However, as has been shown, particularly in Chapter 2, there are some important interactions.

Because of the ascendancy of job-accomplishment goals, an industrial organization frequently tends to submerge the human aspects of people. Such a tendency is influenced by the pressure from economic conditions and the forces of competition, but, also, it undoubtedly represents some social holdover from historically traditional forms of organizations of men. In the past, slave labor, involuntary employment, or the overwhelming substantive objectives of military organizations (which tended to be reflected in the general society) tended to overshadow the man-oriented goals.

The human problems of an industrial enterprise are frequently intensified by the continued lack of attention to human goals. In many cases, a substitute mechanism for forcing attention to man-related goals has evolved, as exemplified by militant unionism or by a socialist-oriented government. (There is no intent to imply that these two should be equated; they are merely given as alternative mechanisms.)

This chapter concerns both job and man-goals, excluding those which are fully covered in the production-control system (and derived from the consideration of product) but including those which are required to support the production-control system and are not explicitly covered by it. This chapter is focused on the control-system activity involved in the attainment of these man-job goals. The separation from the production-control system cannot and should not be absolute because both systems must be directed toward the same objectives, the objectives of the enterprise. Further, this chapter will treat both job and man control together, as a man-job control system; as indicated in Chapter 2, the man-job is considered a basic unit of the industrial enterprise.

In the typical industrial enterprise, the system of man-job control is seldom as well defined as the system of production control. Indeed, in the usual case, the controls related to the man aspects of man-jobs are not recognized as related to a system of control. They are most commonly thought of as a group of independent programs, each of which is loosely related to the objectives of the enterprise.

There are some obvious reasons for the usual lack of perception of the existence of a total system. For one thing, the responsibility for the development and application of the various programs and parts of programs related to man-jobs is usually divided among various groups in accordance with the staff concept described in Chapter 7. The man-job control system does not have a continuous, readily identifiable, substantive output, as is the case with the production-control system; hence, the various staffs do not always realize they are serving the same objectives. The man-objectives of man-job controls are seldom stated explicitly; hence, the various staffs are often in apparent conflict, depending upon their interpretation of the objectives. Second, the lack of recognition of the existence of a system contributes to its obscurity. The requisite flow of intelligence and information is not implemented; consequently, whatever system there is is vestigial. Third, upon frequent occasions, attempts to implement a system have been made by one particular staff group, commonly called *personnel,* or *manpower control,* because of the central theme of "people." This is too broad a category and involves too much subject matter. It tends to defeat the true concept of staff under which activity is divided by *aspect* of problem. When attempts were made to introduce a system concept with such a centralization of authority as appeared in most instances of the type being referred to, the other staff groups in the organization tended to resist the formation of a system of control as too restrictive upon their efforts. Accordingly, the system did not come into visible being.

Staff resistance is related to a series of misconceptions concerning the meaning of control system. It should be noted that the production-control system, as described in Chapter 13, utilizes many distinctly different staff groups, all serving the same problems, without the necessity of a total, centralized authority built around a theme of production. The solution to the problem of creating a true, effective system of man-job control that contributes to the overall objectives of the enterprise lies in the use of a similar objective and problem-oriented outlook rather than in the creation of a single staff group with so broad an orientation, requiring so much diverse knowledge and skill and "owning" a whole diverse group of problems. The latter resembles the older type of hierarchical line, which the staff concept was designed to replace.

In considering the nature of a man-job control system in terms of the steps of control, some confusion can arise if those who control and that which is being controlled are not kept separate. A brief summary of the steps of the concept of control in relation to man-job control seems indicated before attempting a detailed examination of the steps themselves. The parallel to the system of production control should be noted; this can be expected because both systems are only specific applications of the general concept of control, described in Chapter 12.

The objectives of the man-job control system are to provide the needed amount of manpower (men equipped to do jobs) to perform the activity required to achieve the objectives of the enterprise and to assist in the use and maintenance of this capability in a manner which contributes to both the economic goals of the enterprise and to the viability of the enterprise. The latter goal is achieved by maintaining conformity with the conditions stipulated by society with respect to the use of people in the enterprise, so as to maintain the feasibility of the enterprise being allowed to continue. This statement is readily derived from material presented in preceding chapters. The enterprise seeks to make a profit while, at the same time, it protects its capital; the capital must be protected from social threats, as well as from economic threats.

The program-planning step of the man-job control system relates to the development of time-phased plans for creating, using, and maintaining the required man-job capability in a manner that will accomplish the objectives.

The workload-determination step of the man-job control system relates to the development of a statement of the list of activities which must be performed in order to (1) create the necessary manpower capability for performing the man-jobs of the enterprise, (2) use the manpower capability, and (3) maintain the capability, all in a manner consonant with the objectives. This is the work list for the man-jobs which will be used to exercise man-job control rather than a statement of "how many man-jobs will be controlled."

The conversion to required resources, as with the production-control system, concerns the conversion of workload to various types of resources. For instance, in the production-control system, two of the major types of required resources were man-job time and material. In the man-job control system, the equivalents of these are both human and this, at first glance, may cause some confusion. The needed resources of the man-job control system include the man-job time required to perform actively the workload of the system and the man-job time to be acted on through the system, that is, the men who perform the work of the man-job control system and the men who will become, or are, the man part of the man-jobs of the enterprise. There will also be some use of physical plant.

The acquisition of authority to use resources in the man-job control system refers to the use of all of the types of resources mentioned above in carrying out the workloads, implicit in the program, designed to achieve the objectives.

The nature of the remaining steps in which performance is compared with plan can readily be understood from this description of the planning steps.

The preceding general outline of the steps of the man-job control system should serve as a guide for examining in some detail each of the steps of control, the interactions between and among the steps, and the requisite feedbacks.

Concerning goals or objectives of man-control, there are, as noted, various social obligations or required goals affecting any industrial organization in any organized society. In a democratic society, employment is basically voluntary, but various economic forces tend to diminish the true voluntary nature by limiting the number of alternative choices of action available to the individual worker. To compensate for this loss of voluntary action on the part of the worker, society as a whole may impose various goals upon plants as minimum goals in the form of minimum pay laws; maximum hour laws; overtime work and pay laws; laws concerning the development of agreements concerning how hard people may be asked to work; laws concerning the discussion of conflicting goals of management and labor; heating, ventilating, and safety standards; and minimum standards for the various basic amenities. These imposed goals are the way society says, "The plant must achieve, at least, these minimum man-oriented goals for the workers if the plant wants permission to seek its direct, substantive production-profit goals within the society."

In addition to the goals imposed by society at large, organizations of employees, such as unions, further define and enforce goals concerning wages, hours of work, conditions of work, intensity of work, health and safety standards, job security, and amenities and other conditions, above the minimum required by law. Likewise, they impose constraints upon the authority of the hierarchy of managers with respect to the permissible methods of exercising control.

Over and above the desires of the working group and managers for the achievement of man-goals, there are limitations imposed by the external economy of the total society affecting the feasibility of man-related goals. The competitiveness of the country in the world economy, of the industry, and of the individual plant, all tend to limit the goals which can be achieved.

In the background, there is always the unresolved problem concerning the equitable determination of the appropriate relationships between goals for different occupations. For instance, how should the pay or hours of work (or any man-related goal) for the man-job of auto assembler compare with the goal for a steel-mill roller, a coal miner, a grade school teacher, a garment sewer, a maintenance worker in a chemical plant, an ammunition loader, or a dock worker? In a democratic society, the resolution of this problem has been left, for the most part, to the workings of the democratic process with all its ramifications, individual plant and group economics, and attitudes. The number of disputes concerning suitable man-related goals which reach protracted negotiation is evidence of the difficulty of the problem. Further, proof of the difficulty of the problem is evidenced by the number of disputes in the United States which escalate to a point where even the Secretary of Labor, a member of the President's Cabinet, may become personally involved.

The foregoing is not meant to make a case for a substitute approach to the democratic process but merely to explain the reason for the apparent lack of either a system of well-stated, fixed goals or a carefully developed and completely mechanistic system for setting reasonable goals for all groups; the current nature of a democratic society requires the existence of the loose, dynamic goal-setting process. Autocratic societies which have attempted to impress a fixed rationale on the process have encountered difficulties in this area. However, it is feasible during periods of national emergency.

The foregoing should also explain the increasing participation of workers in the man-related goal-setting process. Further, it explains the apparent emotional aspects of many such instances of participation; there is so little available rationale. It is unfortunate that, in many situations, the primary goals related to the job aspects and the man-goals related to the human aspects have become so separated. The separation of the two types of goals often introduces hopelessly conflicting goals in the plant. Men, as noted in

Chapter 2, are not mechanistic and may well argue for man-goals which may not be economically or logically compatible with job or work goals or with the social concepts of a changing society.

The most vivid and perennial example of this type of conflict of goals exists in the number of bills offered each year in the Congress of the United States "to outlaw the use of work measurement in government agencies," despite the imperative need, as made clear in Chapter 12, for some form of work measurement to provide a substantive basis for determining the budgetary needs of government departments, as well as to provide a basis for economically controlling operations.

Similar proposals have been made by worker groups to industrial plants; here the conflict of goals is even greater. For instance, in the preceding discussion of the goals of a man-job control system, one of the objectives noted as being imposed upon the plant was "laws concerning the development of agreements concerning how hard people may be asked to work." Also, in the discussion in Chapter 8, concerning Figure 8.3, page 99, work measurement was indicated as referring to numerous techniques which could be used to determine the time required for a task when the task was performed with some prestipulated level of effort; the technique did not predicate this level of effort but rather took it into account. To eliminate the use of the techniques of work measurement would be to destroy any means of developing a time for a task based on some agreement concerning how hard people would work; further it would destroy any relationship between (1) work-time and the money goals workers impose as concomitant to work-time and (2) job-achievement goals, which are related to the economic objectives of the enterprise and determine the economic capability of the plant to meet the worker-imposed goals. The implicit alternative to the use of work measurement would be to leave the determination of the required amount of job achievement to the individual worker. In addition to the almost inevitable chaos, this procedure would pose an enormous threat both to the economic stability of the plant and to all the goals of workers and managers.

As additional examples, it is generally accepted that a country may establish welfare goals which exceed the ability of its economy to support. A labor union may campaign for higher wages and, at the same time, declare itself against higher productivity. A manager may seek high productivity while attempting to hold man-oriented goals below socially acceptable limits so as to maximize the attainment of the economic objectives of the enterprise. In such cases, industrial peace seldom ensues. Such conflicts have neither served the well-being of men and their society nor enhanced the productive facilities on which they depend. Nevertheless, they appear to be a universal feature of many problems.

To examine the nature of the man-job control system from a control-concept viewpoint requires that it be viewed in the context of the system of work-units given in Chapter 12. The following discussion is organized on such a basis.

The eighth-order work-units of the man-job control system, as implied in the introductory material of this chapter, would be:

1. To provide, use, and maintain at a minimum cost the necessary man-job capability to perform the activity of the enterprise so as to maximize the contribution to the main objective of the enterprise and to make a profit, provided that the following ancillary objectives are also met.
2. The cost of providing the necessary man-job capability will not exceed a given total amount. (The specification of this total amount will be an input to this control system from the top-management control system; the amount is determined on the basis of sales estimates, estimates of material, overhead, other costs, and profits, as the amount of money which will be available for wages and other remuneration.)
3. The economic and noneconomic man-oriented goals of the men in the plant will be met within the economic limitations of 2 above so as to meet the minimum requirements and to exceed these only to the extent that will not seriously affect the profitability of the enterprise.
4. The legal obligations of the plant with respect to man-job goals will be met.
5. To avoid the imposition, from any source, of hopelessly conflicting objectives upon the man-job control system.

It should be noted that, as is characteristic of eighth-order work-units, the objectives are expressed in terms of results rather than outputs. Further, it should be understood that it is not likely that one could visit an actual plant and find a list of this type. First of all, as mentioned at the outset of this chapter, the recognition of man-job control problems as being part of a system is not common. Further, considering the nature of the industrial society, it is doubtful whether it would be expedient for managers to state the objectives publicly in such bald terms. In addition, the managers engaged in this activity have become so thoroughly adapted to it that, like the mechanic or the football player mentioned in Chapter 1, they may find it hard to be logically explicit about their manner of operation.

The eighth-order work-units offered, however, in the preceding discussion are suggested as descriptive of the typical industrial enterprise. Their explicit statement here, like the other materials in this book, is designed to facilitate the development of insight into the activity of industrial management. Particular note should be taken that the use of the word work-unit as used here is not common practice but in accordance with the definition in Chapter 12.

Returning to the list of eighth-order work-units of the man-job control system, it should be noted that some of them are more substantively stated than the typical eighth-order work-units of the upper-level control system. This is quite typical of lower-level control-system objectives. To characterize the nature of the objectives given to the man-job control system as they appeared in the previous list:

1. The first objective given is a true objective; it will be used as a criterion of preference when choosing between alternatives.
2. The second objective is a limiting objective; the value is fixed.
3. The third objective does not have substantive detail and will need amplification.
4. The fourth objective, like the second, is a limiting objective but needs amplification. In addition, it will probably be subject to constant change.
5. The fifth objective, like the first, is a true objective; it will be used as a criterion of preference but in specific types of problems.

As the preliminary action required to perform step 2 of control, plan programs, it will be necessary to convert some of these eighth-order work-units into seventh-order work-units. In the case of man-job controls, this is applicable only to eighth-order work-units of the type represented by numbers 3 and 4 of the list given.

The input of information for the conversion of number 3 would come from the workers themselves, through their representatives, and from those of the managerial group who are primarily concerned with people as people, including direct supervisory managers. (Again, it should be pointed out that it is highly unlikely that the groups mentioned would think of these in the frame of reference, or the terms, used here. Workers would speak of "grievances, gripes, or inequities," managers of "motivations," and so on. The analysis given here, however, faithfully portrays the basic situation.)

The additional information for number 4 would come from three sources: (1) the workers, if organized into a formal union group, through their representative, would probably point out any deviation from legal obligations which affected their interest; (2) various government agencies (in the United States), depending upon the particular industry concerned, would periodically inspect the plant with man-job items, such as hours of work, age of workers, sanitary conditions, and worker health or safety hazards as part of their concern; such inspectors would call any deviation from legal obligations to the attention of the managers; and (3) most plants either have a legal section or maintain legal services on a part-time basis, and such legal services would be expected to prepare information concerning the legal obligations of the plant with respect to man-job objectives.

Subsequently, as a continuation of step 2 of control, these seventh-order work-units, together with the other eighth-order work-units (which do not need conversion to seventh order), would all be converted to sixth-order work-units, or programs.

The basic nature of the programs, or sixth-order work-units required to achieve the seventh-order work-units of the man-job control system, can be separated into four major categories:

A. Maintenance and use of the present man-jobs
B. Acquisition of new employees either to permit expansion of the number of man-jobs or to replace those men lost through attrition or to serve both needs
C. Training both of new employees to integrate the men into man-jobs and of existing employees either to upgrade or to adjust to changes in the production or work procedures
D. Non-production oriented changes to be made which affect man-jobs[1]

The conversion from seventh-order work-units to a quantitative statement of the sixth-order units, as has been previously noted, requires the introduction of additional intelligence. In the case of the man-job control system, the typical required information, at this point, is a forecast of:

1. The anticipated number and types of employees who will be needed to perform the activity of the enterprise by time periods, including information concerning any new skills needed
2. The anticipated number and types of employees who will be on hand by similar time periods
3. Any changes that will be needed to accomplish the conformance with the objectives of the man-job control system, expressed in quantitative terms

The information concerning the anticipated number and types of employees required to perform work of the enterprise, including any new skills needed, is an input of information which must be combined from a variety of sources. The first source is the gross-production control system, which gives the anticipated level of business. Information is also required from the detailed production-control system in order to provide data for converting the gross statement of outputs to a statement of the number of employees based on the current state of the art of using labor to produce outputs. These results must be modified by an input from the product and process design and project-control systems (treated in later chapters) so as to permit the anticipation of changes in the technology of product and process which will affect the number and nature of man-jobs needed. In a similar manner, each indirect area of work, e.g., operation of the production-control system, sales, accounting, and so forth, will be required to determine its man-job

---

[1] The grouping is partially arbitrary and is for convenience. Other groupings could be used as long as they are in conformance with the facts and permit and facilitate the sequential conversion to lower and lower orders of work-units, as described in Chap. 12.

requirements, including a direct feedback from this man-job control system itself. Here we find another reason for the emphasis upon the need for work measurement in indirect activities that was discussed in Chapter 12. If the organization is at all sizable and indirect work requires a considerable number of man-jobs, an inability to include these jobs in the man-job control concept may well make the attainment of the man-job control-system goals impossible. Inasmuch as these goals are directly related to the basic objectives of the enterprise, this is intolerable. To some extent, this fact is generally recognized in a rough fashion in the typical plant, and indirect man-job needs are crudely covered under a procedure usually called "budgeting"; however, the basis of the estimates of man-job needs usually employed is much too primitive to give much more than a rough restriction or constraint rather than a truly effective control. In addition, in many plants, it is not uncommon to have the man-job control activity pertaining to indirect workers or at least part of such control activity handled by a different group from the one used to provide man-job control for the direct workers. If the indirect working group is large, the previous remarks are applicable even with the division of the two control systems. Of course, in the small plant, it may not be appropriate to really formalize the man-jobs in these indirect activities; this conforms to the concept shown in Figure 13.1, page 174.

The information concerning the number and types of employees who will be on hand, number 2 of the list of additional information needed to develop the sixth-order work-units of the man-job control system, will be obtained from another variety of sources. One source for any type of man-job of which a considerable number are employed will be a statistical analysis of the factors affecting the attrition rate in order to develop a method of forecasting the number of employees who can be expected to be on hand by any given date. For smaller groups of employees, individualized analyses may be made to anticipate retirements or personal plans which conflict with continued employment in the plant. In the case of key employees in decisive jobs, periodic analysis would be almost routine. If there is a compulsory draft for military service with the maintenance of job rights, individual data would have to be maintained to indicate, by dates, the anticipated inflow and outflow to the plant capability.

The information concerning the changes needed to achieve conformance to the objectives of the man-job control system is derived from a comparison between the status and the details developed in the amplification of objectives 3 to 5 of the man-job control system.

As with the other control systems, at this point some feedback may be necessary, at times to the upper-level control system, before program planning (or replanning) may continue. For instance, the amount of money available for man-jobs may be obviously less than that required to meet the minimum needs for attaining objective 3,[2] economic or noneconomic man-goals, or 4, legal obligations (including agreements concerning wages entered into by discussions between managers and representatives of the workers[3]). Also, an ancillary objective, which to this point had been considered feasible, may prove to be an item which should have been classified under objective 5.

The alternatives of corrective action which must originate in the top-management control system include allocating more money for man-jobs at the expense of profits, changing gross-production control plans and sales or pricing plans to alter the income of the enterprise, changing the technology of production to change the cost of materials, and so forth. Note that these are trade-offs. Something must give; by definition, incompatible goals cannot be achieved simultaneously.

Some mathematical models may be employed to assist in generating knowledge concerning feasible trade-offs, to develop optimum trade-offs, or to assist in examining the consequences of various alternatives. As a simple illustration, changes in the technology of production may be examined with respect to the different mixes of skills (and cost) associated with various alternatives.

This general step of program planning, performed periodically, is often complicated by the time phasing of the causal system of the potentially incompatible goals. Objective 1 of the control system is constant; the value associated with objective 2 is usually set at a time much in advance of the dates when the objectives are to be met; objective 3, however, may reflect sudden changes in the economy and society; objective 4 is affected either by new legislation or by negotiation with the workers and their representatives and, like objective 3, may be subject to sudden change. Such goals when subject to rapid change may require much rapid action to change other goals and their programs so as to obtain compatibility. (Problems arising under goals of objective 5 are of a like nature.)

To minimize the need for rapid action, it is customary for top managers when faced with a collective bargaining situation to determine the maximum compatible limits for number 4 goals (legal obligations to workers) and to bargain strongly to avoid exceeding these in any final agreement. (A lower settlement may contribute to number 1.) As is no surprise to anyone, the managers, in most cases, initiate the bargaining by offering less than the maximum compatible limits, the union, by asking for more. These are the normal maneuvers of the bargaining process.

The control system, as it is being described, is a continuous process like the ongoing production-control system, but the cycle of repetition of the

---

[2] Although this really involves resource determination, the problem may be apparent at the program-planning level.

[3] Commonly referred to as *collective bargaining*.

initial steps is more like the time frame of the upper-level production-control system.

To return to step 2, program planning, of the man-job control system, the program categories, as originally given, can be quantitatively stated with the additional information indicated, but they are far too broad for converting directly to a statement of workloads. Consequently, these categories must be divided into smaller categories in a manner similar to that used in the production planning and control system, viz., to divide sixth-order work-units into fifth-order, fifth into fourth, and so on, until, as a general principle, third-order work-units, the terms normally required to describe activities, can be identified.

The first program item given previously was:

A. Maintenance and use of the present man-jobs. An examination of the nature of a man-job, as described in previous chapters, will reveal that, apart from the controls implicit in the production planning and control system, some additional control activity is required to maintain the following dimensional characteristics of man-jobs (the identification is by letter and number to facilitate later discussion: the letter conforms to the letter given the program categories; the number is just a sequence number for this listing):

*A*1. Wages
*A*2. Motivation
*A*3. Improvement of method of performing man-job
*A*4. Amount of work achievement required
*A*5. Assignment in the enterprise
    a. With respect to organization
    b. Specific job duties

The second program category given:

B. Acquisition of new employees either to permit expansion of the number of man-jobs or to replace those men lost through attrition or to serve both needs. Because of the nature of this program category, it seems feasible to go directly to third-order work-units. (This occasional skipping of orders of work-units was noted in Chapter 12, but no examples were given.) The third-order work-units are:

*B*1. Recruitment
*B*2. Selection
*B*3. Hiring
*B*4. Basic indoctrination

(Particular attention should be given to the difference in the way program *A* was divided as compared with *B*. This is as it should be and not an attempt to follow a technique. The objective is to portray the nature of the man-job controls, as found in a plant, from a total system point of view, employing the technique of work-units to assist and "bending" the technique as necessary to serve the objective.)

The third program category given was:

C. Training both of new employees to integrate the men into man-jobs and of existing employees either to upgrade or to adjust to changes in the production or work procedures. This program can be divided, usefully, into:

C1. On-the-job training for new direct-labor employees
C2. On-the-job training for new selective-job employees
C3. On-the-job training for new decisive-job employees
C4. Organized training for
    a. Operation of radically new equipment
    b. Special purposes
C5. On-the-job training for existing direct-labor employees to adapt them to changes in product, process, or equipment
C6. On-the-job training for existing selective-job employees to adapt them to changes in product, process, or equipment
C7. On-the-job training for decisive-job employees to adapt them to changes in organization, procedure, technology, or plant
C8. Out-of-the-plant training programs to acquire new inputs of information, including
    a. Conferences and seminars
    b. Professional society meetings
    c. Industry association meetings
    d. Educational institution, degree, or other lengthy course

The fourth program category given was:

D. Non-production oriented changes to be made which affect man-jobs. Typical subcategories found in this program are:

D1. Changes in the amenities provided
D2. Changes in the hours or time of work
D3. Changes in the method of determining wages
D4. Changes in the structure of organization

Category D, it should be noted, will not have any fixed or predictable form for all organizations at all times; instead it will reflect the particular, specific situation. Hence the subcategories given above are less typical illustrations than in the preceding categories.

The work of subdividing these programs and their subparts can be continued until a statement, totally in terms of activities, is arrived at. This is a statement of workload. The additional information, previously noted as required for program planning (converting from seventh- to sixth-order work-units), will permit the extension (if the information is in the proper sort of detail) to quantitative statements of the amounts of each of the workload items, thus completing step 3 of the cycle of control.

All of these subdivisions of the original statements of programs, like the programs they are derived from, represent all of the activity required to achieve the objectives. However, they become so numerous that they are not as convenient as programs for examining some important, basic possibilities of trade-offs, although they are needed to provide the feedback to programs to determine the need for trade-offs. For instance, if the eventual cost of programs B and C is too high, it may be possible to make changes which raise the number of employees retained under program A and so forth.

However, it is convenient to stop the analysis temporarily, at this point, and summarize before proceeding on. The nature of the man-job controls which exist in any industrial plant is being examined from the system concept. A statement of typical objectives was given. This was converted to a statement of programs. The division and conversion of programs to workloads were begun (although not completed) for the purpose of obtaining a statement of workloads which must be performed if man-job control is to be exercised. It is at this point in the analysis that the terms commonly used in the typical plant to describe man-job control activity first begin to appear. This is to be anticipated because, as mentioned at the outset of this chapter, the total system concept is not well recognized in this area of activity, although it is inherent in a realistic concept of management.

It should be emphasized that the control system indicates the path by which problems arise and the manner of developing a solution rather than the hierarchy of authority of the people in the plant. The relationships among the people may be different on different types of problems. Many staff groups must work on a variety of control systems, bringing their specialized knowledge to bear on the problems. It is as if the problems had the real authority. In the area of man-job control, this viewpoint has been somewhat slow to develop. As a consequence, although the typical plant usually engages in most of the activities listed as a further division of the programs given, central coordination is usually tenuous and the various activities are not necessarily performed in a mutually harmonious fashion. This probably reduces the profitability of the enterprise or restricts its productivity.

It seems appropriate, at this point, to examine, at least briefly, some of the pertinent areas of knowledge and technology used in performing the various workload items generated under the programs of the man-job control system. In this manner, the various groups concerned can be suggested in order to provide a better picture of the type of coordination needed to obtain a more effective man-job control system than is commonly achieved.

In respect to the workload items generated under program category A, the technologies required for their performance include:

1. Job evaluation
2. Motivation
3. Job design
4. Work measurement
5. Organization planning

Of these areas of technology, job design and work measurement have been adequately discussed in previous chapters, within the limits of detail deemed appropriate for this book. Therefore, the following discussion is limited to a brief examination of job evaluation, motivation, and organization planning.

Job evaluation, in some form or other, must come into play, even if there are no changes in the basic amount of money from which remuneration will be paid in order to develop and maintain an equitable way of distributing the available funds between and among the employees. In many cases, the employees will participate in the development and application of such plans. Such participation is most frequently channeled through a management group variously designated as personnel, industrial relations, labor relations, and so forth.

Job evaluation was referred to previously as a means of differentiating the pay for different jobs in terms of the amount of each of the factors present in the job which were sociologically acceptable as a basis of differentiation. So-called "evaluation systems," specific formalized procedures for achieving job evaluation, are of four general types:

1. Point plans
2. Comparison-by-factor plans
3. Comparison-by-total-job or rank plans
4. Group-classification plans

As noted in Chapter 8, in different societies, different factors may be deemed appropriate to use as a basis of determining compensation. This does not mean that job evaluation is not used. It merely means that the details of the technology employed may be vastly different: the problem still exists; it has different variables; and it requires a different type of detailed solution.

The following discussion contains a brief analysis of the different basic approaches to job evaluation used in the United States. The plans in use in other countries, in different societies, follow the same general outline, but the factors may be completely different.

Point plans require the listing of the factors which are considered the essential, socially acceptable basis of pay differentiation. Each of these factors must be assigned a weight or importance, relative to the other factors, as well as a scale, which will permit the quantitative differentiation of jobs. Using these factors and these scales, each job can be assigned a total point value. These point values can be related to a wage scale, i.e., more points, more hourly pay. For each job there may be, in addition, a range of pay, depending on length of service. Obviously much judgment enters into this process. The results must still be acceptable to the working group.

Comparison-by-factor plans resemble point plans in that a list of factors must be established to differentiate jobs, but instead of giving numerical values to these factors, they are used to systematize the comparisons between jobs to establish a satisfactory hierarchy of jobs by pay.

Comparison by rank, or total job, resembles the comparison-by-factor plan, except that specific factors are not listed and jobs are compared, in total, one with another to establish a hierarchy of jobs by pay.

Group-classification plans are somewhat different and tend to be used only in large organizations, e.g., the classification plan of the U.S. Civil Service for "white-collar" employees. In group-classification plans, general job descriptions are written for each general occupation, giving the job duties and responsibilities typical of different pay grades within that occupation. Any job assigned an employee is matched against this scale to determine the grade and pay group he is to be placed in. In most of these plans, there is also a series of pay steps associated with the length of service in each grade. The pay steps are usually of sufficient magnitude to cause considerable overlapping between grades.

Most job-evaluation plans, in plants, are more detailed for the production workers than for the managerial and clerical workers. There are several reasons. First of all, there are usually many more production workers than there are nonproduction workers; hence, production work has many more jobs to relate to each other. To reduce the work of employee participation, which could be onerous with many jobs, some form of systematic approach is desirable. (Mere system, however, does not necessarily create acceptability.) Second, many managerial employees are unique and harder to replace than many production workers. Consequently, the method of determining a manager's pay may tend to reflect the individual more than the job. Third, in many cases, the managerial job duties reflect the individual, and the nature of the duties changes when the job holder changes. This also will cause pay rates to reflect the individual characteristics. In large organizations where it may become difficult because of the number of such employees to recognize these individuals, a common failing of group-classification plans, there may be a tendency for unique and particularly valuable employees to move from firm to firm to gain the advantages which they feel entitled to.

Wage and salary structures are designed to attract and retain the desired type of employees, within a cost structure permitting profitable activity for the firm. Some type of procedure is necessary for the man-job control system to relate the money available to pay employees to the number of employees required. As may be anticipated, a great deal of cooperative effort among the various staffs who affect job contents is needed to obtain a suitable result. Motivation is a complex phenomenon. In Chapter 2, in discussing man-jobs, note was taken of the variety of individual reactions possible in a given situation. Managerial activity affecting motivation may well include such aspects as:

1. Supervisory and basic management training
2. A wage-incentive system
3. A system of indirect financial incentives related to
   a. Job security
   b. Promotion
   c. Other rewards
4. A system of nonfinancial incentives
5. An organization designed to provide motivation

It is often said that all managerial employees are also supervisors. This is somewhat true but misleading if taken too literally. Sections of this book have frequently referred to the industrial plant of today as a special type of society where responsibility is more by function, with a shifting relationship among people, depending upon the particular problem, rather than a society with a pervasive, fixed hierarchy of authority. There is, of course, a certain residual authority in the foreman of today (Taylor's gang boss) in that he provides much of the face-to-face contact between the staff and the workers or assists in such contact. There is also, in the rest of the organization, a residual line of authority to assist in maintaining order in the approach to problems. There is also a residual authority with regard to certain types of decisions. Hence, it would be more correct to say that the direct supervisors do much real supervision and most managerial employees do some. Effective supervision motivates and leads rather than provides negative constraints.

Hence, the subprogram item of motivation will also include:

1. Supervisory training
2. Presupervisory training
3. Basic management training

It is possible that some argument could be advanced to classify these under program C, "training." However, in the method of division used in the example being followed, those activities which have a heavy influence on "maintaining the capability" have been kept under program A, "maintenance and use of present man-jobs." The activities classified under C are primarily those training programs which are needed to respond to change. As noted in Chapter 12, the division from objectives to tasks is not an exercise in strict taxonomy but a matter of convenience; there are undoubtedly several ways of listing programs, activities, and so forth; the main purpose is to create a complete plan, examine the trade-offs and alternatives, and constrain efforts to achieve the objectives.

The training of direct supervisors will be examined first. The job of supervising requires many different skills as compared with the jobs being supervised, but it also requires some insight into those jobs. It has long been customary to promote workers to supervisory jobs. This is part of the overall pattern of motivation. Unfortunately, good workers do not necessarily make good supervisors. In addition, even if capable of supervising, workers usually need considerable training before undertaking this new function. Such a training program has many advantages. First, the planning of such a program may acquaint other members of the managerial group with unresolved problems affecting the supervisor. Second, the training program can teach the supervisor how to handle problems he may encounter, without going through a trial-and-error process in the plant, with the consequent problems resulting from errors.

With jobs other than direct supervisor, the supervisory aspects are all too often neglected or the training directed at a level too low to be of real use. As noted in Chapter 7, the society of the plant is changing and requires special forms of behavior. Special forms of behavior are easiest to obtain when they are recognized and described. Unfortunately, as noted in Chapter 7, much remains to be recognized in this area, but most actual man-job control programs include some training of this type, and progress is being made.

Concerning basic management training, as the materials covered to this point must surely make evident, management is not a simple activity, particularly in the large plant. In the small to medium plant, where one individual must perform a variety of functions, a different type of complexity is encountered. The customs and procedures that develop in a particular plant are most certainly highly individualized as compared with material which may be obtained from any general educational program conducted outside, independent of the plant. One essential feature of motivation is to tell the person what is wanted. As a consequence, like the supervisor, most members of management can profit from basic management training conducted in the plant or enterprise that is directed specifically at local problems and practices. Many large organizations, as may be expected, maintain sizable activities of this type.

Most enterprises, as still another means to motivate their employees, maintain a variety of systems of rewards or incentives. There are a great variety of these, although the word incentive is all too commonly associated with financial incentives or systems, such as piecework, payment by results, or wage-incentive plans.

Wage-incentive systems have been in common use for a long period. They are designed to provide a system-based motivation to encourage perform-ance of the desired type from employees. The incentive, for direct em-ployees, is usually related to a direct measure of quantity of performance, although quality or timeliness can also be the basis.

For instance, the time to perform one cycle of a task may be determined by work measurement as one minute. The total number of cycles of the task performed during the day (usually represented by a pieces-made count) would be multiplied by one minute to determine the value of the time earned. This may exceed the time worked; hence, the incentive. For instance, suppose an employee on the job described above made 540 pieces in eight hours of work.

His pay under the incentive system would be

Pieces made $\times$ time value per piece $\times$ rate of pay per time unit

If the hourly rate of pay was $3 per hour, the earnings would be

$$\frac{540 \times 1 \text{ minute}}{60 \text{ minutes}} \times \$3 \text{ per hour} = \$27$$

The wage computed on the basis of time only would have been

8 hours $\times$ \$3 = \$24

This method of wage incentives is referred to as a *standard time plan* be-cause the employee's work is evaluated in terms of the *standard time value* of the work accomplished. There are a great number of variations of such plans. As might be expected, there is often some considerable pressure for participation of the employees in the determination of time values to be used with such plans. This is frequently caused by one of several factors. For one, there is often a lack of agreement concerning what the standard time is supposed to represent. Second, even with such an agreement, there is often some doubt in the minds of the employees as to whether such an agreed-upon concept can be, or is, embodied in the standard time. Some considerable discussion could be undertaken, but for the purposes of this book, the above is sufficient to suggest that the procedures for developing adequate data should be planned, various specialist staffs should participate, and workers should participate at some level.

The workload developed with respect to program category A, page 206, must indicate the general method to be used and the number of jobs for which such data must be developed as part of the maintenance and use of capability.

Indirect financial incentives, such as job security and promotion, are often affected by rules agreed upon by managers and workers, and some activity must be planned to achieve the goal of adhering to these rules with intelligent deviations, as may be required.

Also, in the managerial ranks there will usually be some attrition and some filling in by promotion from in-house. Activity must be planned to help prepare some employees to move up in the organization. This is also a source of motivation but will be discussed under program category *C* because it contemplates "change" before such training would be put to use.[4]

Nonfinancial incentives are, in reality, the most common type in use and, frequently, the least recognized as important factors in motivation. The attitude of the plant as a whole, the general atmosphere, has a significant bearing on the attitude of employees, shown previously to have a marked effect upon production. Letters of commendation or praise, words of praise, or any means of showing approval, all affect productivity. Of course, if the effort to praise is conducted in a cynical fashion, the results may be negative. A feeling of belonging may greatly affect productivity. Such effects were noted in Chapter 2 in the discussion of the classic Hawthorne experiment.

When these nonfinancial rewards are applied differentially, that is, varied with regard to the contribution from the employee, their effect may be quite sizable. A plan for making use of this type of motivation is quite properly a part of man-job control, although again, as with so many of the man-job control programs, much cooperative effort is needed from all of the managers within the plant to establish an effective and acceptable program.

The last item listed previously affecting motivation is the organization. This is of such importance that it is shown as a separate subcategory under *A,* "*A*5. Assignment in the enterprise: *a.* with respect to organization." This is of more concern with selective and decisive man-jobs than with repetitive man-jobs.

Organization is the pattern of authority and responsibility between and among people, aiding them in acting in an integrated and orderly fashion. The purpose of formally setting forth this pattern of relationships is to assist people in understanding the role they must play to perform the work of the plant in the most economical manner consistent with social restrictions. The usual way of portraying the pattern of relationships between and among people takes two forms: the first an organization chart, and the second, an organization manual. The organization chart consists of a box for each job with lines indicating the hierarchy of authority. Because such a graphic presentation is far too simple to convey the totality of the relationship, it is frequently accompanied by much more detailed material called an *organiza-*

---

[4] The reader may feel that this is "hair-splitting." However, it would not be a mistake to put it under category *A;* it just does not seem as convenient. If it had been included under *A,* the same sort of problem would exist. Again, it must be remembered that the classification from eighth-order work-units to third-order work-units is *not* a strict exercise in the taxonomy of work; it is merely a convenient way to plan and constrain; "the convenience," to some extent, depends upon who is doing it, and such borderline cases are not uncommon.

tion manual, which gives the details of the duties, responsibilities, authority, and so forth for most managerial jobs (program *A,* subitem *A5b*). However, as noted, the relationship between people may change, depending on the problem, and many organization manuals would become enormous if this relationship was fully spelled out. However, the more people understand the details of their respective roles, the more effectively they can perform. Therefore, more recently, new types of graphic displays have been developed, such as the *linear responsibility chart.*

The linear responsibility chart is a graphic means of portraying a variety of relationships among people in the order in which these relationships take place during the course of resolving a given type of problem. Typical but not inclusive of the types of relationships which may be shown are:

1. Responsible for doing the work
2. Must be consulted
3. Must be consulted and permission obtained
4. Must be informed
5. Provides general supervision
6. Must be consulted when magnitude of problem exceeds a given size
7. Must be consulted to obtain approval of final answer

This information has been given to indicate the variety of relationships which are typical in an organization. The activity of the man-job control system must include the creating and maintaining of an organization or improving the understanding of it among the personnel of the plant.

The task of determining the quantity of workload with regard to the activities of the man-job control programs is usually divided among the various staffs who will be responsible for performing the work. This division further obscures the total system, with the possible consequence of additional conflicting activities.

The recruitment requirements, program category *B* of the list given in the example, are usually detailed by the industrial-relations group which will work out the detailed activities which must be performed to obtain the necessary number of satisfactory new employees. The same group will usually work out the details of the basic indoctrination training to be given to new employees. The amount of such training may vary with the type of new employee. With decisive jobs, the training may be extensive. Such additional extensive training will be discussed in reference to program category *C.* Also, as with the make-or-buy decisions within the production-control system, decisions must be made (particularly where high skills or managerial abilities are involved) whether to promote and train or hire from the outside to obtain the requisite employees. Such decisions will be influenced by general economic conditions, growth rate of the plant, quality of present employees, agreements, and social customs. In addition, all individual decisions will be influenced by characteristics of individuals in the plant being considered for specific jobs, although there must be some general program decision. Such decisions can shift workload from program B, "recruit," to program C, "train."

A short perusal of the subcategories shown under program C will quickly suggest that a large number of different members of the organization will be involved in performing this workload. Most supervisory managers or those with any supervisory responsibility at all will take part in on-the-job training activities. Top and middle managers will, in most cases, also take some initiative in suggesting themselves for participation in out-of-plant training courses. Concerning item $C4$, Organized training, the industrial-relations group or a subgroup therein called training[5] will be involved in the activities which must be conducted. However, since other staff and line groups in the plant will be planning for a certain amount of employee development and preparation for advancement, plans for training will also be made within those groups. The industrial-relations training group will find itself if performing properly taking two different roles, one, planning training programs for new employees, and two, assisting in coordinating training programs, planned by other groups, for which the other group will also provide the manpower required to conduct the course, and so on.

In many of the training tasks under program C, the training of employees on new jobs or of new employees will require the development of all of the data associated with a job design, as indicated in Chapter 8, with the involvement of all of the kinds of managerial staff mentioned in that chapter.

The categories shown under program D, "Non-production oriented changes to be made which affect man-jobs," are more or less self-explanatory. Further, it should be noted that the range of activities shown will involve members of management ranging from plant-engineering (design of physical plant) to top managers. Subcategories of other activities, properly included under this program, will be related to needs, such as may be indicated by a list of jobs which are sources of difficulty and need redesign, i.e., job enlargement or job simplification, to reduce the difficulty of finding people who can perform them, to reduce sources of friction with the workers, or to reduce conflicts with the work assignments as they are developed under the production-control system or other control systems.

The purpose of the foregoing extensive digression into the technologies used to perform the activities of the man-job control system, the manner of performing them, and the examination of the groups in the enterprise which would normally be involved was to highlight the relationship between

---

[5] There are enough people engaged in activity of this type for there to be a professional society called "The American Society of Training Directors."

the concept of control and the authority hierarchy between and among people. Obviously, the total hierarchy of authority among the members of the managerial group cannot be arranged in an order which conforms to the requirements of the man-job control system; the same can be said with regard to the production-control system. Many members of management have duties related to both control systems. As will be seen later, they also have duties relating to other control systems as well. The relationships between and among people must constantly alter, depending upon the control objectives. This is not an easy type of behavior to develop and maintain, but this is what effective performance requires. The task is more difficult when the concept of the control system is not perceived, and the problems must be approached in an unstructured fashion.

To return to the main theme of this chapter, after the statements of the workload of the man-job control system have been prepared in the form of quantitative statements, the next step of control is to determine the resources required to perform these activities.

The ease or difficulty of performing this step depends primarily upon how accurately the workload was expressed in quantitative terms. Concerning such items as the number of jobs requiring evaluation, the number of tasks for which job designs must be developed, and so forth, a good quantitative estimate is usually available. However, most of these activities will be performed by specialist staffs other than the industrial-relations group. Coordination among these staffs must be effected to obtain control. Conflict usually develops when the "coordinating" group attempts "direction."

On the other hand, the amount of organizational design work to be performed is difficult to determine. Further, much of top management takes a deep interest in this work. This part of the program of man-job control is seldom accurately converted to workload in a formal manner.

For the most part, the conversion to required resources is relatively simple as compared with this step in the production-control system. The interdependencies between and among third- and fourth-order work-units, equipment, tooling, materials, and so forth do not exist. Further, the coefficients of conversion of workload to required resources are usually far less complex. As contrasted to the details connected with repetitive-job time standards, the details of the selective and decisive job are left, as previously noted, largely to the discretion of the job holder. The coefficients of conversion of workload to required resources, the work-measurement data, may take a form such as "one recruiter per X number of jobs" or "one trainer per two weeks of all-day training per month." On the basis of such values, manpower is allocated to the various staffs for the man-job control-system activity they undertake.

Some of the items of workload in the man-job control program are even easier to convert to amount of resources required. For instance, the number of new employees needed, when converted to type and time period, can be expressed in monetary terms simply by the addition of data concerning wages which are already available in the statement concerning the structure of wages as derived from the job-evaluation plan. This is far simpler than the development of a statement of the varieties of tools and materials, and the amounts and their prices required to support the production-control system.

As with the other control systems, when step 4, conversion of workload to required resources, is completed, a feedback to objectives must take place to determine if there is a compatible relationship. In the man-job control system, the need for such a feedback should be obvious. When incompatibility occurs, much recycling takes place until the conflicts are adjusted and authority can be granted to proceed. As noted much earlier in this chapter, some of the corrective action to promote feasibility may take place in the top-management control system or in the gross-level production-control system.

In the step of using resources to accomplish the workload, a variety of subsystems of control are commonly used. The systems are usually simple because the input of new bits of intelligence is relatively small, and simple controls are both economical and effective.

The determination of the workload accomplished, step 7 of control, is usually also a simple step. For instance, two weeks of training usually takes exactly two weeks. (This may sound inane, but some of the comparisons are of this level of simplicity.) The amount of new intelligence fed back into the control system is relatively simple in nature, although there are a variety of inputs related to the diversity of the activities. For instance, there is usually a feedback from the ongoing production-control system which indicates the "excess" labor on hand or the amount of work which was scheduled but could not be accomplished because of the lack of manpower. These data are used to assist in correcting the input of capability. There may also be a feedback from the production-control system, indicating the number of jobs awaiting the development of a time standard in order to convert them into an estimate of required resources or to assist in scheduling and constraining the productive activity. These data will be used to guide the work-measurement effort. There will be feedback from the area of industrial relations, indicating the number of jobs needing a job evaluation. Because of the sensitivity of this work and its result, rapid handling of such problems is usually given a high priority and schedule conformance is usually attained.

The determination of the program accomplished, step 8 of control, is seldom formally recognized as such. There are two reasons for this. First, the critical items are usually brought under control at the level of the first feedback and comparison, the comparison of activity with workload. This is usually true of the acquisition of employees, their training and their motivation; the application of job evaluation; the creation of job designs; and the setting of time standards. Second, most of these parts of programs are carried on by separate staff groups, and each staff group usually reports independently concerning its contribution to the operating objectives of the plant. Consequently, industrial-relations staffs will report on the number of employees acquired and the cost of acquisition and training; the work-measurement group will report on the value to production of the standards they set; and the job-design group will report on the value of the designs they created. These diverse data are seldom brought together. In consequence, the usual man-job control system is difficult to see as a complete system, although the necessary functions are performed.

The determination of the degree of accomplishment of goals, as with program, is done in diverse places. There is a general tendency to substitute a feedback from the top-management control system concerning profit for any detailed evaluation of goal accomplishment, although this is also the main goal of the man-job control system.

In summary, having shown the similarity of the man-job control system to the production-control system, it is pertinent to point out some of the differences which may clarify the reasons for the incomplete system developed in the usual plant. In the production-control system, the number of new bits of intelligence entering the system and the problem of detailing these into actionable form ordinarily constitute a formidable task. The actual use of resources to perform the work is relatively routine in most cases, although the problems of control, including corrective action, may be large. In the man-job control system the problem of adding details to the objectives to make them actionable is relatively simple but the carrying out of the action often constitutes a formidable task. The tasks of training people, evaluating jobs, designing jobs, planning organizations, and so forth are often difficult tasks, calling for not only complex knowledge and skill but also skill in dealing with people. Consequently, in most man-job control-system activity, primary attention is given to the actual activities performed rather than to the control system in which they take place. In many cases this direction of attention goes too far, with a considerable loss of effectiveness as compared with that which could be achieved if all of the diverse functions concerned with man-job control were coordinated more fully as a system of control.

REFERENCE TOPICS

Personnel	Job evaluation
Industrial relations	Wage incentives
Labor relations	Incentives
Labor legislation	Executive attitudes
Wage administration	Management training

Motivation   Communication
Supervisory training   Organization
On-the-job training   Linear responsibility charts
Employee recruitment, selection, testing

SUGGESTED THEMES

1. Compensable factors in different societies
2. Changes in industrial relations
3. Trends in labor legislation
4. Examples of collective bargaining patterns
5. Status assigned jobs as reflected by pay
6. Anomalies in society concerning status and pay
7. Incentives and disincentives in given situations
8. Union attitudes, ostensible and real, comparing statements and actions
9. Management attitudes, ostensible and real, comparing statements and actions
10. Discussion of "reasonableness" of profits
11. Guidelines for wage differentials among industries
12. Varieties of relationships between and among people in organized groups
13. Analysis of various job-evaluation plans
14. A study of the rewards in any selected organization
15. A description of the organization of any selected enterprise
16. The means by which any selected organization carries on the steps of control with regard to man-job control

SUGGESTED CASES

Cruickshank, H. M., and K. Davis, *Cases in Management,* 3d ed. Homewood, Ill.: Richard D. Irwin, Inc., 1962. Cases beginning on pages 3, 11, 17, 42, 110, 123, 129, 138, 140, 151, 155, 161, 164, 166, 229, 271, 273, 276.

Greenwald, D. U., *Elementary Case Problems for Industrial Engineers.* New York: The Ronald Press, 1957. Cases beginning on pages 12, 14, 16, 18, 108, 110, 118, 121, 125, 128, 129, 133.

Mantel, S. J., Jr., *Cases in Managerial Decisions.* Englewood Cliffs, N.J.: Prentice-Hall, Inc., 1964. Case beginning on page 15.

Terry, G. R., *Case Problems in Business and Industrial Management,* 2d ed. Dubuque, Iowa: William C. Brown Company, Publishers, 1955. Cases beginning on pages 23, 124, 125, 126, 127, 129, 130, 131, 139, 141, 142, 144, 150, 151, 158, 159, 165.

Ziegler, R. J., *Casebook in Production Management.* New York: John Wiley & Sons, Inc., 1962. Cases beginning on pages 128, 131

15 CONTROLLING PHYSICAL PLANT

Physical plant was defined in Chapter 1 as "all of the physical adjuncts to productive activity." This included building, equipment, and tools. Physical plant, it will be noted, is used to serve the programs of the production-control system and the man-job control system.

As indicated in the last chapter, some aspects of man-job control are included directly in the production-control system. The aspects included are those related to the use of man-jobs in performing the tasks explicitly described in the production-control system. In a like manner, some aspects of physical plant control, particularly the planned, scheduled use of equipment to produce the outputs of the enterprise, are also included in the production-control system and do not have their own system of control apart from the production-control system. This chapter concerns only those aspects of physical plant control which are not included in the production-control system.

Hence, the objectives, or eighth-order work-units, of the physical plant control system may be described as:

1. To maintain the equipment in operating condition in a manner that achieves a maximum economic contribution to the enterprise
2. To maintain the building in condition to protect and house the equip-

ment and to provide the necessary conditions for man-jobs in a manner that achieves a maximum economic contribution to the enterprise

3. To maintain an effective configuration of equipment so as to serve the needs of processes in the most economical manner

These objectives are sufficiently independent so that in usual practice three independent control systems are used to achieve these objectives, with some borrowing of manpower capabilities between the first two control systems. In this chapter, the control systems related to the achieving of the first two objectives will be discussed together because, as will be seen, they are very much alike, differing only with respect to the nature of the outputs and in some of the skills required for the man-jobs. The control system devoted to the third objective will be discussed subsequently.

The control of the condition of equipment was recognized as an important problem very soon after the introduction of mechanical equipment. At that time, because of the great disparity in the cost of equipment as compared with the cost of labor, attention was centered on maximizing the use of equipment. This is a continuing problem because, as noted in Chapter 6, in dealing with time and money, the fixed cost of equipment is essentially independent of use. Idle equipment shut down for repair continues to contribute to cost, without the production of any offsetting value. It may also make it impossible to use other equipment.

The statement of objectives is sufficiently simple so that it may be converted to sixth-order work-units, or programs, directly, without recourse to intermediate seventh-order work-units. The additional intelligence is relatively easy to obtain. For instance, in both the equipment-condition control system and the building-condition control system, the program list consists of the total list of objects under control. However, as is typical of all program statements, there is a variety of alternative ways of stating even these programs. The list of equipment could be described in terms of the equipment for various products, the individual pieces of machinery, the areas of the plant, or the components of machines. Likewise, the building could be listed in terms of floors of building; areas of building; or components of buildings such as floors, windows, piping, and elevators. Inasmuch as the purpose of making a program list is to facilitate the identification of workload and required resources, some knowledge of how the need for activity is generated should be used in determining the most suitable form for the list of programs.

In the most usual case, the program list for equipment is in terms of various pieces of equipment, with the occasional addition of selected items of pieces of equipment, such as truck tires, high-pressure oil pumps attached to other machines, and so forth. The usual program list for building is by building components by location.

The conversion to workload requires some considerable additional information. Note that fourth-order work-units do not appear in these systems as separate and discrete from third-order work-units.

Maintaining equipment and building in adequate condition permits of two major alternative approaches. One way is to wait until some piece of equipment or some aspect of building fails and then repair it. A second alternative is to inspect and repair periodically before failure occurs to minimize the costs associated with failure. It may be more economical to conduct some programs in this fashion, although an overemphasis on this approach can raise costs beyond economical limits.

Considerable study may be needed to determine which programs should be handled on a preventive basis, as well as to determine the appropriate intervals between maintenance periods. Naturally, there will be various items clearly indicated as preferable to handle by one or the other method. For instance, plant windows can usually be washed periodically even for office areas, but broken window glass in office areas cannot be averted by preventive maintenance. Critical machines in line manufacture cannot be allowed to run to failure in most instances. The loss incurred by the unplanned shutdown of the whole line would probably greatly exceed the cost of inspection and repair on a preventive basis. The equipment used by a company providing a service, such as the airplanes of an airline, must obviously be subjected to preventive maintenance.

The workload items of the programs to be treated with preventive maintenance, in most cases, can be converted readily to statements of required resources, although some items may not be determinable until after some experience under a system. The man-job time may be determined by some form of work measurement. The skill required by the man-jobs and the equipment required to perform the work can be determined from the job design for the preventive activity, but the materials required cannot always be estimated in advance.

The time phasing of the programs, the scheduling of the man-jobs, and the comparing of performance with plan may be facilitated by the use of Gantt charts or by the use of other techniques, as already described in Chapter 13.

Indeed, as far as the preventive workload goes, the system of control for the equipment condition and building condition will greatly resemble the production-control system, except that the number of bits of intelligence passing through the system is nominal in most cases. Exceptions can be found. An airline, as mentioned earlier, is an excellent example of such an exception.

The consideration of the airline makes it particularly easy to suggest one additional constraint under which the control system must usually operate. In the case of the airline, preventive maintenance of the aircraft, while it is being performed, obviously prevents the use of the aircraft for producing the direct, substantive outputs of the organization. The same is true of the preventive maintenance, for the most part, of the equipment of any organization. Hence, some interface with the production-control system is needed so that the capability lost during maintenance is removed from the capability considered as available within the production-control system. As another alternative, the preventive-maintenance cycle may be defined within a given range of time or use and the production-control cycle may indicate, within these limits, when it is most convenient with respect to the production of outputs to shut the machine down for inspection and repair. The costs of the various alternatives must be compared, taking into account the costs within both systems, in order to approach full optimization. If the preventive-maintenance cycle is controlled within the equipment-control system, the equipment-control system will usually make the most effective use of its man-jobs. However, in the usual case, the costs and values associated with the productive use of the equipment are greater. In the typical plant, the maintenance-control problem is complicated by having to respond to some of the random fluctuations within the other system. Obviously, cooperation between the people responding to the two systems is required.

The second part of the workload contained in the programs of each of the two maintenance-control systems under consideration consists of emergency events, or unpredicted work (at least not predictable in detail). Such a workload cannot be detailed in advance or exactly converted to a detailed statement of the required resources as accurately as can be the preventive work. On the other hand, sufficient data may be evolved to determine the required resources in advance of performing the work, once an event has been identified. Further, the total of such a workload for an extended period, in terms of the resources of man-jobs and the money value of material required, can be estimated to a fair degree in advance of the events and added to the capability maintained for scheduled preventive work to determine an estimate of the total capability required to be on hand. Such information may be fed to the man-job control system to serve the purposes of that system.

In the scheduling activity, within the equipment- or building-condition control system, this excess capability may be given a definite assignment when an emergency event occurs. The subsequent steps of control, once an emergency event is identified, will be handled, again, in a manner identical to the procedure used for productive work in the production-control system.

The activity performed is compared with the work planned so as to continually update the knowledge concerning when and where maintenance has been performed and to carefully evaluate the need for capability as demonstrated by experience. If emergency work does not occur at the rate anticipated over a considerable period of time, there is the possibility that excess labor will be expended upon the preventive activity, performing it to a degree of perfection above economical limits. If emergency work occurs at a rate greater than anticipated over a considerable period of time, there is the possibility that preventive work will be neglected, leading to more emergency work and eventual chaos in the plant. A variety of corrective actions, similar to the variety encountered in the production-control system, are possible.

In most cases of equipment- and building-condition control, the costs associated with the performance of the work can seldom be considered by themselves. In the usual case, they must be compared with the costs which would be incurred if the work were not done or if the work were delayed. Therefore, the materials used in such work can also be divided usefully into two distinct types, those for preventive maintenance and those for emergency work. Those materials and supplies consumed in preventive maintenance can be predicted, for the most part, well in advance of their use. Hence, they may well be subjected to a material-control system, designed to minimize the cost of obtaining such materials; such a control would contribute to the profit objective of the enterprise. However, emergency events are of such a nature that the amount of material required to remedy the undesired condition cannot be predicted in advance, except for certain basic materials. It is normal for the group performing the work of equipment- and building-condition control to have, therefore, at their immediate disposal certain basic stocks of materials and repair parts, even though the cost of these materials adds to the working capital of the enterprise. Obviously, there will be many occasions where the trade-off, speed of obtaining versus price, mentioned in Chapter 11, will be useful. The determination of the resources required for the operation of these control systems should include a suitable amount of money for this, as well as adequate authority to make purchases from these funds without recourse to the normal routines of purchasing. Failure to provide for this often creates much friction among people, as well as excess costs from the operation of these control systems.

The remaining control system, related to the control of physical plant as indicated at the beginning of this chapter, relates to the control of the configuration of the plant (layout) and the quantity of equipment. As with man-job control, the tasks within such a system usually overshadow the mechanics of the system to the extent that the system, as such, is often difficult to perceive in an actual plant. This condition probably tends to reduce the benefits obtained. In the absence of a basis for comparison, even this is difficult to evaluate.

The objective of a system related to the control of the configuration and capability of the plant is to adjust the layout and the capability so as to maximize the long-run opportunity for profit. Because such an objective relates to future events containing many uncertainties, the programs are not usually given in the same degree of detail as the other control systems which have been discussed. The programs consist in taking advantage of innovations in process equipment and process sequence and in materials-handling equipment, as well as reacting to advantages made possible by changes or potential changes in the quantity of product, mix of the different products, and available capital for investment.

The workload in such a control system is seldom ascertained with any detail because it is difficult to develop a definite list of things to be done in specific terms to perform such a program, although, as will be shown in Chapter 17, it is feasible to do so and it may be profitable to do so. As a consequence, the resources required to perform the workload instead of being ascertained in advance are, in most cases, applied as long as it appears profitable to do so, i.e., as long as savings or increases in profit exceed both the cost of maintaining the man-jobs engaged on such work and the cost of making the changes to the plant. The amount of workload generated depends, to a great extent, upon the ability and ingenuity of those charged with the responsibility for such activity. It should also be obvious that the individual problems within the type of workload described have many interrelated aspects. Many of the items of workload are sufficiently important and unique to be given their own one-time-use control system, as will also be described in Chapter 17.

In somewhat more detail, the problems or tasks within the workload may be such as:

1. Maintaining an up-to-date record of the location of equipment and service facilities, such as water, air, steam, and electricity, so as to provide a starting point for any change. Such data are usually kept in the form of a model, consisting of plan-view drawings, plan-view and profile drawings, or three-dimensional models, appropriate to the nature of the plant.

2. Providing for the location of additional equipment brought into the plant and providing for services to such equipment.

3. Examining new process possibilities resulting from innovations originating outside of the plant, as well as within the plant, and the economics of such innovations. Such innovations may concern both process sequence and process equipment. Studies of this type are greatly influenced by changes in the volume of production and must be coordinated with product- and process-design activity.

4. Examining the desirability of new materials-handling equipment and comparing alternative materials-handling equipment, as well as the alternatives of changing the location of production equipment. As with the preceding item, such studies are greatly influenced by the volume of production and by the stability of production.

5. Evaluating the effect of changes in the quantity of production upon

the desirable production equipment, layout, and materials-handling equipment. This type of problem is similar to those given in category 3 and 4 above, but the source of the input of new intelligence generating the problem is different.

6. Evaluating the effect of the mix of the different products and the layout upon the profit.

7. Evaluating the most profitable type of new equipment for consideration as an investment, taking into account marketing problems created by the additional production.

8. Changing the layout of equipment when the equipment is modified so as to facilitate economies in man-jobs assigned to the equipment.

9. Rearranging office and laboratory space to allow appropriate conditions for indirect work and to accommodate changes in such work.

In some cases, relatively rigorous mathematical methods are available which will assist in the solution of some of the above types of problems. Of course, such mathematical models have their limitations. They are usually based on certain assumptions concerning markets, marketing problems, costs, maintenance of price structures, and so forth. However, they are helpful in determining the most logical course of action with such assumptions. Thus, they are superior to intuitive methods but certainly not infallible.

From a consideration of the type of problems encountered in performing the workload of the control system just discussed, it should be obvious that the intelligence stimulating such problems may originate in many places in an organization. Many skills may be involved. It is not necessary that a particular person or a particular group of persons be assigned such activities to the exclusion of other types of problems or that such activities be exclusively assigned to a given group. The functions of control, however, must be performed if the plant is to achieve its goals by other than fortuitous means. The conditions just outlined indicate one of the real problems concerning organization and one of the reasons that staff activity, as outlined in Chapter 7, is preferable to a strict hierarchy of authority typical of older and simpler societies. To handle problems of the types which have been presented, a flexible and constantly shifting relationship among people permits the development of the necessary specialized information and managerial skills and their effective coordinated use.

REFERENCE TOPICS

Plant maintenance
Preventive maintenance
Maintenance standards

Plant engineering
Materials handling
Equipment-replacement policy
Plant layout
Tool repair
MAPI

SUGGESTED THEMES

1. Costs and values with respect to the time period selected for preventive maintenance
2. Preparation of maintenance lists
3. Evaluation of preventive-maintenance programs
4. Analysis of power-grid or -system failures
5. Plant-layout models
6. Discussion of costs and values of optimum assortment of maintenance materials for selected situation

SUGGESTED CASES

Cruickshank, H. M., and K. Davis, *Cases in Management,* 3d ed. Homewood, Ill.: Richard D. Irwin, Inc., 1962. Cases beginning on pages 51, 262.

Greenwald, D. U., *Elementary Case Problems for Industrial Engineers.* New York: The Ronald Press, 1957. Cases beginning on pages 101, 102, 104, 106.

Terry, G. R., *Case Problems in Business and Industrial Management,* 2d ed. Dubuque, Iowa: William C. Brown Company, Publishers, 1955. Cases beginning on pages 46, 72, 73, 74, 75.

Ziegler, R. J., *Casebook in Production Management.* New York: John Wiley & Sons, Inc., 1962. Cases beginning on pages 64, 95, 98.

16

CONTROLLING MATERIALS

This chapter concerns the control of materials. Materials were defined in Chapter 1 as "the physical objects consumed by the work group in creating its output." In Chapter 11, materials were classified into four categories: raw material, components, operating supplies, and equipment and plant supplies. The control of the last category, equipment and plant supplies, was discussed in Chapter 15. Therefore, this chapter will be confined primarily to a discussion of the control of raw material, components, and operating supplies; the term *materials control* will be used in this restricted sense.

Most commonly, the materials-control system is directly interfaced with the sixth step, use resources, of the ongoing production-control system and receives an input of quantitative substantive goals or objectives across this interface, after the production-control system has operated to acquire authority to use resources. However, as will be discussed later, there are instances in which it is more advantageous to obtain an input of goals from an interface with a higher control system and to use the production-control system to provide an interface with a later step of the materials-control system to aid in guiding corrective action.

In addition to substantive goals which are derivative from other control systems, the materials-control system has a guiding economic goal. This economic goal is *to supply materials to the productive facility in a manner designed to maximize the profit potential of the plant.*

Sub-optimization, such as cheaper supplies or raw materials, when the savings from lower unit costs are more than offset by the increase in processing or handling costs, is to be avoided, as well as the use of cheaper materials whose unreliable or slow delivery causes delays which offset purchasing savings. Similarly, excessive stocks whose carrying charges (interest, storage, deterioration) exceed purchasing advantages do not contribute to the economic objective. The converse, small stocks with low carrying charges, may also be economically disadvantageous if there are frequent delays in production due to stock limitations. The economic objective is served by facilitating the production-control system at the lowest total cost, considering all costs and values. An adequate interface between the two systems is an obvious necessity. This interface is somewhat more critical in most manufacturing enterprises than the equivalent interface between the production-control system and the man-job control system or the interface between the production-control system and the equipment-condition control system because the materials-control system is less susceptible to minor corrective action. For instance, if the man-job control system supplies the requirements of the production-control system with a somewhat smaller number of men than are actually needed, some corrective action may be taken by using overtime until the proper number of men is supplied. Also, if a machine breaks down, it may be repaired at night or over a weekend to minimize the delay; overtime may be used to make up the lost time; or substitute equipment may be used while the preferred machine is out of order. However, an insufficient supply of material can be corrected only by getting material; there is seldom an alternative. As noted in Chapter 15 with regard to repair materials, this aspect may be of prime importance in the design of a suitable control system.

The materials-control system also interacts with the problem of selecting a material. Some of the cost factors and some of the value factors associated with the selection of a material are affected by the operation of the materials-control system. In Chapter 11, which dealt with the problem of selecting a material, seven cost factors and three value factors were listed. The lists are repeated below, with an asterisk preceding the factors which are affected by the materials-control system.

The cost factors are:

 1. Basic unit cost from the supplier
*2. Cost of maintaining a contractual relationship
*3. Cost of moving the materials from source to plant
*4. Cost of storing
*5. Cost of verifying the characteristics of the material

*6. Cost of internal handling
7. Cost of processing

The value factors are:

1. Suitability to satisfy the requirements of the product
*2. Availability of the requisite quality and quantity when desired
3. Compatibility with man-jobs

It should be noted that the weighting, or relative importance, of these cost and value factors will be different for each individual material. In some cases, it may be advantageous to change a material to take advantage of a gain possible through the operation of the materials-control system; in other cases, the system may need to be altered to accommodate the peculiarities of a material. Rather than create a materials-control system which represents a compromise among the various characteristics of the various materials, it is common practice to divide the system into several programs which resemble subsystems. Each program has all the essential steps of a control system, with differences in the manner of performing the steps.

There are additional factors contributing to this type of program division. As with a production-control system, the complexity of the materials-control system tends to increase with the number of bits of information which must be handled per unit of time to maintain control. The purpose of control is to achieve the objectives from both the substantive and the economic view. In order to reduce system complexity and thereby reduce the cost of operating the system, various categories of materials are frequently separated and controlled by subsystems which have only a generalized interface with the production-control system. These subsystems are designed so that they do not require a detailed input of substantive goals from the production-control system to reduce the information-handling costs.

In a sense, therefore, this chapter is concerned with the complex of subsystems designed to supply the substantive needs of the production-control system with respect to raw materials, components, and operating supplies, while approaching full optimization of the costs associated with the supply activity. As in the previous chapters dealing with control, the materials-control system will be examined in terms of the major steps of the general concept of control.

The objectives of the materials-control system are both substantive and economic. These were briefly discussed in the introduction to this chapter. The substantive objectives were described as being derived from various interfaces with the production-control system or other managerial control systems.

Some of the factors which affect the selection of the location and the design of the nature of the interface if the economic goals are to be achieved to the maximum are:

1. Lead time in procurement (the time lag between placing an order and receiving material)
2. Lead time in manufacturing (the time lag between the receipt of an order to manufacture at the "do" step of the ongoing production-control system and the inception of processing on or with the material)
3. The uniqueness of the use of the material or component and the cost of nonuse
4. The value of the material and the cost of holding it in storage
5. The amount of fluctuation in the use of the material
6. The amount of fluctuation in the price of the material and the causes of such fluctuation

The lead time in procurement must be compared with the lead time in manufacturing, as well as with the other factors. For instance, when the lead time in procurement exceeds the lead time in manufacturing but the material is not unique for each order, the interface, to obtain the substantive objectives of the materials-control system, may be moved from its usual position to the "do" step of the top-management control system or the upper-level production-control system. With simple materials, such as staple fibers, rubber for tires, sugar for candy, iron ore, or wool, this may easily be feasible. Such an interface overcomes the lack of sufficient time between the computation of the detailed resources requirements in the ongoing production-control system and the time of use. In the ongoing system, the time between these two steps may not be sufficient to allow the acquisition of materials without continuous and severe disruptions to the production activity that are due to shortages of materials and are accompanied, of course, by much corrective action. Such a location of the interface may also be extremely useful when there are large fluctuations in the price of the material because the increased time for procurement allows some freedom in avoiding the acquisition of materials during the periods of high price.

In the latter situation, there is always the chance that the operation of the materials-control system may become primarily a speculation in the raw material. It is not the purpose of this chapter to discuss the merits or demerits of such a condition, but it should be noted that such a development indicates a radical change in both the substantive and economic objectives of the materials-control system and should not be considered an appropriate activity unless such substantive and economic objectives have been assigned by top management.

When the materials-control system is interfaced with the top-management control system for a particular material, the statement of that program of the materials-control system becomes: ". . . holding a given quantity of (material) designed to fill needs, without excessive supply, but minimizing the cost of supply and replenishing at a rate which at least matches usage, except for (the means of reacting to the price problem, as mentioned in the preceding paragraph)."[1]

When, in addition to the lead time in procurement exceeding the lead time in manufacturing, the component or material is unique to the order, it may be necessary to change the production-control system so as to process the information concerning the unique components or materials separately from the remainder of the information concerning the fifth-order work-unit. In this way, for any given order, there are two inputs to the materials-control system from the "do" step of the ongoing production-control system: the first input or information concerns unique parts and the second and much later input, at the time of actually issuing "do" orders to the shop, contains the nonunique materials, components, or supplies.

Violent fluctuations in the amount of use of a material can be met in a variety of ways. The simplest solution, to avoid disruptions caused by a failure to have material, is to maintain a large stock in reserve, although with expensive materials this also may be undesirable with respect to the objectives. The preferred solution hinges on the relationship between the lead time for procurement and the lead time for manufacturing. If the lead time for procurement is the lesser of the two, the material may be procured as needed, purchasing at least the average amount needed to obtain price advantages from quantity and adding to the order when usage jumps. If the lead time for procurement is greater than the lead time for manufacturing, the interface for the input to the materials-control system must be moved. The alternatives are the special processing of the information in the production-control system, moving the interface for the input of information to the materials-control system to the resource-computation step of the production-control system rather than waiting till the "do" orders are issued, moving the interface to the program-planning step of the production-control system to obtain the procurement information from the "make or buy" list, or moving the interface to the "do" step of the upper-level production-control system.

Of the methods listed, two are the most commonly employed methods in connection with the important materials of the typical industrial enterprise. These two methods are:

1. Interface the materials-control system with the "do" step of the on-going production-control system.
2. Interface the materials-control system with the "do" step of the top-management or upper-level production-control system.

---

[1] The parentheses would contain specific items in any actual statement in contrast to this general example.

In addition to these, there are other types of common or usual subsystems. When the materials are not unique to any particular order and when the cost of holding or carrying is not high, the interface with the production-control system may be nondetailed; that is, the interface may be used to obtain only a general figure for the rate of use of the materials, regardless of which production program they are used in. Subsequently, materials controlled in this fashion will have their own subsystem, with their own individual order points and order quantities. The *order point* is the amount required to avoid exceeding a certain minimal risk of running out of stock during the replenishing time. The *order quantity* is the amount of material which provides the most advantageous procurement, considering all cost and value factors. Materials included in such a program reduce the requirement for information through the interface between the production-control and the materials-control system.

The fourth and final type of program is used with materials of relatively low value where it is economically advantageous to order a sufficient supply for a lengthy period, replenishing either by periodic review of the stock on hand or when the physical stock on hand is noted as reaching some particular level.

Almost all of the materials to be procured will be assigned to one of these four programs of the materials-control system. The division will be in terms not of the physical characteristics of the materials, but of their control problems. Within programs, there may be further divisions into subprograms, in terms of source, type of material, and so forth, to aid in fitting the necessary activities into man-jobs. This division may tend to mask the real separation into programs. One man may work with similar materials from more than one program.

The workload of the materials-control system consists of the preparation of a more detailed description and quantification of the amount of each specific material needed at a time when the knowledge of such a need is appropriate. In the performance of this step, the various programs show marked differences.

With major materials whose control is interfaced with the top-management control system, this step is merely vestigial. With materials which are interfaced in detail with the ongoing production-control system, this step consists in collecting like needs from different production orders and developing a schedule of need with respect to time. With materials operating under the self-control of the order point and order quantity, there will be an interface with the performance or "do" step of the production-control system to provide a continual updating of the amount actually on hand, as well as a flow of information whenever an order point for a given material is reached. For materials covered under the noting-physical-stock-on-hand method, the interface will be with the actual disbursing operation, and information will flow only when a stock is noted as being low. For materials controlled by this method, there will also be a periodic inspection of the stock to determine needs for replenishment or disposal of items no longer needed.

For materials operating under the self-control program, we may find a workload being detailed by a standardized clerical procedure, by a book-keeping machine operation, or in the case of large numbers of items, by some punch-card or computer system.

The resources required to perform the workload, like the resources of the man-job control system, are of two types. One type of resource is the man-job capability needed to perform the work. The other type of resource is the money needed to purchase the materials. For effective control, both of these must be estimated in advance. For instance, in the operation of the top-management or upper-level control system, some estimate of needed resources for the contemplated production program should have been made; this estimate constitutes one of the inputs to the materials-control system as an economic objective. This is a limiting objective, a type noted in connection with the man-job control system. The main objective of the materials-control system is to minimize costs, that is, to perform at least within the constraint of the estimated resource requirement but to use less resources if possible.

With respect to the required man-job capability, this also should have been estimated as a function of the contemplated top-management program and the necessary data collected as part of the man-job control system, which also supports the top-management control.

The actual performance of the workload of procurement may be carried on under a control system which is identical to that used for the ongoing production-control system, although, with fewer bits of intelligence and with fewer types of activity taking place, it may be a relatively simple system. A similar condition was noted previously with respect to the equipment-condition control system.

The detailed actual conversion of the workload; with respect to the resources required for the actual purchase of the materials, is performed when the requirements for materials are converted into financial terms by means of actual offers from vendors to supply these materials.

The step of acquiring authority to use resources, as with the other control systems, is used to provide a feedback to the first step of control. The first step of the materials-control system has a variety of interfaces with other control systems for this feedback, although these interfaces are not necessarily used to provide an input of objectives for the original program planning. These feedbacks, in the usual plant, exist with the top-management control system, the production-control system, and the money-control system (to be described in Chapter 19). As a result, the necessary authority to acquire materials is usually obtained in small bits and carefully constrained for a variety of possible reasons.

As mentioned earlier, with natural raw materials which may have a considerable seasonal as well as some unpredictable variation in price, the workload of the materials-control system may contain the peculiar characteristic of speculating with the material, i.e., attempting to purchase, not only with the cost and carrying charges in mind but, in addition, with the purpose of taking advantage of the peculiar price fluctuations. Hence, subsequent to the determination of resources required (obtaining offers from vendors), the step of obtaining authority to procure may well be subject to strong constraints until top management approves of the action contemplated.

Also, the price of raw materials may be so critically related to profit that top management may check on each acquisition of material to prevent a mistake which could be severely damaging or fatal to the enterprise.

There is still one more reason for these interfaces, which is peculiar to the nature of materials. Earlier in this chapter, it was pointed out that the materials-control system is less susceptible to minor corrective action than the other systems of control; there is no substitute for materials. Hence, in the usual case, there is probably some overstocking of materials to prevent disruptions to the productive activities. This tends to increase the use of working capital. In view of this, it should be obvious that if the money-control system indicates a need to reduce or curtail the use of working capital, the simplest place for rapid corrective action is through the materials-control system. It is difficult, expensive, and relatively undesirable to temporarily reduce the man-job capability, and the fixed costs of the plant are not readily changeable; hence, the feedback of the statement of required resources through the interface with the money-control system may cause some change in the timing of the acquisition of materials. The change is not in the objectives, but in the timing related to their attainment.

In other instances, where the price of the materials moves in a relatively predictable fashion within a relatively narrow range, where the rate of use is relatively fixed, or where the cost of the material is slight in relation to either the value of the product or the cost of the procurement, the authority to use resources may be granted in an overall fashion, with a standing constraint concerning the amount of money to be used, or the range of price fluctuation under which the authority may be used, and so forth.

Hence, it may be seen that for the most effective use of the system of control, the step of acquiring authority to use resources will be somewhat different in each of the four major types of programs of the materials-control system.

In addition to the reasons given in the above discussion, tight control of the acquisition of authority to use resources may also reflect a suspicion entertained by top managers of the degree of control obtained through the materials-control system. There may not be an accurate interchange of information through the interfaces with the production-control system, the top-management control system, and the materials-control system. Indeed, true control is frequently missing or defective. Certainly, the more effectively the top-management control system is designed and the more effectively the objectives and limitations are constantly fed to the other control systems, the more likely it is that the use of resources can be fully constrained within these objectives and that there will be less need for constant review of the requests for authorization to use resources, at least on an item-by-item basis, unless the lower-level control systems are not operating properly. In such cases, basic corrective action should be taken to eliminate the deficiencies in control rather than to add to the controls.

In addition, in the discussion of the condition-of-equipment control system and the condition-of-building control system, circumstances were noted in which the cost of the materials could be insignificant in relation to the loss associated with slow procurement. It was further noted that the price advantage obtainable by careful procurement of such materials may also be relatively small in comparison with the potential loss. Subjecting such materials to the operations of a lengthy and slow materials-control system is a case of control for control's sake. This is not suggested as a suitable objective. If such materials are controlled within the materials-control system, a fifth program, designed to provide fast procurement as its objective, must be added. This fifth program should be interfaced with the equipment- and building-condition control systems and respond to those control systems' input across the interface with a minimum of additional constraints. This does not mean an uncontrolled use of resources because the limitation on resources should already exist within the planned programs of the condition-of-equipment and -building control systems. Continuous checking on these materials requests is almost a certain indication of a failure to establish a real system of control. It creates much unnecessary managerial activity and in most cases detracts from the attainment of objectives.

In the step of using the resources to perform the activities, the usual activities are commonly described in more detailed terms, such as:

1. Purchasing
2. Receiving
3. Inspecting
4. Accepting and paying
5. Storing or warehousing
6. Issuing

The term *purchasing* refers to the locating of possible vendors, the determining of the most desirable source, the developing of possible trade-offs in material or the developing of information leading to the examination of potential trade-offs, the creating of a contractual relationship with a selected source of supply, and the maintaining of the relationships required to complete the contractual relationship. At first glance, such a description might appear to conflict with the previous separation of the activity of materials selection or the steps of materials control. However, it should be recalled that all control systems require a variety of feedbacks between and among the steps of control; also, the assigning of duties to a person or group of persons may involve different steps from different control systems. Certainly, as has been frequently reiterated, the task of operating the various control systems is too complex to be handled by a simple hierarchy of authority.

Receiving refers to the actual physical receiving of the material, the physical handling of it, and the recording of the event. *Inspecting* refers to the ascertaining of the characteristics of the materials received and the matching of these with the desired characteristic, in both quality and quantity. It also requires the creation of a flow of information to *accepting and paying* to permit these activities to take place. It must also create a flow of information either to supervisors or to records maintained to determine when an order point has been reached, depending on the program under which the material has been placed, in order to permit subsequent steps of control to be performed or corrective action to be taken when such data have not been received and the assumption can be made that the material is not yet available.

Storing or warehousing refers to the physical holding of the materials under suitable conditions, to the maintaining of the characteristics of the materials, and to the holding of them in a manner that will minimize the total cost of handling and holding the materials.

Issuing refers to actually taking the materials out of storage and entering them into the productive process. Again, a feedback must be created for each program to maintain a knowledge of that which is being controlled.

Subsequent to the use of the resources, the materials-control system will exhibit a series of evaluation steps, as noted with the other control systems. However, because of the duality of the types of resources, the steps may involve two types of comparisons. For instance, concerning the resources being used, the money expended for materials will be compared with the money anticipated as necessary for the materials. Also, the amount of material estimated as being necessary will be compared with the actual amount of material used. The man-job capability used will also be compared with the amount of man-job capability estimated as necessary. The workload performed will be compared with the workload estimated as necessary, particularly with respect to the time when it was performed, although this last comparison is most likely to be made in the simple control system constraining the man-job capability used to perform the activities of materials control.

The purpose of the comparison steps in the materials-control system, as with the control systems previously discussed, is to detect deviations from plans and to assist in determining the most appropriate corrective action at the lowest possible level in order to minimize the time required to institute such action.

If the materials are costing more money than anticipated because of higher-than-anticipated unit costs, several types of corrective action are possible. A change may be made in the specification of the material or materials causing the deviation in order to reduce costs; another source of supply may be sought which will provide a better price; or offsetting evasive action may be taken with some other material to bring the total cost of materials into conformance with plans. This is corrective action within the materials-control system. Still another alternative is to change the amount of resources available; this is a corrective action at a higher control cycle.

If the amount of money being used is in excess of plans because of the increased use of some material, again, various types of corrective action are possible, depending upon the reason for the overusage. If excessive waste was the reason, corrective action must be taken in processing. If the waste was inevitable in processing, the computation of the required amount of material must be altered for future production and corrective action taken with respect to the required amount of money, as previously indicated. Excessive usage may also result from poor storing, with loss from deterioration, pilferage, or unauthorized usage. In such cases, corrective action must be taken at the performance step. If the production-control system is enlarging its programs (more production than had been anticipated), corrective action cannot be determined until an evaluation is made from an overall point of view of the desirability of the higher-than-anticipated production. It is entirely possible that higher-than-planned production of a particular item may not be compatible with the profit objectives of the organization. It may be the source of an unbalanced and uneconomical use of facilities or the cause of excessive storage costs connected with other materials on hand for other products.

As still another step of evaluation, the operation of each major program must be summarized and compared with program plans to determine if corrective action is necessary at this level. For instance, the question may easily arise as to whether a particular material should be moved from one program to another in order to achieve more appropriately the objectives of the materials-control system.

Finally, the total operation of the materials-control system must be compared with goals or with norms (figures on previous performance) in terms such as the cost of material expressed as a percent of the finished-product price or value, the amount and cost of production delays caused by materials-control failures, the value of excess materials, the value of spoiled materials, and the costs of warehousing and carrying charges. Quantitative terms, such as these, are needed to evaluate the attainment of the objective of minimizing overall costs. A comparison of this nature will indicate any need for corrective action, as well as assist in the formulation of future goals in a realistic manner.

The discussion to this point has treated materials-control systems in general terms. Many of the details of such systems would have to be fully understood before one could attempt to design a system of any complexity. The design of a system would entail the identical steps involved in the design of a production-control system; hence, they are not repeated here. Therefore, the remainder of this chapter deals only with some additional fundamental aspects of materials-control systems.

Many of the problems encountered in operating a materials-control system, like problems connected with other controls, can be conveniently represented by various types of mathematical models. These may range from simple equations to complex matrices, depending upon the nature of the problem.

For an example, take the problem of determining how much of a bulk-purchased standard item to procure and at what intervals. The following information is required:

1. The amount of annual usage
2. The relationship between unit price and purchase quantity
3. Lead time required to obtain the material
4. Range of fluctuation in the rate of usage
5. The cost of a delay in production caused by an out-of-stock condition of the material
6. The cost of storing the material
7. The carrying cost of the money tied up in stock
8. The indirect costs of making a purchase (other than for the material)
9. The cost of spoilage or deterioration in storage as a function of the time of storage
10. The cost of receiving, inspecting, paying, and so forth

From the above data, equations can be set up to assist in determining the order point and the order quantity, as well as in determining the possibility of being out of stock, and so on. Likewise, from similar data, equations may be constructed to assist in determining in which program of the materials-control system the particular material should be placed.

Another type of problem arises when a number of plants of the enterprise are located in different places and a number of suppliers are involved. The material in question may be limited in supply at one or more supply points.

In determining how much raw material should go from each supplier to each plant, a linear programming model may be used similar to the ones used for the sausages example in Chapter 11 and for the product-mix example in Chapter 13. When supplies are coming from more than one source and there is some randomness in the availability of the material, a queuing model may prove helpful.

Another basic aspect of materials-control systems is the usual interaction with, and need for interfacing with, other managerial activities. Some of these were discussed in the general presentation of the concept of the materials-control system. However, to carry this concept further, reference should be made to the variety of trade-offs possible in material selection, as given in Chapter 11. Certainly, the selection of materials must be interfaced with the materials-control system and vice versa, so that material unused because it was replaced with a cheaper or better material (but the action was taken too soon) is not stored indefinitely and so that materials selection is influenced by control problems to obtain full optimization with respect to all the factors associated with costs and values.

It should also be noted that the actual carrying out of the performance step of materials control is affected by the design of the storage area and its manner of use, by the selection of materials-handling equipment, and by the correlation of the handling equipment with the packaging specifications given to vendors. Hence, some considerable interchange of information must be established with the plant-configuration control system.

It has also been noted that a form of production control must be evolved to plan and constrain the carrying out of the materials-control system. This concept of control within control was stated in Chapter 12, which described controls in general; this illustration is merely another example of how this configuration of controls evolves.

Finally, as manufacturing increases in complexity and as the number of different materials and components increases, the amount of data which must be handled by the materials-control system may become enormous. In the constant search for economy of operation, it is not surprising to find it preferable to systematize or mechanize much of the data handling. In the early literature, there are many references to formalized clerical procedures with standardized forms to reduce the effort; later changes involved posting machines; finally ADP (automatic data processing) with large-scale computers has been brought into the activity in large plants. The changes in size and the changes in mechanization do not change the essential nature of the control system. The same steps of control exist and must be performed. If the mechanization does not really serve the steps of control, if the interfaces with other control systems are improperly designed or operated, or if the outputs do not provide the necessary feedbacks, the mechanized confusion can be monstrous. All properly designed systems which serve the objectives must have the general characteristics of a control system as set forth in this chapter.

REFERENCE TOPICS

Purchasing	Materials handling
Traffic	Vendors
Receiving	Salvage
Inventory	Materials-control systems
Economic lot size	Automatic data processing
Testing	Stores control and ledgers
Acceptance sampling	Materials accounting
Stores	A-B-C materials control

SUGGESTED THEMES

1. Analysis of selected materials-control systems with respect to the method of performing each step of control
2. Economics of automatic data processing
3. Development of a model of the most economical purchase quantity
4. Use of acceptance sampling in selected industries for incoming materials
5. Design of materials warehouses for selected enterprises

SUGGESTED CASES

Cruickshank, H. M., and K. Davis, *Cases in Management,* 3d ed. Homewood, Ill.: Richard D. Irwin, Inc., 1962. Case beginning on page 240.

Greenwald, D. U., *Elementary Case Problems for Industrial Engineers.* New York: The Ronald Press, 1957. Cases beginning on pages 25, 28, 40, 42.

Mantel, S. J., Jr., *Cases in Managerial Decisions.* Englewood Cliffs, N.J.: Prentice-Hall, Inc., 1964. Case beginning on page 146.

Terry, G. R., *Case Problems in Business and Industrial Management,* 2d ed. Dubuque, Iowa: William C. Brown Company, Publishers, 1955. Cases beginning on pages 24, 87, 89, 90, 94, 96, 97, 99, 177.

Ziegler, R. J., *Casebook in Production Management.* New York: John Wiley & Sons, Inc., 1962. Cases beginning on pages 67, 71.

17 CONTROLLING PROJECTS

In this chapter, the word *project* is used to describe all of the activity associated with the attainment of a goal when the activity necessitates some extensive, unique responses, different, in many details, from previous performance of tasks employing the same area of knowledge or different in that considerable ingenuity may be required in devising or developing an answer.

The word project, in common use, has a variety of meanings; a special meaning is being assigned only to promote clarity in the discussions which follow. The selected meaning for this word is as follows: A project exists when the goal is to produce an advance in the state of an art, to develop a design with unique features, to select a preferable course of action from among many alternatives, and so forth. Project activity is differentiated from production activity for the primary purpose of recognizing the similarities and differences in the control problems associated with the work. In general, production results in the creation of items of intrinsic value, the outputs of the enterprise. Projects result in the creation of items of extrinsic value. This basis of differentiation is not absolute because indirect work performed in offices also results in the creation of items of extrinsic value; moreover, projects and production may be combined. The classification, therefore, is only a guide.

As used in this chapter, the meaning of the word project will include the performance of the design activities within an industrial enterprise, such as physical-plant design; product-process design (including research and development); man-job design (including the relationships between man-jobs); control-system design; or the design of a method of employing a specific technology to handle a problem within a control system, e.g., the design of a mathematical model and the development of the method of solving such a model. A pure research activity would also be described as a project or a series of projects, depending upon the singularity or multiplicity of the separable goals, as well as upon the level of control being examined. A project, therefore, may be considered as a unique fifth-order work-unit, a one-of-a-kind output, containing highly individualized problems.

In most organizations (excluding those devoted to research and development work), in place of a single control system for projects or a limited number of control systems, each type of project or even each project may have a unique type of control system, if it has any. Further, the multiplicity of systems will usually exhibit an extremely large amount of variation with respect to formalization and complexity. The term *formalization* refers to recognized and stated characteristics; the term *complexity* means the amount of detail taken into account and the number of types of relationship among various activities brought into conformance by the control. The usual range is from a completely informal system whose details do not go beyond stating the objective (often in general terms) and the desired start date and finish date to a highly formalized, detailed system of control which may involve the use of much specialized system technology. Such special technologies will be discussed briefly in this chapter, not in depth, but only to an extent sufficient to relate them properly to the control-system concept.

At the risk of belaboring the point, the difference between a control system and a hierarchy of residual authority must be reiterated. The existence of a control system for projects should not be interpreted as implying the need for a central authority for projects. Properly applied, the control system is used as appropriate by managers for work in their respective areas of activity and for maintenance of conformity with the objectives and sub-objectives which guide the entire organization.

In the usual case of a properly designed project control, the complexity of the system chosen (or designed) will be a function of the same four factors that affect the desirable complexity of a production-control system. In actual practice, a not infrequent failure to understand the real concept of control will lead to excessive informality in many instances where a more formal and detailed system would greatly improve the chances of success for the project and enhance the value of the consequent cost-benefit ratio; the reverse, overformality, can also produce less desirable results.

The four factors affecting the desirable complexity of a project-control system and rephrased from the list given in Chapter 13 for a production-control system are:

1. The number of independent bits of intelligence which are fed in per period of time; the number of fifth-order work-units
2. The difficulty of obtaining the necessary knowledge to add to the intelligence; the difficulty of converting from fifth-order work-units to third-order
3. The complexity of detailing the intelligence into actionable form; the interrelationships between units of product (outputs of any kind), steps of process, and third-order work-units
4. The number of bits of intelligence which are generated by the activity and which must be compared with plans to maintain control; the number of separate, discrete third-order work-units

In the most usual type of case, the project-control system must respond to the following conditions, although, as will be seen later, there can easily be exceptions. The number of independent bits of intelligence which are fed in per period of time is relatively small; the flow is usually a one-time or very intermittent input rather than continuous. The program and workload are not, in the usual case, continuously revised with daily inputs of new bits of intelligence. The difficulty of obtaining the necessary knowledge to add to the intelligence is usually considerable; each occurrence has some unique characteristics, making the man-job involved either heavily selective or decisive (as these terms were used in Chapters 2 and 8). The conversion of objective to program and program to workload does not follow a routine procedure using routinely available knowledge. The complexity of detailing intelligence into actionable form does not usually require fine detail, but the number of alternative courses of action to consider is usually quite large. Also, there are usually only a small number of equally satisfactory alternatives. The number of bits of intelligence which are generated by actions and which must be compared with plans to maintain control is usually quite small. Of course, it is not difficult to find enormous projects with large numbers of such bits of intelligence, but these are not the common form of projects. For instance, the literature concerning project-control systems abounds in information about massive projects, such as the development of the U.S. Navy Polaris missile or the exploration of space. However, projects of this scope are relatively rare in comparison with all the projects being constantly undertaken in normal industrial activity; further, as will be seen later, such massive projects are really project-production hybrids.

In order to examine more fully the concept of project control, a general example is helpful, such as a product-process design project. A product-process design project (as described in Chapter 10) has a fairly well-fixed general form, although some of the steps or the sequence of some of the steps is subject to change, depending upon the details of the problem.

In Chapter 10, step 1 of the sequence of steps in handling a design problem was given as: "Specification of the need to be filled and the desired cost, sales-price, volume, and profit relationships and restrictions in order to establish specific goals and criteria for subsequent steps."

This step provides the specifications for information which must cross the interface between the top-management control system and the project-control system as a project objective. When the overall control system of the industrial organization indicates a need for corrective action in order to meet the profit goals of the enterprise, one of the alternative courses of action is the creation of a new product. An analysis of the market and of the unscheduled man-job and plant capability, together with the magnitude of the deviation from meeting the profit goal, would aid in providing a detailed communication across the interface.

The objective for the product-process design project, as it comes through the interface, might take the following form. (Note, in the example, the use of general terms rather than a single specific case and the avoidance of extraneous, specific details; parenthetical notes indicate where specific, problem-oriented facts would appear in an actual case. This method will be used throughout the illustration.)

Design a new product and the accompanying process by (date) that will meet the existing need found in (describe situation and need), with sufficient customer satisfaction, and a cost, sales-price, and volume relationship that will contribute (amount) to the profit of the company, preferably without exceeding the unscheduled man-job time of (type and amount) and the unscheduled plant time (type and amount) anticipated as occurring as of (date), and without requiring more than (amount) of working capital.

In instances where managers are not really controlling, the objective may not be detailed to this degree. It is necessary to point out (even though this is tautological) that in such situations one can expect great difficulty in attaining the unspecified objective. However, people cannot work in such a situation so the objective would probably be developed or tacitly assumed by the product-process design group in order to provide some framework for their activity. In such circumstances there is a very good chance that the objective will not conform to top-management requirements, and much waste effort and needless expense may readily be encountered.

As noted earlier in this chapter, a project concerns the production of a unique fifth-order work-unit. The preceding statement describes such a work-unit. The sixth-order work-unit, of which this is a part, is "all of the product-process design outputs." From this point of view, one may readily understand how the project-control system may be operated by many managers, where each devotes some of his primary attention to a different program but where all programs are controlled in the same general manner, without a central project-control authority. Also, as with production-control systems, several levels of control are feasible if necessary.

The next step of project control, program planning, requires a preliminary explanation of terms. The objective is stated as a fifth-order work-unit; hence, the next step of control must be performed in terms of the next lower order of work-unit, the fourth order. While this is not in conformance with the names given in Chapter 12 to the orders of work units, it conforms to their definitions, and, as mentioned when the list was first given, the list was not to be taken as a strict exercise in taxonomy. The concept of the program within the project must be kept separate from the larger concept of program in the preceding paragraph.

With a product-process design project within a project-control system, the program-planning step, step 2 of control, will require the development of a time-phased plan for the performance of the remaining steps (steps 2 to 13) of the list of steps given in Chapter 10 for such a project.

The fourth-order work-units (using only steps 2 and 3 to shorten the illustration) would appear as follows:

2. Determine by (date) the general specification of (the required product) with respect to the function it must perform:
   a. Basic; exactly what must the product do?
   b. Reliability; what is the contemplated duration of use and the frequency of use without risk of failure?
   c. Convenience; what are the appropriate criteria and what advantages must the product possess over alternative products which might be used?
   d. Accuracy; what dimensional limitations relate to the performance of the product?
   e. Cost; what limitations are attached to the cost of operation of the product?
3. To complete by (date), the general design concept:
   a. Configuration and size; what should be the general arrangement of parts either in terms of "black boxes," known units, or mechanical elements, or in terms of parts, together with limitations on size, weight, and so forth?
   b. Material; what are the characteristics required by the environment of use?

c. Processing cost; what probable limitations relate to the processing cost?

Two characteristics of this type of program statement are reasonably obvious; first, the statement, in general, is like the original tabulation of steps, although some specific descriptive material is added. Second, the dates given with the program steps can be determined from the overall objective, together with past experience with such problems, to serve as tentative goals. However, the real feasibility of these dates cannot be determined until the workload is described; the resources which will be required are determined; the required resources are compared with the available resources; and finally the objective, programs, workload, and resources required are brought into a desirable relationship.

To continue with the illustration, the performance of program step 2*a* (general specification of the required product with respect to the basic function it must perform) may require the following workload to be accomplished:

1.1.   Examine (a given number of) locations where the need exists, and summarize all the basic functions the product may be required to perform.
1.2.   List all the variations in basic function caused by the variations in the nature of the things to which the product is applied.[1]
2.1.   Have the sales department obtain information similar to 2*a*.1.1 directly from the leading salesmen in each of the (number) territories of sales.
2.2.   Have sales comment on the validity of the information submitted.

In a similar fashion, each of the substeps of program steps 2 to 12 would be converted to a statement of workload. In the usual case, an estimate can be made of the resources, on a very rough basis, to fit the program and workload tentatively into the target dates given by the objective or to locate difficulties where alternatives must be considered.

With projects of some considerable complexity, this simple listing method may not be an effective aid in adjusting for the possible overlap in time of some of the substeps. In such cases, a graphic technique may be very helpful.

For instance, a modification of the Gantt chart, as shown in Figure 17.1, might be used. In this chart, each bar represents either a program step or a workload item, and the length of each bar indicates the relative duration

---

[1] For instance, if the contemplated product is a front-end alignment device for use with automobiles, one bit of needed intelligence is the difference in the manner of use with different makes and models of cars.

of time anticipated for performance. The numbers on the same line as each bar identify the item charted and in Figure 17.1 conform to the numbering system used in the example being discussed. The "angle mark," at the left end of a bar, indicates the latest possible start date; the similar reversed mark, at the right end of the bar, indicates the latest possible completion date to meet the objective. To draw such a chart, some estimate must be made of the required resources and the intensity of their application, e.g., two man-months, where two men work one month coordinately. If the problem of determining the resources required is of some difficulty, a tentative chart might be drawn on the basis of rough estimates and a more accurate chart made after the required resources have been determined by more formal methods. There are a variety of such graphic techniques based on scalar representation.

Another commonly employed set of techniques might best be categorized

Figure 17.1   The Gantt chart used for project control

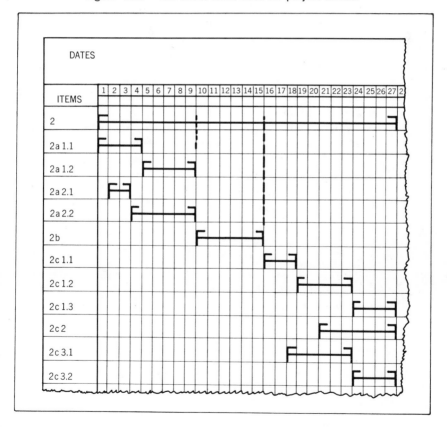

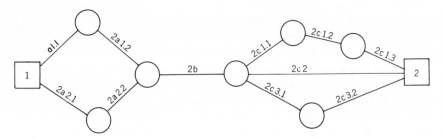

Figure 17.2   A simple network diagram

as *network diagrams*.[2] The network diagram of Figure 17.2, like Figure 17.1, is a graphic display of the relationships between and among program and workload steps of the illustration being discussed, but a different set of graphic conventions is used to portray, or model, the situation.

Each circle of Figure 17.2 represents a status achieved by the performance of activities. The performance of the activities is represented by lines. A square may be used in place of some of the circles to represent an important status or the completion of some critical activities in the project, so as to make the chart easier to read. Hence, the meaning of the square is essentially the same as that of the circle. (Various other charting conventions can be used.) The relationship between and among the activities is indicated by the configuration of lines, circles, and squares. This method of charting emphasizes the dependencies. The term *dependencies* refers to the requirement of completing some activities before being able to start other activities, regardless of the number of men on the project. For instance, in the charting method used in Figure 17.2, all the activities which terminate in one circle, going from left to right, must be performed before the activities which depend on the status being reached may be initiated. The activities which depend on the status being reached are represented by the lines going from the right side of the circle.

Either the list, the Gantt chart of Figure 17.1, the network diagram shown in Figure 17.2, or any combination of these or any other presentation may be used to assist in performing the tasks of program construction and workload determination; in decision making concerning the feasibility, com-

[2] Such diagrams have been widely publicized in connection with the control system used with development of the Polaris missile. The control system was called PERT, an acronym for "Performance Evaluation and Review Technique." Hence, in many instances in the literature, they are called PERT diagrams. Other versions are called "critical path planning," "link diagram," and so forth. Network diagram has been selected as a more generally descriptive term, not to be identified with one technique, but to refer generically to all.

pleteness, or desirability of the plan; and in generating alternatives for comparison.

The network diagram compared with the Gantt-type chart has an advantage in that it can be drawn without any estimate of the amount of resources needed to perform any activity; further, such information may be added later to the network diagram without redrawing it. Hence, it is coming into common use. On the other hand, the Gantt chart permits scheduling (assigning actual start dates to work) more readily. In some cases it may prove helpful to convert the final network chart to a Gantt-type presentation. There are also hybrid types. It is particularly important, though, if we are to avoid confusing the concept of management with technologies, to recognize that whatever technology is used adds nothing, by itself, to the program. The techniques which have been discussed are only symbolic devices and not essential features that are used upon occasion to help the people who do the planning of the steps within the project-control system.

In general, when the number of dependencies and step details is small, the list-type approach is sufficient; when the number of details is high but the interdependencies simple, the bar-type time-scale presentation of the Gantt chart is the most effective aid; when the dependencies are very numerous and complex, a network-type diagram is more effective than the other two types of approach; in some cases all three types of planning aids or modifications of the types shown may be used simultaneously to approach the problem most effectively.

At this point, let us consider some of the factors that aid in determining how far to go in program and workload detailing. If the uniqueness of the project is relatively low (in terms of experience) and the known chance of success high, then past knowledge and experience may be used to guide the project either as a relatively informal base or as an outline control covering only the major steps. Also, the control would tend to be rather informal when the amount of time and money to be spent on the project is relatively small; in such cases, much planning time would, obviously, be out of order because the possible gain is small. As project uniqueness increases, as the certainty of success diminishes, as the amounts of time and money to be spent on the project increase, as the importance of minimizing risk of failure increases (failure with respect to either substantive or time objectives), the desirability of detailed program planning and workload planning increases, together with the desirability of formalized control, viz., the use of a project-control system with well-defined rules.

To return to the discussion of the general steps of a project-control system, the step subsequent to workload planning is the step of converting workload to a statement of the resources required to perform the activities. Reference has been made to the use of experience in the development of rough estimates.

It is interesting to note that the supposed difficulty of performing the conversion of workload to required resources has often, in the past, been cited as a stumbling block to real control of projects. Questions have frequently been raised, such as the following:

1. If the project is really unique, how can one anticipate how long a step will really take or what quantity of resources will be required?
2. If the steps really require ingenuity or creativeness, how can we preassign a time or resource to them?

These questions may be attributed to three underlying areas of misunderstanding:

1. A failure to understand the full meaning of control and the objectives of control
2. A failure to understand how workload may be described in detail in a general frame of reference
3. A failure to understand the mechanics of innovation or the mechanics of the exercise of unique approaches

To correct such misunderstanding, there must be an understanding of the full meaning of control and of the objectives of control. Control, as the term is used herein, refers to the setting forth of objectives; the determination of what is necessary to attain such objectives; and the determination of the resources required to attain the objectives, followed by the important feedback step that compares required resources with objectives to assist in determining if the objective is worth seeking. Control, of course, goes further, but this point should be examined first. Even in those cases in which there appears no objective basis for the resource determination, it is almost always possible to generate a statement concerning the amount of resources worth spending or the amount of resources worth risking to carry the project through the first complete cycle of control, the first cycle designed to determine only feasibility. When the first full cycle of control is completed, a decision can be made as to whether to extend the project or terminate it. Hence, even if an accurate, or reasonably accurate, determination of the required resources cannot be made, an important use can be made of the substitute value which can be generated.

To return to the concept of control, control also includes a series of steps wherein workload performed, program performed, and objectives attained are compared with plans in order to assist in detecting the need for (and to assist in taking) corrective action to cause plans and performance to conform. To permit such comparisons and corrective action to take place usefully (rather than as a project post-mortem), the steps of program and workload must be broken down in sufficient detail so that the resources required can be determined; this requires that the step be detailed to the point where it can be compared with something in past experience or with available data.

To describe the list of workload items in a manner that will permit the determination of the amount of resources required, the activity must be divided into steps which are sufficiently homogeneous to permit a person familiar with the work to estimate with reasonable accuracy the amount of resources (man-job time, travel time, money, material, and so forth) required to perform the work. As an alternative, if the person is not familiar with the work, he may have recourse to data which describe the relationship between work and required resources. If project workload is divided properly, such data may eventually be accumulated to bolster the informalities of experience. When project activity is properly broken down into programs and descriptions of workload,[3] an estimate can usually be made for each item of the workload. The individual items may be summarized by program steps, as well as for the entire project, to permit the first feedback (the comparison of resources and objectives) to take place, as well as to serve as a basis for the ongoing control during the performance of the project. Even with steps involving ingenuity, past experience could be used with adequately divided steps to place reasonable dimensions on the resources required. The meaning of reasonable is critical to this discussion.

Reasonable means suitable for the purpose. With steps involving the exercise of ingenuity, it can be assumed that the detailing of the workload into homogeneous steps separated this activity from the more predictable events. The ingenuity, in most cases, will be required from only one person or from a relatively small group. That person or group would be expected to assist in developing an estimate of the required resources for such a step, including how much of his (or their) time would be needed. This estimate represents a goal or target for that person or group. It represents an agreement concerning accepted responsibility. Such a situation should generate a performable estimate. However, examine the worst eventuality.

Perhaps, when the project is actually undertaken, the workload item involving ingenuity is not performed in the anticipated time or within the resources allocated. This nonconformance to plan will be detected with the aid of the control system, and a need for corrective action will be indicated. The need to generate alternative courses of action, to evaluate these alternatives, and to select and apply the best alternative is indicated. Either the activity will be brought into conformance by the allocation of other resources or the plans or goals may be changed. Certainly, corrective action will be taken with respect to all dependent activities to prevent chaotic disorganiza-

---

[3] Such a list is sometimes referred to as a *technical plan*.

tion. These responses, as previously noted, are the real reasons for having control systems; these are the benefits obtained.

Hence, even an estimated value is reasonable; it serves the purpose. Of course, the higher the reliability of the estimate in terms of predicting the subsequent performance, the less corrective action needed, and the lower the costs associated with corrective action.

It should also be noted that the more experienced a group becomes in constraining projects under a control system of this general type, the more skillful they will become at using it because the separation of activity into workload steps helps in codifying their experience. This increase in skill will increase the chances of selecting project designs with good cost-benefit ratios or ratios at least as good as possible.

Hence, it may be stated that there are a variety of ways of determining the resources required for project-type activity, all of which permit the attainment of the various benefits associated with real control systems. The technology of determining such estimates may be far simpler than the equivalent technologies employed with direct productive work.

Now let us return from the discussion of the problems of resource determination to the discussion of the major steps in a project-control system. In comparing workload performed with workload planned, in the simplest case, the workload performed, dates of completion, and resources expended could be compared with plans kept in the list-type form. The list could also be used to detect late items of workload. Corrective action could be started in all cases of nonconformance and control attained. In those cases where the Gantt-type presentation of plans is used, the information concerning performance could be posted for comparison with simple modifications of the basic conventions of such charts and the need for corrective action detected. Likewise, the network-type presentation could be used to compare plans and performance graphically and thus to assist in obtaining true control. It is worth noting that it is possible to take network-diagram data and convert them into a form suitable for use as an input to a computer. Periodically, these plans, together with performance data, can be fed into a computer and information concerning nonconformance of plans and performance retrieved from the computer in a multiplicity of formats, such as:

1. Workload steps due to be completed but not yet finished
2. Workload steps completed ahead of schedule
3. Workload steps which have used more or less resources than anticipated
   a. And are completed
   b. And are not yet completed
4. Workload items that are dependent upon other items which have not been finished on schedule

A computer used in such a fashion adds nothing to the essential concept of control; it adds only an increase in the capability of handling large numbers of bits of information in a given period of time. The computer would be used only in those cases where it is more economical to operate the control system with mechanical aids because of the number of bits of information and the complexity of the dependencies among these bits.

The preceding short discussion of the use of the computer in project-control systems has been introduced to assist in keeping the analysis of a problem and the use of a technology for certain general configurations of problems in their proper perspective.

Much earlier in this chapter, it was suggested that complex projects could easily be generated and that they are not uncommon. With the increasing tempo of the modern industrial world, particularly with respect to projects affected by strong competitive forces, e.g., rapidly changing design capability with respect to products sold in a price and performance-sensitive market or items connected with national defense, it is not always possible to sequence projects and production. In many cases, they are integrated rather than sequenced, and the interfaces between the project-control system and the production-control system are so numerous that it is easier to treat both controls as a single system. With the project of designing and the task of producing and testing completely integrated, the details of program plans and workload plans and their dependencies may attain a staggering complexity. This was typical of such project-production hybrids as Polaris, the spacecraft Comsat, and the production of a new-generation aircraft. Network planning and the associated control activity received their greatest publicity with respect to their use on such hybrid problems. The details to be handled were monumental; the time frame extremely restrictive. Therefore, the success gained on the projects must be ascribed not only to excellent performance in the substantive technologies but also to the development and use of a technology for handling the data relating to planning and performance in a systematic fashion (embodying all the essential steps of control) to constrain all the diverse activities of a large number of groups of people into an orderly and economical process.

The largest and most complex project-control problems are found in upper-management control systems which are interfaced either with a large number of individual projects within lower-level control systems or with a large number of hybrid project-production problems controlled by lower-control systems. The operation of the Federal facilities of the United States of America by the President, Congress, and the Supreme Court might be cited as the prime instance of such a project-control problem; the operation of a large corporation, such as General Motors, contains a less complicated but still monumental problem. While there may be some doubt as to whether control technology has advanced to a state of the art sufficient to assist, in such cases, in a real optimization of the attainment of objectives with respect to the resources employed, there should be no doubt that even imperfect controls produce better results than merely leaving all events to the random workings of a chance-cause system. While such a philosophy has been implicit in the discussion of project-control systems, it would seem that in most cases the benefits from the use of project-control systems are demonstrable.

REFERENCE TOPICS

PERT
Network diagrams
Critical path planning
Programming
Research and development
Project control
Gantt charts

SUGGESTED THEMES

1. Network diagram for an assigned project
2. Development of a program structure for a research and development laboratory for a selected enterprise
3. A network diagram of the activities leading up to a historical event
4. A Gantt chart for the plan of an assigned project
5. An analysis of selected uses of a network diagram as described in periodical literature

SUGGESTED CASES

Cruickshank, H. M., and K. Davis, *Cases in Management,* 3d ed. Homewood, Ill.: Richard D. Irwin, Inc., 1962. Case beginning on page 220.

Mantel, S. J., Jr., *Cases in Managerial Decisions.* Englewood Cliffs, N.J.: Prentice-Hall, Inc., 1964. Case beginning on page 69.

Terry, G. R., *Case Problems in Business and Industrial Management,* 2d ed. Dubuque, Iowa: William C. Brown Company, Publishers, 1955. Cases beginning on pages 80, 163.

Ziegler, R. J., *Casebook in Production Management.* New York: John Wiley & Sons, Inc., 1962. Case beginning on page 44.

18 CONTROLLING QUALITY

The preceding chapters have dealt with the control of certain aspects of "things," as originally classified in Chapter 1. For the most part, these chapters have discussed quantitative controls, although in Chapter 15 some discussion of the control of attributes (quality) of the physical plant was included; in Chapter 16 the problem of attributes was mentioned; and in Chapter 17, the emphasis was on a single unit of output.

This chapter deals with the quality-control system. *Quality* may be defined briefly as the attributes of materials, components, and products. The quality-control system was identified previously as an additional system of control which had an effect within the overall production-control system, as defined at the end of Chapter 12 and discussed in Chapter 13. Of course, as will be seen, the quality-control system has additional impacts.

At this juncture, a brief discussion and recapitulation to clarify areas of possible misunderstanding is in order. First, the order in which the various systems of control have been presented does not reflect priority or relative importance. All the controls had to be discussed separately, and something had to come first. The concept of production control, the grand integration of the results of all controls, presented a natural place for a beginning.

Subsequently, the controls of things, in keeping with the organization of this book, followed. A quality-control system, which cuts across these controls of things, is easier to discuss if it comes after them. Second, the use of the term *quality control* in this chapter is somewhat different from its use in much of the currently available literature, which concerns the technology of developing solutions to problems commonly encountered in the operation of systems. Care should be taken to avoid confusion arising from the use of this term, quality control, for describing technology; the use is not improper, but this chapter is concerned primarily with system rather than technology. Third, this chapter contains a discussion of a system of control which should not be identified directly, in its totality, with the duties of an in-plant group which may have a similar title because most of the group's effort is devoted to part of this system of control. This distinction was frequently mentioned in the chapters dealing with the design of things and reiterated in the chapter on "Controlling Man-Jobs." The quality-control system, as described herein, is not to be thought of as the work of a quality-control group in a plant. To be sure, their work will be part of such a system, but so will the work of many others.

The objective of the quality-control system is to assist the substantive control systems of the organization (production, man-job, physical plant material, and project) in achieving the basic economic objective (profit) by controlling all the factors affecting the ratio of usable and unusable raw material, components, products, man-job time and machine-use time to produce the optimum ratio with respect to profit, considering all costs and values. The aspects to consider range from customer satisfaction and product reliability to raw-material selection and determination of source. Hence, the quality-control system serves the same eighth-order work-units as the other systems of control.

In more detail, the seventh-order work-units will be to assist in the design (or selection) and use of man-jobs, equipment, material (including direct and indirect material, components, and supplies), product and process. The focus will be on the factors affecting needed attributes of inputs and created attributes of outputs to achieve, from the profit aspect, a desirable combination or cost-value relationship, and further, to assist in the operation of the various substantive control systems with respect to obtaining conformance of the attributes of the subject of the system to the goals.

Thus it may be seen there will be two main groups of programs to achieve these objectives. One group of programs will be related to the design activities and one group to the substantive control systems. The number of factors taken into account in the design activities, and all planning and performance factors and variables in the control systems that affect both quality and the consequent cost-value relationship, is a large number. Hence, it should be obvious that the two groups of quality-control programs will most certainly require a complex series of interfaces among themselves and with the substantive design and control activities. These interfaces are so complex that in many actual instances, instead of attempting to operate the part of the quality-control system which is related to the design activities as an integrated system, it is divided into a series of delimited projects, which are handled as a group of semi-independent projects within a loose project-control system. The necessity of dividing the activity into semi-independent projects will become more clear as the complexity of the details of the quality-control programs is examined.

There are four major areas of activity for the programs of the quality-control system as they relate to the design activities of the organization: man-job design, physical plant design, product-process design, and material selection. However, quality-control programs in these areas, for full effectiveness, cannot be divided into completely independent programs because of the interactions which take place between and among these four groups of things with respect to quality. This same general characteristic was noted with regard to the design activities.

To illustrate, there will be a quality-control program with the product-process design activity or participation in the pilot design, pilot runs, and so on, to assure the economic feasibility of obtaining the desired quality of product. However, the performance of this quality-control program must involve the consideration of the interactions among product-process design and physical plant, material, and job design. In carrying out this program, there will be a considerable amount of feedback to the guiding objectives to bring the economically feasible quality and the desired quality into conformance. Certainly, the assigned quality, as an objective, must not exceed the design capability, the process capability, or the real market desires. For instance, an automobile designed to last twenty years may be within design and process capability and, from a purely logical economic point of view, desirable. However, the market desires are not necessarily limited to such narrow logic. In a modern society, changing style may have a higher value. Such a view, of course, could be debated, and such debates are obviously a part of the feedback in this type of situation. It should be apparent that the quality-control program cannot be isolated from the design program.

The terms design capability and process capability, used in the preceding paragraph, are worth discussing. *Design capability* depends upon the state of the art, and the limitations on design are imposed by the lack of full knowledge or by economic conditions; these limits are constantly changing. When commercial jet airplanes were first introduced, the ratio of thrust to engine weight and to pounds of fuel consumed per hour was limited by the knowledge of jet-engine design; this limited airframe design. The advance of knowledge to fan-jets, which gave roughly a 30 percent increase in the ratio of thrust to engine weight and in fuel economy, changed the design capability with respect to aircraft. Subsequent innovations will further alter the design capability. External factors also have an effect. Aluminum was once extremely rare and costly in the metallic state. Aluminum furniture and windows could have been designed at that time, but this would have been an academic exercise; no one could have afforded to make or use them. Hence, the economic factors also impose limits on design capabilities. In addition to the economic limitations, the lack of knowledge in other fields may affect design capability. For instance, petrochemical knowledge, at one time, limited the production of gasoline, on an economic basis, to about 80 octane. Thus, the design of engines to use fuels of higher octane ratings would not have been of much value at that time other than to demonstrate the advantages to be gained from greater petrochemical knowledge concerning the economic production of high-octane gasoline. The Eiffel Tower in Paris was essentially such an exercise. One of its purposes was to demonstrate the capability of creating steel-frame structures and to assist in setting new objectives for rolling mills by expanding the state of the art of design.

Process capability, a term used frequently in literature on quality control, is a parallel type of limitation. The term concerns details, such as the amount of variation in size or other attributes, associated with a process (or a step in a process) but reflecting a more subtle aspect of the state of the art. Naturally, it is not entirely separate from design capability. For instance, when James Watt's first steam-engine cylinder was bored on a special boring mill in Newcombe's plant in Birmingham, England, the process capability of the boring mill was such that the cylinder was not less than ⅛ inch "out-of-round." This was considered, in those days, an exceptionally good process capability for work of such size. Naturally, to design Watt's steam engine with fine piston rings would have been useless; Watt used a leather packing like a hand water pump. In the usual case, process capability refers to the amount of variation with respect to some attribute that is typical of a particular type of machine, particular machine, or process. For instance, in the making of gray-iron castings from one pattern using sand molds, there will be some variation in the size of the final castings. The variation is one measure of the process capability. In making pieces on an automatic screw machine, there will be some variation in the roundness of the parts. In pumping a saline solution into hog bellies preparatory to making bacon, there will be considerable variation in the amount of solution absorbed by each belly.

In actual practice, various mathematical measures have been devised to describe process capability, e.g., *range* and *probability of exceeding certain limits.* Process capability, for most situations, is defined in such terms; these mathematical statements should be thought of as mathematical models of the process capability. Obviously, process capability is usually much easier to define with some exactness than design capability.

The program, within the quality-control system, of working with the product-process design activity should take advantage of the definability of process capability to assist in designing the details of process to conform to the requirements of product and vice versa. The program should include the determination of:

1. The steps in the process having a bearing on critical attributes
2. The process capabilities of each of these steps with respect to machines, molds, dies, patterns, and so on
3. How process capabilities may be altered
4. Alternatives for process steps

Such activity will naturally interact with the selection of materials, the selection of physical plant, and the design of man-jobs. It will also interact with the quality-control-system programs which relate to the operation of the substantive controls of the organization. The program of working with the product-process design activity may be likened to the gross production-control system because this program of the quality-control system sets the objectives for the lower-level quality-control-system program. The lower-level quality-control system will be interfaced with the production-control program concerning actual performance. In cases where the upper-level quality-control program is relatively nonexistent (and this is not uncommon), we will find the lower-level program using industry norms or historical norms for scrap, defects, yield, and so on, to set goals as a substitute for the objectives which should have come from a higher level of control.

The purpose of this detailed discussion is to show why the programs of the quality-control system that are concerned with product-process design activities should not be thought of as independent programs and to show why a project-type control system is appropriate. A similar presentation could be made for each of the programs of the quality-control system which relate to design activities.

The second program area of the quality-control system, related to the design activities of the organization, will consist in working with the man-job design group to assist in creating work methods that will economically contribute to quality. In some cases, the requisite details may be minute. In the assembly of radio tubes, the hand that picks up the cathode must not touch the grids or plates because the consequent contamination, the transfer of emissive material, will affect the attributes (noise level) of the vacuum tubes. Also, a man-job design may require the assignment of some of the responsibility for inspection to the production worker. This assignment, in turn, may affect the optimum location of formal inspection (with respect to costs and values) in the process and may have a bearing on alternatives of process design or process sequence.

The third program related to design activity will concern the relationship with the material-design (or material-selection) procedure in order to optimize the interactions among material, cost, and quality. Naturally, as noted previously, the material selected is not independent of product-process design, man-job design, or physical-plant design.

The number of factors related to each of these programs and the number of interactions possible create a serious risk that the outcome will be suboptimization of the cost-value relationship rather than full optimization. Therefore, an iterative-type cross-feed must exist among the various programs.

The fourth program, concerned with design activity, will relate to the design of physical plant. The effect of the production equipment upon the process has already been noted. In addition, the location of the equipment with respect to other equipment will have, in some cases, an effect upon product attributes, as will the "climate" (air conditioning, temperature) of the plant; both location of equipment and climate will interact with man-job design.

The programs of the quality-control system which relate to the other control systems will also have a complex relationship with these other controls. Indeed, these programs of the quality-control system cannot be separated entirely from the programs related to the design aspects. As has been shown, the design activity affects objectives, and objectives are the inputs to the ongoing control systems. Further, for really effective control, information must flow both ways across the interface; there must be a feedback from the control of actual performance to the system used in determining objectives.

For instance, mention was previously made of the existence of a program area within the quality-control system, involving participation in the selection of materials to be procured and setting up of the specifications to be met. There will also be an ongoing program within the quality-control system of rendering assistance by continually determining whether incoming materials do meet the specifications, interfaced with projects of assistance in reducing the cost of materials (total costs, including inspection). This latter phase may involve, for example, teaching the vendor how to send only materials that meet the specifications. The ongoing quality-control program (working with the materials control) must also generate information concerning the results of the selection of materials and the setting of specifications to feed back to the upper-level control to improve the selection process. Such a feedback will also affect process design, and so on. An examination of the activity within the ongoing quality-control program may reveal that the activity involved is included in the substantive program being carried on by the materials-control system. The procedures used may be designed, as a project, by a quality-control specialist, but the routine operations may appear to be within the materials-control system, although the activity is part of that which is being called a quality-control system. It will be recalled that earlier in this chapter, the chapter was said to be concerned with system rather than with the activities of one particular group. It should also be noted that the method of determining the characteristics of the incoming material may well have been designed by a materials specialist. The function is still part of the quality-control system as that term is used here.

With regard to the production-control system, the quality-control system must include a program of developing (or selecting) test equipment for ascertaining the quality during the process, at appropriate points, by suitable and economical means, and, further, of having a continuous ongoing program of application of this equipment. This will be particularly true with respect to "life testing" and "reliability testing," which do not fit readily into a processing sequence. At any rate, the quality-control system must include some program for continually assisting the production-control system at the performance level to measure adherence to quality standards, to recommend appropriate corrective procedures when trouble spots develop, and to seek continually to improve process capability and reliability. Such a program will also contain projects which involve a study and analysis of operating data and customer complaints.

In a similar fashion, for the system of controlling physical plant, there must be an ongoing program of quality control to assist in monitoring equipment, particularly with respect to the maintenance of machine capability, as well as projects related to the development of preventive maintenance cycles, and so forth.

With respect to the control of man-jobs, the quality of performance is an important aspect. Typical mistakes or failures to perform properly must be identified and corrective measures fed back to supervisors and to the training programs to improve product quality by better performance of the productive tasks. From the foregoing discussion, the complex interactions between and among the programs of the quality-control system and the other control systems should be apparent.

The determination of the workload implicit in the operation of the programs of the quality-control system will require the identification of all the places where the program activity must be performed and the detailing of the nature of that activity. The activity can be divided into two major categories, repetitive and intermittent. The repetitive, or ongoing, programs can be controlled in the same way as direct productive activities; the intermittent activities will usually be handled under a project-type control.

Typical locations for repetitive activity are:

1. Materials receiving
2. In-process inspection
3. Final inspection
4. Life testing
5. Reliability testing
6. Equipment monitoring

Typical locations for intermittent activity are:

1. Packaging testing
2. Machine-capability determination
3. Process-capability determination
4. Preventive-maintenance-cycle determination
5. Participation in design activity with
   a. Man-job design
   b. Physical plant design
   c. Product-process design
   d. Material selection and specification
6. Customer complaint analysis
7. Shop-mistake analysis
8. Machine-capability improvement
9. Vendor improvement
10. Training shop operators in inspection procedures which are part of productive jobs
11. Inspection equipment design or selection

The conversion of the workload with the repetitive activities to a statement of the resources needed, as with other control systems, will require that the method of performance of the work be determined. The technology relating to this workload within the quality-control system provides many alternative methods. Just as in the production-control system the amount of man-job time needed to machine a gear depends upon the selection of the equipment, e.g., milling machine or hob or gear shaver, so the amount of manpower needed to man an inspection point depends upon (1) the inspection equipment to be used and (2) whether a 100 percent sorting inspection plan or some acceptance sampling plan is to be used.

For clarity, the two terms in 2 should be examined briefly. A 100 *percent sorting inspection* plan refers to examining every unit of a product fully in comparison with standard attributes and discarding nonconforming items. It is worth noting that in actual practice, this sorting may not result in sorting out all the defective items. The accuracy of the "sort" is a function of the precision of measurement, the stringency of the specifications, and the attention of the inspector.

Sampling refers to testing carefully a selected portion of the total quantity and creating, from the data obtained from the sample, a mathematical model of the attributes of the whole group. This mathematical model is used as a guide to make a decision concerning the proper action to take with the whole group. Other factors must be taken into account, but typical alternatives of corrective action, when nonconformance to objectives is encountered, may be such as the following:

1. Reject the entire lot.
2. Sort the lot for defects by a 100 percent inspection.
3. Send the lot on for the next step of processing.
4. Resample.
5. Restate material specifications. (Note that this alternative requires a feedback to higher control cycles.)

The mathematics of most sampling plans has been used to produce specific decision rules, giving direct statements of action to be taken as a function of the data obtained from the sample so that the model concept is obscured from the casual view.

With bulk materials, carefully planned methods are used to obtain a sample which is representative of the batch, and these methods are usually formalized in industry standards. Some of these procedures require a considerable amount of work, but such workload can readily be converted to a statement of the manpower resources required.

There is a third type of inspection which has considerable use, wherein individual items are sorted by size to match other parts also sorted by size, e.g., the careful measurement of automotive cylinders, which differ in size, even with the best of boring equipment, to mate with pistons, which also vary in size.

It is not the purpose of this book to discuss in detail the mathematical models involved in performing some of the workload of the quality-control system. Reference was made to them only to indicate that they do exist and to show the place, in the totality of a quality-control system, where they are appropriate. The use of different inspection procedures in the design of the man-job in the quality-control system may have a marked effect upon the resources required to perform the workload; this is an additional illustration of the variety of knowledge required to perform man-job design adequately.

With the intermittent activities within the workload the conversion of workload to a statement of manpower resources required is somewhat different from the methods used with repetitive man-jobs, as was indicated in Chapter 8, "Designing Man-Jobs." The method of determining the resources for such workload items was discussed in detail in Chapter 17, "Controlling Projects," and will not be discussed here to avoid repetition.

The acquisition of authority to use the resources, as with the other control systems, involves a continuous comparison of the benefits to be obtained and the cost of obtaining them and a consideration of all the alternatives (trade-offs) in order to optimize the cost-value, or cost-benefit, ratio.

In a quality-control system, because of the large number of interactions with other control systems, the range of trade-offs is enormous. The following list is designed only to show the range; it is not definitive:

1. Sampling versus sorting to reduce costs of inspection
2. Sorting versus sampling to reduce the costs of processing defective material
3. Change in material supply to reduce inspection cost and thus total cost or vice versa; more inspection of cheaper material to reduce total costs
4. Changes in the location of the inspection points in the process to optimize costs
5. Changes in design to reduce inspection costs, leading to lower total costs
6. More thorough final inspection, raising unit costs, but leading to better customer satisfaction, greater sales, and greater total profits

The evaluation of the workload performed in comparison with the workload planned is normally handled in a manner similar to the method used with a production-control system. If much repetitive inspection work is performed, a relatively complete subsystem like the production-control system may evolve; this may be an economical approach. The control may appear to be absorbed into the substantive control system.

The evaluation of the program accomplishment will be somewhat more complex. The achievement of a given set of attributes in the production of a given product must be compared with goals stated in similar terms. Usually, percent of scrap, percent defective, percent rework, or percent yield goals are set by the quality-control projects which are associated and integrated with the design activity, or by norms associated with the product, process, or industry. The anticipated cost of the ongoing quality-control program is determined when the required resources are computed. The achievement can, from these data, be evaluated, but it is difficult to ascribe the correct amount of the accomplishment to either of the programs within the quality-control system. As has been amply discussed, the quality-control programs are almost inextricably interfaced and integrated with the other programs; hence, a completely independent evaluation of the quality-control program becomes extremely difficult, and in most cases much ingenuity is required. Certainly, each instance poses unique problems. Similarly, with respect to the evaluation of the achievement of goals, the success or failure to achieve the goals can be determined but the determination of whether the quality-control system achieved these or whether the achievement can be more properly attributed to the operation of some other control system is often extremely difficult. A general procedure for the sorting out of the contribution of each program cannot be given; each problem of this type must be handled on an individual basis.

In summary, certain general facts may be noted. First, the broad outlines of a quality-control system are similar to the other control systems examined in previous chapters; the generalized concept should assist in recognizing the steps to be performed to use such a system effectively. Second, the technology of quality control, because of the interrelationships between the programs of the quality-control system and other control systems, should not be thought of as something to be used independently of the technology associated with product-process, physical plant, material, or man-jobs. All of these technologies must be integrated for effective use. Third, many forms of mathematical models may be used effectively and economically in handling information concerning attributes; one must learn much about these models to understand fully the problems of a quality-control system. Fourth, and finally, the quality-control system, like the man-job control system, should not be thought of as the province of one group only; it is a system of control which should pervade all the other control systems in the enterprise. Certainly this concept is consistent with the idea of an integrated group serving the needs of problems as opposed to separate groups each owning special problems. There are, of course, as with the other areas of control, special types of problems which call for specialists in the technologies involved; this should not be confused with exclusive ownership of all such problems.

REFERENCE TOPICS

Statistical quality control
Probability
Forecasting
Risk
Sampling
Inspection
Testing
Quality standards

SUGGESTED THEMES

1. Discussion of the risks and advantages of sampling in selected situations
2. Discussion of assigned standard sampling plans

3. Discussion of the factors affecting the optimum location for inspection points
4. Organization of the typical quality-control department
5. Locations in an assigned organization that participate in the system of quality control and the method of participation
6. Cost and values of an inspection situation

SUGGESTED CASES

Cruickshank, H. M., and K. Davis, *Cases in Management,* 3d ed. Homewood, Ill.: Richard D. Irwin, Inc., 1962. Cases beginning on pages 211, 218.

Greenwald, D. U., *Elementary Case Problems for Industrial Engineers.* New York: The Ronald Press, 1957. Case beginning on page 62.

Terry, G. R., *Case Problems in Business and Industrial Management,* 2d ed. Dubuque, Iowa: William C. Brown Company, Publishers, 1955. Cases beginning on pages 30, 82, 102, 103, 104, 105.

Ziegler, R. J., *Casebook in Production Management.* New York: John Wiley & Sons, Inc., 1962. Cases beginning on pages 101, 109, 114, 118, 138.

19 MONEY CONTROL

The term *money control* will be used to refer to the control-system activities which deal either with money or with substantive activities when they are translated into financial values. As noted in Chapter 6, time and money are two additional dimensions that are used to describe the four groups of things recognized as constituting an industrial enterprise. Up to this point, the discussion of control systems has stressed the time aspects of events which are controlled. To separate the events from their time dimensions would, obviously, greatly reduce the meaningfulness of a discussion of plans and performance.

In an economy where the use (consumption or time-use) of the four things making up an industrial enterprise is obtained in exchange for money and where the overriding goals of an organization concern the final effect of all activities upon both profit and the security of the initial money (capital) of an enterprise, money, like time, should be an integral part of any control system. In actual practice, unfortunately, this is often not so. The accounting, or money-control activity, is often handled in an entirely separate manner, leading to numerous additional interfaces and coordinating activities and to much more complexity and difficulty in obtaining control. In such cases, money control, or financial control, as it may also be called, is usually thought of as a single control system, without recognition of the separable parts.

The activities related to money control can be divided into three general categories. In this chapter, these three categories will be briefly defined and then individually examined, with particular emphasis on the differences among the separable aspects of money control.

The first category of money control is the control related to the authority implicit in the ownership of the money. Money is required to initiate or operate an industrial enterprise. In the modern economic world, ownership connotes certain privileges of choice, limited, of course, by general and specific restrictions laid down by the organized society in which the enterprise exists. The choice of use is exercised at the fifth step of the control pattern, viz., the acquisition of authority to use resources, shown in each of the control systems previously discussed. This fifth step was described, in all cases, as having a feedback to the first step, determining objectives. The first step was also indicated as having an interface with the top-management control system. Hence, this first type of control is integrated into the top-management control system and is used to indicate the substantive programs which have been chosen for action, as well as to indicate the permitted money dimension of such programs. Money control of this type also indicates the money dimensions of goals for the lower control system. However, it is important to recognize that such a control system grants permission to the lower control system to acquire or to use resources in terms of their common denominator, money. This category of money control is the source of the money-oriented information crossing the interface of the top-management control system with the subordinate substantive control systems.

The second type of money control concerns the activities related to the money dimensions, which, from the first type of control, are implicit in all the other control systems, such as production control; product process design, and other cases of project control; quality control; man-job control; physical plant control; materials control; and sales control.[1] All these control systems deal with activities toward subgoals, using things and taking place in a time continuum, but the goals also have economic dimensions. The program planning and workload determination are carried forward under economic constraints. The permission to acquire and use resources, even when these are expressed as things, must also mean permission to use their money equivalent to acquire or to use them. The comparison of plans with performance must also be made with respect to the money dimension, as well as with respect to substantive quantities and time. Money control, there-

---

[1] Sales control will be discussed in the next chapter. It is so heavily interfaced with top-management money control that it appeared logical to discuss the money controls first.

fore, must be an integral part of such systems of control if control, as it has been defined, is to take place in a completely meaningful fashion.

The commonly used term *budget,* usually referring to an allocation of money, cannot be kept separate from the other dimensions of goals. To separate the authority to use things in their substantive sense from the authority to use their money equivalent would create two control systems with an excessively heavy interchange of minutiae at their interface. Such a condition usually leads to much frustration on the part of those performing the directive activity. Of course, such situations, while undesirable, do occur.

The third aspect of money control is the direct control of the actual money. Money, like the things of an industrial enterprise, has a physical embodiment (or the equivalent), as represented by cash, checks, or other instruments conveying ownership. Because money has a physical embodiment, it must be controlled in the same general way (although different in detail) as the use of the actual material from which product is made. However, it should be obvious that this aspect of money control must be fully interfaced with the money-control aspects of the substantive control systems, as well as with the top-management control system. It must serve both but not as an intermediate level of control between them because the substantive control systems and the top-management control system already have an interface for *money information.* A second set of interfaces leads only to unnecessary activity.

The actual direct money control is a subordinate service control, which must respond to the other control systems. Great care must be exercised to see that it facilitates the objectives of the substantive controls.

The three aspects of money control, as they have been defined in this chapter, may be summarized as follows:

1. The top-management control system, wherein alternative programs in terms of their money dimensions are compared with goals, and the programs chosen together with the money dimensions permitted for such programs are designated for the lower-level control systems. This control expresses the exercise of the rights of choice implicit in ownership. The money dimensions in this control system will be used to evaluate the results of activity with respect to the overriding economic objectives of the enterprise.

2. An implicit part of the substantive and project-type control systems that is related to the money dimension of activities.

3. A subordinate control, direct money control, to provide an interface between the peculiar physical characteristics of money and its actual use in a control system.

In other literature, the three types of control differentiated in this chapter may be roughly equated to common terms as follows:

1. The first type of control may be associated with the work performed under the titles of *treasurer, controller, financial planning,* or *budgeting.*
2. The second type of control may be compared with much of the activity carried on under the titles of *cost accounting* or *accounting.*
3. The third type of control activity may be described under the titles of *cashier* or *disbursements.*

The italicized terms in this list have been avoided in the preceding discussion because, first, the division, as will be seen later, is not exactly the same. Second, the aim, in this chapter, is to examine the essential money-control functions in an enterprise and their interrelationships, without confusion with techniques or common job titles.

To confuse the three aspects of control which have been differentiated in this chapter, to assume that they are similar because they all deal with money, or to apply the same detailed system to all three would seem as unrealistic as applying the details of a production-control procedure for controlling ship construction to the manufacture of hairpins because they are both made out of steel. Each of the three systems of money control needs its independent statement of objectives, programs, and so forth. This does not necessarily predicate the use of either the same or different people to operate each of the three aspects of money control or to perform the activities within the control systems. It has been emphasized frequently that job duties can be constituted into man-jobs in a variety of ways, and a combination of duties does not require that they all be performed in the same way. Indeed, to perform them all in the same manner would be to deny the essential differences in the variety of duties. It should be remembered that in the initial discussion of control, the need was noted for a complex set of relationships between and among people and duties to achieve goals.

One additional aspect of such relationships must be increasingly discernible at this point. The relationship between two people in an organization cannot be assumed to be a single relationship; it must change, depending upon the requirements of the activity which creates the need for the specific relationship. To illustrate briefly, the top manager may approve or disapprove of the use of the resources proposed by the person responsible for a substantive activity. The top manager has this decision making authority. However, if approval is given, the top manager may be expected to respond subsequently to the "order" of the substantive manager concerning the final detailed choice made for disbursing the money under the approved plan; the decision making authority has been reversed.

To examine the controls in more detail, top-management control, as concerns money, is related to the ownership of the money and the concomitant right to choose the uses to be made of the money. However, except in those cases where the enterprise consists of an *individual proprietorship* (a single owner of the money) who also operates the top-management control system, there may be another skeleton control, representing ownership, interfaced with real top-management control. The term *skeleton* is used because, in most cases, very little detail is processed through such a control system. The skeleton control representing the ownership and spread among the holders of corporate stock (shares of ownership) operates merely to set general guidelines,[2] and the real top-management control, which provides the interface between the enterprise and the external community, is delegated to some individual or small group of individuals. A *partnership,* wherein ownership is shared among two or more individuals, with varying degrees of formalization of the relationship between and among the owners, can be seen as obviously leading to occasional confusion if the skeleton control is not kept separate from the true top-management control; hence, a consensus is needed for each decision. Such a consensus can often be maintained over long periods of time, but the situation is basically liable to instability.

The skeleton control concomitant with corporate stock ownership, which provides an interface between money ownership and top-management control, also permits an easy change of parts of ownership, without necessarily deleteriously affecting the continuity of top-management control; and vice versa, the actual people operating the top-management control can change without requiring changes in ownership. Each social unit, e.g., county, state, and country, usually has laws governing the relationship between ownership and top-management control; these alter the details of the allowable relationships but cannot and do not alter the need for top-management control or the need to consider the financial aspects of such control. Even where the laws of the society create a whole new concept of ownership or in the case of a governmental organization where ownership is vested in the society as a whole, the details of the money-control system, implicit in top-management control, will change but the essential cyclic nature of the control system and the steps given as inherent in such a control system will remain unchanged if the enterprise is to have a coherent purpose.

In the industrial enterprise, the first task of the top-management control system is to examine the external environment of the economy and of the society in which it exists and to set feasible goals for the organization. This general analysis also includes the use of a *sales-control system,* which will be examined in the next chapter, after the description of the financial or money-control system, with which, in addition to others of the control systems, it must be interfaced.

Top-management control may be said to be interfaced with the external

[2] This will depend, of course, upon the number of shareholders and the percent of ownership held by any shareholder.

world. Inasmuch as the overriding goal of an industrial enterprise is to make a profit while protecting the security of the capital, goals at such a level must certainly have an economic or money dimension, as well as substantive dimensions.

It is worth noting that the performance of this step of setting objectives is the primary differentiating characteristic between the top-management control system of an industrial enterprise operating in a free economy and either an industrial enterprise operating in a state-owned economy or the top-management control of a government organization. The top-management control system of an enterprise in a free economy has economic objectives; there is considerable freedom of choice in developing substantive programs to achieve these objectives. An enterprise in a state-owned economy usually has substantively stated goals assigned to it. It may have some freedom of choice with respect to the economic aspects of achieving them, but in stringent economies, such as represented by communist or fascist states, these economic choices may be either severely delimited or nonexistent.

A governmental organization, even in a free economy, usually has substantively stated goals, which are either assigned or derived from more general statements of the nature of desired achievements; in addition, there are usually numerous economic restrictions concerning the allowable nature of programs to be followed in achieving the goals. With the additional limitations and restrictions, the complexity of controls usually increases to avoid excessive, continuous corrective actions.

To return to the discussion of the industrial enterprise operating in a free economy, the economic goals must be translated into statements of substantive production programs, with each separable program dimensioned not only with respect to the quantity and quality of production as a function of time but also with respect to money. The money dimensions will include the anticipated use of capital and the cash flow, the amount and rate of flow of money in and out of the organization.

Before such program dimensions can be determined, there must be a forecast, or prediction, of both the amount of sales and the rate of sales. In addition, the substantive programs must be converted into a statement of workload, things that must be done; the statement of workload must be converted into a statement of the amount of resources required, including man-jobs and machine use, not only in the substantive sense but also with respect to their money dimensions. The resources computed as required must be expressed in terms of both capital use and cash flow, so that each program may finally be evaluated with respect to goals and a set of objectives compatible with available resources may be achieved. Naturally, in a large organization, such data cannot be dealt with intelligently in detail. Hence, gross measures derived by statistical procedures from lower-level control systems will be used, rounded to comprehensible terms, provided these data inputs are reliable.[3]

In all cases, the goals, the resources required, and the resources available must be brought into conformance. A variety of alternative courses of action usually exist to assist in achieving such a balance, such as acquiring more resources by either increasing capital or obtaining the temporary use of money (borrowing), curtailing programs, altering financial objectives, or planning to change the factors affecting the use of resources to achieve programs. In some cases, alternatives may be referred to the owners (stockholder meetings) for a decision, although such a referral is a function of the degree of delegation from the skeleton control of ownership to the actual top-management control system.

Subsequent to the development of a compatible structure of goals, programs, workload, and resources, the results are transmitted through the interface with the next level of control, which earlier in this book was described as middle management. It is worth noting that the dimensions of goals thus transmitted leave much less opportunity of choice for the next level of management than was exercised by top management.

The middle management of an enterprise in a free economy is thus restrained in approximately the same fashion as the top management of an organization in a state-controlled economy. In a state-controlled economy, the top government officials operate the top-management control system. It is obvious that such a top-management control is enormous in scope. This poses problems of handling amounts of information which probably exceed human capacity, even when supported with the most sophisticated data-processing equipment. However, of greater importance is the realization that in such a case, the ownership is vested in the whole of society and the control relating to this ownership may easily become more and more of a skeleton control, with fewer and fewer restrictions concerning the delegation to the administrators of the right to make choices. The skeleton control cannot cope with a problem of this magnitude. Hence, top-management control (in this sense) by government must inevitably become more and more dictatorial and the people more and more dependent upon the personality of the officials. Human nature being what it is, this does not appear to be a desirable situation, and the past history of modern dictators in state-owned economies certainly indicates the validity of such a conclusion. The major point of differentiation between state-owned enterprises in democracy and state-owned enterprises in a state-owned economy is the fuller implementation of the right of choice within the skeleton control related to owner-

---

[3] In common financial statements of large corporations, these figures are often rounded to the nearest thousand dollars. In the presentation of some of the budgets of agencies of the United States government, the figures are rounded to the nearest million dollars to keep the numbers intelligible.

ship, which is exercised through the periodic election of representative government. Also, the government control does not encompass the total economy, and the choices to be made in exercising control can be understood by those who operate the skeleton control system.

A full study of the implications of such an analysis as the foregoing is clearly beyond the scope of this book. The digression was included for three reasons:

1. To underscore the importance of a clear theoretical concept of control by indicating the magnitude of events to which it is related.
2. To substantiate the validity of the concept of control which has been offered by showing how such a concept readily explains events which have occurred.
3. To indicate that formal society is a system of control and must for its most fruitful form, wherein freedom of opportunity, security, and material wealth are to be maximized, carefully design a socioeconomic system in which the requirements of control are met, without limiting the multiplicity of goals and the feasibility of achieving them.

To return to the discussion of the industrial enterprise, the steps of comparison of performance with plans in the top-management control system are, usually, heavily oriented toward the money dimensions, although substantive dimensions of goals, programs, and workloads should also be used. If corrective action is required from the top-management level of control, this is a clear indication of the lack of, or the failure to achieve, control at lower levels. If any time lag is involved between the actual events and the making of the comparisons of plans with performance at the top-management level, the lag may create a need for corrective action which is more drastic than if the corrective action had been instituted or achieved at a lower level of control that was more closely associated with the actual events. Consequently, in most cases, the mechanics of the interface of the top-management money-control system with the middle-management control system is designed to provide a rapid feedback of financial data to the top-management money-control system. This need often leads, erroneously, to a separation of the financial dimensions from the substantive dimensions of the middle-management or substantive control systems. The reason for calling this erroneous is that the separation often removes the ability to control, with regard to money, at the middle-management control-system level, thereby creating a greater need for corrective action at the top-management control-system level. The top-management control system is usually further removed from the causes of the out-of-control condition; hence, corrective action is usually delayed, is more complicated, and involves more people. Such conditions are not the most effective for economy of control.

The money-control aspects of the substantive control systems must also be carefully examined. The money-control aspects of these systems may be understood readily if the money dimensions are recognized as merely one of the dimensions of the goals toward which control systems are used to constrain activity. In the previous chapters in the discussion of substantive control systems, frequent mention was made of the problems of trade-offs and corrective action. Most of these problems have either time or money dimensions as their main criteria. The money-control aspects of the problems of the substantive control systems also require that information concerning money be gathered and summarized in a form compatible with the substantive control. For instance, in producing products *A, B,* and *C,* the information concerning the expenditure of money must be gathered separately for each of the three products. Further, to provide for control, money spent for the time-use of man-jobs on product *A,* for the time-use of physical plant to produce product *A,* and for the material used to produce product *A* must be reported in such a way that it may be identified with a given quantity of product *A* produced over a given period of time. With direct costs, those directly related to the actual production of an actual number of units of product, the requisite separation and reporting of costs are not too difficult. However, much of the cost of an industrial organization is indirect, that is, not directly attributable to specific units of specific products. Common examples are such cost sources as the maintenance of washrooms and lunchrooms, negotiations with labor unions, general factory supervision, general factory repair, and foreman training. Some way to attribute or report these costs, or money expenditures, to each product and product group must be developed, and this distribution of costs must be integrated with the collection of direct costs, so that the totals may be used to evaluate the status of the programs subject to control.

In addition to reporting costs in the manner just indicated, there is a need to develop an input of data for use in computing taxes and for serving various top-management needs. For such uses, the total of all money spent must usually be resummarized differently to indicate the total amount spent for labor, materials, new equipment, physical plant maintenance, local taxes, and so forth. Further, because it is common practice to keep a top-management money-control system operative on accruals (obligations rather than completed transactions), the system of reporting money information must include amounts payable but not yet paid and amounts receivable but not yet received. From the foregoing, it can be seen that a bit of intelligence concerning the money dimension of events may need to go to several tabulations to serve different uses.

There are two basic alternative approaches to the problem of reporting money information in a variety of formats. One solution is to pull together all the controls concerning money and to operate this as an independent control system. The other approach is to provide, by manual means for small operations and by automatic data-processing equipment in large operations, a variety of different summarizations of the money information to serve the different needs of the substantive and top-management control systems. While the latter alternative would seem to be more appropriate, the former is probably more common, representing the common mistake of identifying things as similar on the basis of the technique employed rather than the identification of objectives. Whichever alternative is selected, there will still be a data-processing activity, involving the use of man-jobs to process data in a variety of ways to serve the objectives of the various control systems. The mere processing of the data itself, however, must not be regarded as a money-control system.

The third type of money-control system which was identified concerned the handling of the actual money, the direct money control. One of the basic purposes of such a system is to provide for the mechanical handling of the money or its equivalents. Money must be disbursed; money received from sales, after it has been subjected to the sales-control system, must be "held."

The goal of such a system is to facilitate the operation of the composite plans of the top-management control system and the substantive control systems and to provide the mechanics of letting money flow in and out in accordance with the programs of these systems, with a minimum of effort on the part of all concerned and with a minimum chance of either misusing the money or miscalculating the true status of affairs.

The programs of the direct money-control system are the servicing of the needs of the other control systems. The workload consists in paying out and receiving money in terms of a given number of documents, as well as reporting to the data-processing procedure in terms which permit the feeding of information to the various control systems. The workload might be expressed in terms of the amount of money handled each period of time but only when there is a statistically reliable relationship between such a value and the amount of activity to be performed.

The resources required for the operation of such a control system would be most correctly stated in terms of the required time-use of man-jobs, the amount of space needed, the required time-use of data-processing equipment to handle the data and to create the necessary records and financial instruments, and the equipment needed to protect adequately any money held in the form of actual money. It would be incorrect to include in the statement of required resources the amount of money that would be handled because this money is already under the control of both the top-management money-control system and the various substantive control systems.

The comparison of plans with performance and the indication of the need for corrective action would be of two types: (1) relating to the actual operation of the money-control-system activity, under a sort of production-control system (internal to the money-control system), and (2) relating to the disbursing of money within the confines of the goal constraints developed as part of the other control systems. The need for corrective action or for some trade-off would be reported only when the total amount expended under any particular account (a subdivision of a program) exceeded the planned amount, an out-of-control condition which should have been detected in the substantive control system.

The particular type of money-control system under consideration would respond, from the preceding point of view, by servicing the requests of the other control systems under the authority implicit in the permission already acquired within such control systems. Its function may be compared with that of the carburetor float in the initial description of control in Chapter 12.

It is of interest to note that in many organizations the disbursement of money often follows an authority channel identical with a strict interpretation of the hierarchy of authority within a plant, in complete disregard of the systems of controls which may have been established. A request for an expenditure may need to be processed through a long series of people, although the basic authority for the particular expenditure may be clearly implicit in the goals and in the authority to use resources assigned, through a top-management control system (and possibly through other subsequent controls), to a particular group or individual. Such a situation, which is so common that it must be mentioned in this book, is the result of a failure to recognize fully the nature of control and the requirements for effective systems. The failure frequently creates a situation wherein the taking of direct goal-directed action, corrective action, or the adoption of desirable trade-offs is often much more difficult and time consuming than it needs to be. Further, its effect upon the human component of an enterprise is often devastating.

REFERENCE TOPICS

Accounting
Cost accounting
Balance sheet
Profit-and-loss statement
Standard costs
Cash flow
Overhead distribution
Equipment-replacement policy
Cashier
Disbursement

Controller
Comptroller
Treasurer
Finance
Ownership
Political economy
Budgets
Forecasting
Procedure analysis

SUGGESTED THEMES

1. An analysis of money control in assigned organizations
2. An analysis of money control in the U.S. government
3. An economic analysis of an assigned inventory situation with respect to working capital
4. An analysis of disbursement procedures for an assigned enterprise
5. An analysis of the budget statement of an organization with respect to the money-control aspects

SUGGESTED CASES

Cruickshank, H. M., and K. Davis, *Cases in Management,* 3d ed. Homewood, Ill.: Richard D. Irwin, Inc., 1962. Cases beginning on pages 13, 26, 34.

Greenwald, D. U., *Elementary Case Problems for Industrial Engineers.* New York: The Ronald Press, 1957. Cases beginning on pages 7, 84, 87.

Mantel, S. J., Jr., *Cases in Managerial Decisions.* Englewood Cliffs, N.J.: Prentice-Hall, Inc., 1964. Cases beginning on pages 1, 27, 108, 164.

Terry, G. R., *Case Problems in Business and Industrial Management,* 2d ed. Dubuque, Iowa: William C. Brown Company, Publishers, 1955. Cases beginning on pages 1, 2, 3, 21, 31, 32, 169, 171, 176.

20 SALES CONTROL

The term *sales control* describes the complex of control systems used to assist top management in operating across the interface with the external economic world with regard to the outputs of the enterprise. The sales-control-system complex (there are usually several subsystems of control) essentially relates to the control of the process of exchanging goods (or services) from the plant for money from the users of the outputs of the enterprise. The basic pattern of sales control has some resemblance to the system of production control because both usually involve at least two levels of control.

In the sales-control system, one level of control is a gross control which is based on an annual or similar time span, depending upon the nature of the product, the market, and the appropriate sales method. The gross control is usually closely interfaced with the top-management control-system step of setting objectives; its inputs are used to assist in setting feasible goals for the enterprise. Indeed, in the small organization the integration may be so close that one can hardly speak of two systems. The second level of control is an ongoing control which is usually closely interfaced with both the upper-level sales-control system and the objectives-setting step of the production planning-and-control system, although it may be buffered from the production-control system with an inventory. The term *buffered* is used to describe a stock of finished goods used to lessen the impact across the interface between the two systems. Both levels of sales control, as well as the possible use of inventory for buffering, will be described in this chapter.

In actual practice, the assignment of responsibility to a sales department may differ greatly from the functions described as part of a sales-control system as presented in this chapter. There are several possible reasons for such deviations.

First, the concept of a system of control does not, as has been frequently reiterated, predicate any specific man-job design or set of designs; a variety of job configurations may be used to achieve any given set of desired results. Man-jobs were defined as the combination of men and work assignments. Feasible assignments depend upon the availability of men and their characteristics. Sales is not only an important area of activity but one in which the individual nature of the men employed has an important bearing. Many values rendered by the sales group are difficult to describe in direct monetary terms or in direct substantive terms. Manufacturing defects, in the broad sense of deficiencies in design or cost as compared with competitive products, may be overcome by appropriate sales activity; the performance of such activity is greatly affected by individual personal characteristics. Particularly in the sales area, activity cannot be considered in purely mechanistic terms. Hence, one can readily expect many unique man-job configurations to arise in specific enterprises.

Second, the system concept may not be fully recognized, and much intermittent management effort may be used to achieve the desired sales results in a poorly formalized fashion, requiring much extra effort. However, such a condition may be hard to identify separately from the first condition given unless the situation is examined thoroughly.

Third, the decisions made within the upper-level sales-control system may not result in a full delegation of authority to the lower control level. Some of the decision making authority concerning details of the workload may be retained within the upper level. This tends to take place when the effect of such decisions is important and large and the number of such decisions is small. In such a case, the two systems will not be fully separated and will not have really different time scales for all activities. It must be noted that this may be a desirable condition but that it will also increase the difficulty of perceiving the cyclic nature of the control activity and the relationship between the two levels of control.

Fourth, the objectives of the gross-level sales-control system are usually contained within the objectives of the top-management control system, and although these are only a part of the objectives, they are such a vital part that the gross sales-control system is not always considered a subsystem. In the small organization, as noted earlier, this may lead to an integration of the top-management control and the sales control rather than to an interface between two systems.

The usual objective of the gross-level sales-control system is to achieve an exchange of goods or services for money from the customers of the organization in a manner that will achieve the financial objectives of the enterprise. The objectives must be within the financial and physical capability of the enterprise and of the outside economy, and short-range goals must be compatible with long-range goals.

The objectives of the system will usually be the following eighth-order work-units:

1. To sell, during the period covered, a sufficient amount of the product at some given price and at some desired rate of selling per period of time to achieve a given amount of profit for the enterprise. Such an objective must be realistically within the capability of the enterprise, both physically and economically, and may include plans for buffering the flow of production with inventory. (This is related to profit.)

2. To maintain a given number of accounts (satisfied customers). This is based on the rendering of service factors not directly related to quantities of products and is related to the security of the enterprise.

The programs (sixth-order work-units) of the gross-level control systems will be similar to the following:

1. A series of items, each related to a specific product or group of products, indicating the amount of sales anticipated for each time period and giving price, credit dimensions, and market area
2. To handle, in some cases, a given amount of returned product
3. To carry on a campaign of advertising and face-to-face sales efforts
4. To provide support services to sales, including credit determination, traffic (the routing of the shipments to the customers), and billing

It is particularly worth noting that much of item 4 may be done by people not designated as sales people. However, this work is still part of the sales-control system.

To plan programs in a realistic manner, some forecasting must be done of the feasible total amount of sales, the rate of sales, the pattern of sales, the sales price, and the manufacturing cost, as well as the costs associated with inventory if this is to be used as a buffer. In many cases, mathematical models of the external economy and the costs of manufacturing, holding, and selling may be made and used to develop and evaluate alternative courses of action in terms of the probable profit and the risks involved. As one might anticipate, such models can be very complex. They represent a rather specialized field of study beyond the scope of this book, but note should be taken of this area of technology.

At the gross control-system level, the estimate of the workload will be made for all of these programs on the basis of assumptions concerning the manner of carrying them out. This is typical of upper-level control systems.

The computation of the resources will require an estimate of the amount of money needed to perform the activities within each program and the amount of money needed to finance the operation of the inventory system and the sale of goods on credit. These should be considered a resource requirement of the gross sales-control system to provide this system with the full range of dimensions under which it must operate and to permit a full design of the programs. A full design of programs, in turn, will lead to more effective comparison of plans with results and quicker, more appropriate, and more realistic corrective actions when needed.

The acquisition of authority to carry out the sales activities must include the stating of the procedures or policies under which the resources to handle inventory and credit may be used, to reduce to a minimum the amount of information flowing across the interface with top management, thereby freeing a maximum amount of managerial time for the examination of deviations from plans and the design of appropriate corrective action.

The performance step of the gross control system will consist in feeding across the interface with the lower-level sales-control system (if there is one) the detailed objectives of the sales-control system as refined by the completion of all the steps of planning, indicating also the specific authority delegated and the types of problems which are to be referred to the higher-order system because such authority is not delegated.

The comparison steps of the gross control system will be performed on a gross time scale, smaller than the total time scale of the planning steps but larger than the ongoing comparisons typical of the lower-level sales-control system. In most cases, these comparisons will concern workloads and program performance and goal achievement with respect both to total sales and to the distribution of resources to the specific programs, such as the actual dealing with purchasers, maintaining accounts, advertising, maintaining inventory position, and acquiring new accounts. Total performance will also be compared with net profits. As one might anticipate, such comparisons are of direct interest to top managers. Consequently, in many cases, it is difficult to differentiate the man-jobs related to this part of the gross-level sales-control system from top management.

The objectives of the lower-level sales-control system are acquired from the upper-level sales-control system, as is typical of lower-level control systems. The degree of detail, in the case of the lower-level sales-control system, resembles the degree of detail given in the ongoing production-control system. The programs must be developed in terms of a substantive breakdown, such as product lines or models, areas of sales, or types of customers or markets, depending on the type of product and the degree of detail developed in the upper-level control system. Of course, all these programs must have dimensions with reference to the amount of sales and the rate of sales and must fit within the constraints pertaining to the amount of resources available for credit and inventory.

The pattern of activities or workload must be planned within each of these programs to accomplish the programs of the upper control system. The activities must, at this level, be described in sufficient detail so that the actual resources required may be determined in an objective manner and compared with the resources allocated from the upper-level control system in order to develop a compatible relationship.

The actual carrying out of the sales activity must be considered as a problem similar to the actual production of product, even though the product, in this case, is a service rather than a physical product. Certain basic types of problems can be anticipated and readily identified within the larger problem of "carrying out the sales activity." The success of each individual sales effort involving a confrontation with either a customer or a potential customer may be examined in order to determine a possible need for corrective action and the means of taking it. The distribution of available resources for the various types of sales efforts may be continually examined and redistributed in order to take advantage of, or react to, sales successes or failures, changes in goals, changes in the economy, or changes in the society. Also, the physical location of sales manpower may need to be continually examined in order to maximize the production of direct sales effort rather than have time lost in indirect efforts such as travel. Further, the interaction of product and customer must be continually appraised and reacted to with respect to both the services required or extended and the implicit qualities of the product which are continually affected by the competition encountered. Information must be fed not only to the design of sales programs and workload but also to the product-process design activity, the production-control system, and the quality-control system to maximize the potential for achieving the sales-control system objectives.

The comparison of the performance of workload with the planned workload and of program achievement with program plans must be made not only on the basis of the terms used to state the details of workloads and programs but on the basis of the achievement of the real objectives of the control system. Hence, the achievement of goals must be watched on a similar short-time span. For instance, the sales-control system should be designed to ensure not only that a given number of face-to-face sales calls are made with respect to a given product and a given segment of the market but that a given percentage of calls will result in some anticipated amount of sales. In this respect, the results are somewhat more tenuous than with a production-control system. In the usual production situation, the application of production equipment to raw material usually results in an anticipated amount and quality of product. Sales actions take place in a far less mechanistic environment. Hence, the comparison with goals must be frequent, and considerable flexibility must, in most cases, be maintained with respect to program and workload. Decision making is somewhat more difficult than in the more mechanical areas of managerial problems. Consequently, an adequate sales-control system is particularly valuable in that it may assist in supplying data for logically evaluating managerial decisions or for evaluating alternatives.

The problem of buffering sales with inventory has many facets, some of which have been indirectly discussed in previous chapters. For instance, in Chapter 13, "Controlling Production," the problem of maximizing profit by making an ideal mix of product was discussed. In Chapter 16, "Controlling Materials," the problem of buffering with regard to raw material was examined briefly. It should be obvious that neither of these problems can be realistically examined without reference to the sales-control system and the information emanating from that system.

The problem of buffering is affected by what can be sold, as well as by what is profitable to sell. It is also affected by the nature of the industry. With enterprises in which the specifications of the final product are determined by the customer, the only feasible type of buffering may be with raw materials or with components. In industries in which the product undergoes considerable processing to bring it to the customer's specifications, it may be possible to do considerable work without bringing the product to a highly specific form. For instance, steel may be poured into ingots for rolling or forging to create a stock of ingots of different alloys from which plate or rod or shape or tube may be made for the customer with less interruption to the production process than under a procedure where the obtaining of an order only started the ingot production. In such a case, the question becomes "Is the saving from the reduction of interruption in steel making more than enough to offset the costs associated with holding a stock of ingots?" However, this is not a simple question because a complete answer would indicate how many ingots of each kind to hold. If too many are held, the holding costs are certainly larger than they need to be; if too few are held, some orders may be lost. The ideal solution would be the quantity which will maximize the profits. However, each order may not really be considered by itself. If a potential customer found that one of his orders or part of an order could not be handled, he might take all of his business elsewhere, to a concern which would provide quicker and more complete servicing.

Another type of buffering problem occurs in industries where the rate of sales undergoes considerable fluctuation during the course of a year. The alternatives are to vary production to meet demand or to buffer the fluctuation of sales with inventory. The more products involved, the more complicated such a problem becomes. Also, the provision of steady work affects plant morale and productivity, although these may be difficult to assess precisely in economic terms.

Another type of buffering problem occurs in an industry where the number of different products made exceeds the capacity of the plant for simultaneous production, a rather common condition. The cost of making such products is usually affected by the size of the lot produced at one time. The ability to service customers will depend upon the frequency with which the different products are made, the quantity made at one time, and the amount carried in stock; but so will costs.

Further, in any inventory buffer, there is always the danger of obsolescence of product or deterioration in storage, in addition to the basic costs previously described under "Materials."

In view of all the factors and considerations involved, it would seem reasonable to conclude that an informal solution to the problem of buffering would be unlikely to produce an answer approaching an optimum solution, except in the simplest of situations. Hence, some formal methodology of treating such problems must be used. The inputs must come not only from the substantive control systems of the plant but from the sales-control system to ensure that the programs of the sales-control system are compatible with the programs of the other systems. Unless all aspects are considered, it would be relatively easy to have conflicting goals for the various control systems; a great deal of management effort would be wasted in resolving the resultant difficulties, or, in the worst case, the organization might fail to meet its basic objectives and be destroyed by the force of economic circumstances.

REFERENCE TOPICS

Sales	Sales programs
Market research	Sales promotion
Forecasting	Filling orders
Price trends	Delivery
Salesmen, sales force	Traffic
Pricing	Advertising
Product planning	Distribution
Product research	

SUGGESTED THEMES

1. The nature of sales as affected by type of market and type of product
2. Methods of forecasting sales in use in assigned industries or enterprises

3. A proposal for a method of forecasting sales and price for an assigned enterprise
4. Changes in the sales of selected lines in relation to the gross national product
5. Cultural changes reflected in changes in sales patterns

SUGGESTED CASES

Cruickshank, H. M., and K. Davis, *Cases in Management,* 3d ed. Homewood, Ill.: Richard D. Irwin, Inc., 1962. Cases beginning on pages 29, 55, 209.

Greenwald, D. U., *Elementary Case Problems for Industrial Engineers.* New York: The Ronald Press, 1957. Cases beginning on pages 44, 135.

Mantel, S. J., Jr., *Cases in Managerial Decisions.* Englewood Cliffs, N.J.: Prentice-Hall, Inc., 1964. Cases beginning on pages 6, 8, 50, 82, 135.

Terry, G. R., *Case Problems in Business and Industrial Management,* 2d ed. Dubuque, Iowa: William C. Brown Company, Publishers, 1955. Cases beginning on pages 9, 10, 13.

Ziegler, R. J., *Casebook in Production Management.* New York: John Wiley & Sons, Inc., 1962. Cases beginning on pages 75, 135.

PART 4 CONCLUSION

21 DECISION MAKING

In the opening chapter of this book, the scientific method of making decisions was described and the method illustrated with some simple examples. Also, the need for a framework for organizing facts was noted. In the following chapters, increasingly complex aspects of the task of management were examined in an attempt to build the requisite framework and nomenclature. From the preceding chapters, it is apparent that in almost any conceivable set of circumstances encountered in performing the task of management, many alternative courses of action exist. The day-to-day task of managers will consist in determining appropriately detailed criteria, developing a list of alternative courses of action, and choosing from among these alternatives. Decision making will be the focus of the task of the manager. This concept is not in conflict with the general statement, made in Chapter 12, that to manage means to exercise control; decision making and control are inseparable. To make a decision requires an objective which is to be achieved; decisions cannot be made in a logical fashion without such an objective; to talk of decision making implies that control is being sought. To control suggests the desired events or conditions will not take place of their own accord; decisions will be needed to constrain factors affecting the final results.

This chapter will discuss some additional aspects of decision making which are vital to effective management decisions but which were omitted from the opening chapter because, at that time, the task of management had not yet been examined in detail. The various parts had not yet been described, and nomenclature had not yet been developed. In addition, some small amount of material from Chapter 12 is restated here to tie together the scientific method, the control concept, and the decision making process.

An example of the typical situation in which a decision is required will be encountered when the gross, or upper-level, production-control system of an enterprise indicates a future date when the available productive resources of the enterprise, equipment and man-jobs, will exceed the requirements of the workload. Inasmuch as the basic objective of the enterprise is to make a profit, obviously some decision is needed as to whether to use these available resources to produce product, to dispose of these resources, or to allow them to be wasted. To illustrate, let us assume that the product-process group has examined the nature of these available resources and determined that one of two products, identified as *A* and *B,* can be made.

Of course, many decisions were involved in developing this input to the decision making situation under consideration. The examination of the problem of what to do with the anticipated excess resources will illustrate the approach to all.

There are four basic alternatives:

1. Produce product *A*.
2. Produce product *B*.
3. Dispose of the excess resources, viz., lay off workers and sell equipment.
4. Allow the excess resources to be wasted, viz., tolerate idle equipment and idle time or "make-work" for the men.

Certainly, alternatives 3 and 4 will contribute to the main objective of the enterprise only in a passive fashion; they will reduce costs as compared with making unwanted product. Alternative 3 will reduce the expenditure, for the time being, by not spending money for unneeded resources, but it will also reduce the program capability of the enterprise. It may also have a deleterious effect upon the morale of employees. Alternative 4 will only minimize the effect of a bad situation; the cost of the unused resources will not contribute to the main objectives of the enterprise. Hence, it is obvious that alternatives 1 and 2 should be given more detailed consideration.

The part of the decision making process examined to this point has resulted in a tentative decision. A tentative decision usually does not lead to a substantive course of action; more commonly, it leads to a continuation of the decision making process. The particular tentative decision in this illustration may also be said to have a high degree of obviousness; that is, the relationship of the alternative to the objectives was clear and obvious. Further, this decision can be said to have a low degree of finality; that is, it can be altered later with no particular difficulty or loss. This is more or less typical of tentative decisions, except when the time allowed for a final decision is short.

The next step is to follow the tentative decision and obtain the required additional information. For instance, each product will have an anticipated cost of production. For this illustration, let the anticipated cost of producing the feasible amount of product A be represented by AC and the anticipated cost of producing the feasible amount of B be represented by BC. It may be anticipated that each product will produce a profit. Let the profit associated with product A be AP and the profit with B, BP.

It is possible that there will be hazards to the health and safety of the employees associated with the production of each product. Let the hazards associated with product A be represented by AH and those associated with B by BH.

With regard to the cost of production, three conditions are possible, as follows:

AC is equal to BC, which can be written as $\qquad AC = BC$
AC is greater than BC, which can be written as $\qquad AC > BC$
AC is less than BC, which can be written as $\qquad AC < BC$

With regard to the hazards associated with the production of the two products, three similar conditions are possible:

$AH = BH$
$AH > BH$
$AH < BH$

Finally, with regard to the profits, three similar possibilities exist:

$AP = BP$
$AP > BP$
$AP < BP$

If all of these possibilities are independent, the totality of all possible situations can be represented as:

$$
\begin{vmatrix} AC = BC \\ AC > BC \\ AC < BC \end{vmatrix} \times \begin{vmatrix} AH = BH \\ AH > BH \\ AH < BH \end{vmatrix} \times \begin{vmatrix} AP = BP \\ AP > BP \\ AP < BP \end{vmatrix}
$$

Expanding this mathematically phrased statement will show that there are really twenty-seven different possible situations, which can be divided into six groups:

1. Situations where the choice of A or B makes no difference

2. Situations where the choice of product A is clearly preferable to product B
3. Situations where the choice of product B is clearly preferable to product A
4. Situations where the magnitude of the cost may affect the desirability of product A by requiring excessive resources as compared with those required to produce B
5. Situations where magnitude of the cost may affect the desirability of product B by requiring excessive resources as compared with those required to produce A
6. Situations where the unlike dimensions of increased profits must be weighed against the dimensions of increased hazards

In detail, the twenty-seven possible situations classified into the foregoing six groups are as follows:

1. Situations where the choice of A or B makes no difference:

$AC = BC, AP = BP, AH = BH$

2. Situations where the choice of product A is clearly preferable to product B:

$$AC = BC, \quad AP = BP, \quad AH < BH$$
$$AC = BC, \quad AP > BP, \quad AH = BH$$
$$AC = BC, \quad AP > BP, \quad AH < BH$$
$$AC < BC, \quad AP = BP, \quad AH = BH$$
$$AC < BC, \quad AP = BP, \quad AH < BH$$
$$AC < BC, \quad AP > BP, \quad AH = BH$$
$$AC < BC, \quad AP > BP, \quad AH < BH$$

3. Situations where the choice of product B is clearly preferable to product A:

$$AC = BC, \quad AP = BP, \quad AH > BH$$
$$AC = BC, \quad AP < BP, \quad AH = BH$$
$$AC = BC, \quad AP < BP, \quad AH > BH$$
$$AC > BC, \quad AP = BP, \quad AH = BH$$
$$AC > BC, \quad AP < BP, \quad AH = BH$$
$$AC > BC, \quad AP < BP, \quad AH > BH$$
$$AC > BC, \quad AP = BP, \quad AH > BH$$

4. Situations where the magnitude of the cost may affect the desirability of product A by requiring excessive resources as compared with those required to produce product B:

$$AC > BC, \quad AP = BP, \quad AH < BH$$
$$AC > BC, \quad AP > BP, \quad AH = BH$$
$$AC > BC, \quad AP > BP, \quad AH < BH$$

5. Situations where the magnitude of the cost may affect the desirability of product B by requiring excessive resources as compared with those required to produce product A:

$AC < BC,$ $AP = BP,$ $AH > BH$
$AC < BC,$ $AP < BP,$ $AH = BH$
$AC < BC,$ $AP < BP,$ $AH > BH$

6. Situations where the unlike dimensions of increased profits must be weighed against the dimensions of increased hazards:

$AC = BC,$ $AP < BP,$ $AH < BH$
$AC = BC,$ $AP > BP,$ $AH > BH$
$AC < BC,$ $AP < BP,$ $AH < BH$
$AC < BC,$ $AP > BP,$ $AH > BH$
$AC > BC,$ $AP < BP,$ $AH < BH$
$AC > BC,$ $AP > BP,$ $AH > BH$

It is worthwhile to examine some features of the foregoing analysis. A basic knowledge of the situation was used in a systematic fashion to develop a list of all possibilities. Basic knowledge concerning the importance of costs, profits, and hazards was used to categorize the possible situations. Thus, it was found that additional criteria were needed concerning these categories, in addition to the criterion of profit, in order to make a decision.

However, in addition to the above, something else was done. Symbols were used to create a model. A *symbol* is an abstract representation of an object, an event, a condition, or a relationship. For instance, the letters used to write words do not resemble either the sound of speech or the object they refer to. (There are some languages of which this is not true.) The signs of mathematics, such as $+$, $=$, or $-$, are used as aids in describing an event, a condition, or a relationship, but they have no resemblance to the actual event. A *model,* on the other hand, is a kind of representation of a real object, objects, event, or events, in the real world, which has some of the characteristics of that which is being represented. For instance, a scale model may be a reduced or enlarged version of a real object, possessing the same intrascalar relationships, the same colors, and so forth, but not all the capabilities of the real object. An equation may be used to create a model in terms of symbols of an inventory situation. The configuration of the symbols possesses some of the properties of the real situation; for certain purposes it may be more convenient to work with than the real situation, even though it cannot be sold or used like real inventory; it is a model. As will be seen later, there are many forms of models used to assist in making decisions.

In the decision making situation of the example, symbols were used to create a model which assisted in developing a list of all possible situations which might be encountered in comparing the desirability of making product

A with the desirability of making product *B*, as well as comparing whether one of these two alternatives was preferable to the other alternatives originally listed. The word "assisted" is important. It aided in examining the facts which knowledge indicated as worth consideration. *Knowledge,* as defined in Chapter 1, consists of organized information concerning past events, objects, or situations, stored in some manner which will facilitate retrieval when needed. In the typical industrial decision making situation, the industrial objectives will initiate the retrieval of information; hence, industrial knowledge must be organized around the various possible objectives. For this reason, the preceding chapters devoted so much space to an examination of the systems of objectives, subobjectives, programs, and so forth, which are typical of the systems of control.

To continue, as was also mentioned in Chapter 13, in addition to knowledge to help in making a decision, there is a need for intelligence. *Intelligence* is defined as new information concerning a specific or current object, event, condition, or situation. To be really useful, it should be in a form readily suitable for comparing with knowledge or using with knowledge for evaluating alternative possibilities with respect to the objectives or criteria.

For instance, the model constructed in relation to products *A* and *B* would not be of much value until sufficient intelligence was obtained to determine which of the situations given as possible alternatives represented the real condition. However, as noted in the listing of the alternatives, even with sufficient intelligence to determine which situation is obtained, there cannot be a certainty of an immediate decision with respect to the preferability of *A* to *B* or vice versa, except in certain cases such as those given as groups 2 and 3 on page 294.

In addition, any intelligence obtained concerning the cost of production, the associated hazards, or the profit will have a property called either uncertainty or reliability; the intelligence is a prediction rather than an observable fact. The terms *uncertainty* and *reliability* refer, in a general sense, to the degree of trust to be placed in information. With respect to quantitative data, more specifically, it should be used to refer to chances of a given figure being within certain limits. *Chances* may be described quantitatively by statements such as 3 out of 4 or 99 out of 100. *Limits* may be stated by giving the upper and lower values within which the true figure lies if chances given are accepted as sufficient for trust.

For instance, the cost of production for product *A* may be given as probably AC dollars, with 95 chances out of 100 of being within $AC + K$ and $AC - K$, where K represents a monetary value. The preceding statement is knowledge. If an estimate from one of the control systems is used to substitute numbers for AC and K, this is intelligence. The cost of production for product *B* might also be stated in similar terms, as BC dollars, with 95 chances out of 100 of being within $BC \pm L$, where L is some monetary value probably different from K. It is not unusual that the following relationship may exist, although it is far from inevitable:

$$AC < BC, \quad \text{but} \quad (AC + K) > (BC - L)$$

Further, there is still a chance (5 out of 100) that the cost of production of product A is above or below the limits $AC \pm K$ and the same chance that the cost of production of B is above or below $BC \pm L$. Therefore, if, on the basis of the intelligence which indicates that the cost of product A is less than the cost of product B, the decision is made to select product A for production, there is still some risk.

The term *risk* refers to the chance of obtaining undesired consequences and should be thought of as having three dimensions. The three dimensions of risk are:

1. Chance
2. Magnitude
3. Finality

Chance refers to the likelihood or, as defined before, to the uncertainty or reliability. *Magnitude* refers to the values which are concerned; in the example under discussion, these values are the total costs associated with producing A or B or following the other two alternatives. Magnitude also refers to the amount of profit anticipated. The magnitude of both costs and profit must be considered in relation to the total costs and profits of the enterprise. The magnitude or size of the hazards indicates the seriousness of the possible results. *Finality* refers to the reversibility or revokability of a decision or its consequences.

To return to the illustration, the decision may be to make product A. If the intelligence was right, if the cost of A is probably within $AC \pm K$, and if the profit associated with the production of A, given as AP, is much greater than K, the risk of not making a profit, in terms of chance, is low. The risk is low because even if the costs exceed the estimate, profits will still exist. For various values of AP, the chances of risk may be stated as:

$AP = \frac{1}{2}K$;   high risk
$AP = \quad K$;   2½ out of 100 (the true cost may be below $AC - K$)
$AP = \quad 2K$;   low risk

To continue, the magnitude of the risk depends upon how large AP, AC, and AH are in terms of an appropriate standard or criterion. Certainly, if the costs associated with the possible production of A are low in relation to total plant expenditures and other profits and if the same is true of the profits associated with B, the magnitude of the risk is relatively small and not important. Risk, with respect to magnitude, can best be evaluated in terms of relative importance.

The degree of finality has a considerable influence on the decision making process. For instance, in the illustration, if products *A* and *B* are made from the same raw material and on the same machines and if the lead time between production and sales is short, should it turn out that the decision to make *A* was based on faulty intelligence and that the plant really should be making *B*, it would probably be easy to change. In such a case, the decision has a low degree of finality. Taking another possibility, if the production of *A* requires very different tooling and materials from *B* and if the lead time to procure tools and materials is high, a decision to make *A* rather than *B* may have a great deal of finality, or a high degree of finality.

Still another problem raised by the model created was the comparison of unlike values. There were six possible situations where increased profits and reduced expenditures would have to be compared with greater hazards. The possibility of hazards is a second form of risk; it has the same three dimensions. The actual hazards in a situation must be evaluated in this form to assist in arriving at a suitable decision.

In summary, to arrive at a decision in the illustration, the first requirement was an objective which, in this case, was to make a profit.

Next, there was a problem, a difficulty to overcome: in this case, anticipated idle resources. Knowledge was used in making a list of major alternatives. A tentative decision was made quickly because this first tentative decision had a high degree of obviousness and a low degree of finality. Knowledge was again used in developing a more refined list of alternatives, which assisted in making clear the additional objectives, knowledge, and intelligence needed. In using the intelligence to make a decision, reliability and risk had to be considered. Certainly, if the magnitude and degree of finality of the risk were high, further attempts would have to be made to minimize uncertainty and chance.

However, in the situation examined by means of the model, only three factors were considered: costs, profits, and hazards. Certainly the examination of the typical industrial enterprise contained in the preceding chapters would suggest that this is a greatly simplified example compared with those encountered in the actual plant. As noted in Chapter 12, in the usual case many more factors would be involved and many more criteria considered. In such a case, it would be even more important to use the scientific method and to consider the problem in the fashion described because most problems will require decisions which have a low degree of obviousness, and informal analysis will have little chance of picking an appropriate alternative. In applying the scientific method, a large number of bits of information may well be involved. The quantity may be such that they cannot be gathered in the time allowed for making a decision (by the forces requiring it), or the quantity may exceed the human ability to handle data. Further, every problem cannot be approached as though it were unique. Every necessary bit of intelligence cannot be obtained by some unique procedure, which is initiated only when a problem is identified. The comparison steps of the control systems must be continually operating to allow an early, routine identification of problems requiring a decision and to provide a maximum of intelligence in a suitable form.

In the usual industrial enterprise, the use of the scientific method will be facilitated in two ways:

1. By the use of formalized techniques or procedures either for continuously carrying intelligence into retrievable form that is suitable for comparison by managers with knowledge and criteria or for quickly gathering such intelligence when control systems indicate such a need
2. By the use of the techniques of management science for creating and manipulating models to assist in examining the variety of alternatives that may exist, the additional criteria required, the consequences of various alternatives, and the additional knowledge or intelligence that may be required to make a decision

The models which may be created may be such as:

1. Schematic models, using symbols, to show the probable or present flow of a product or a network diagram to show a flow of actions
2. A time-scalar model, such as a Gantt chart, to show the sequence of events and their magnitude on a time continuum or a network diagram with the time for each event
3. An idealized mathematical model, possessing some of the properties of the real situation but ignoring minor characteristics, such as an equation showing the relationships between the major factors governing the most economical purchasing quantity for a material
4. A static scalar or mathematical model, such as a scale model of a plant, or the model of alternatives such as the one used in this chapter
5. A simulative model, which is either scalar or mathematical, embodying a large number of properties of the real object or situation so as to permit rapid manipulating of these factors using fewer resources or less force in a shortened time frame rather than experimenting with real risk, such as a pilot model of a product, a miniature version, or a set of equations for determining an optimum mix

The following list of research areas, used by the American Institute of Industrial Engineers in classifying articles,[1] although not fully consistent in its division into subject areas, does give a good idea of the variety of technologies and areas of management science in which procedures for data gathering and model making have been developed and in which areas, therefore, knowledge exists.

The list is awesome in size but serves to illustrate the wealth of knowledge, technology, and science available to serve the decision maker. Note also that the list includes some "catch-all" classifications to pick up knowl-

[1] *The Journal of Industrial Engineering,* vol. 17, no. 1, January, 1966, p. 38.

MAJOR CLASSIFICATION	SUBSECTIONS
Work measurement	Procedures preparatory to work measurement
	Timing
	Measuring operator performance
	Measuring job difficulty
	Delay allowances
	Machine control and interference allowances
	Personal allowances and fatigue
	Basic motion standard data
	Elemental standard data
	Control of standard times
	Special labor category standard times
	Work sampling
	Micromeasurements
Methods	Nonrepetitive work analysis techniques
	Repetitive work analysis techniques
	Basic principles investigation
	Evaluation procedures
	Testing procedures
	Installation procedures
	Operations design
Facility planning	Plant layout analysis techniques
	Plant layout basic principles
	Plant layout evaluation procedures
	Plant layout testing procedures
	Plant layout presentation procedures
	Materials handling analysis techniques
	Materials handling basic principles
	Materials handling evaluation and selection procedures
	Materials handling testing procedures
	Materials handling equipment design
	Maintenance
	Plant location
	Plant design and construction
	Safety
Applied psychology	Motivation and psychological aspects
	Physiological aspects
	Sociological aspects
	Biomechanics
	Arbitration
	Collective bargaining
	Labor
	Training
	Learning
	Job evaluation
	Wage-incentive plans
	Selection of personnel

Engineering economics	Replacement theory Amortization theory Interest rate concepts Decision making
Organization planning	Decentralization concepts Social scientist's aspects Control designs Communications Information theory Organization design Financial planning
Materials processing	Tool engineering Process research Mechanization and automation Inspection Product research
Production planning and control	Inventory control Forecasting Scheduling Dispatching Routing Packaging Analysis and measurement techniques for planning and control Receiving and shipping Stockkeeping and warehousing Control models and simulation
Data-processing systems design	Digital computers Analog computers Accounting equipment Desk equipment Auxiliary equipment Analysis techniques Information retrieval
Applied mathematics	Mathematical programming Waiting line theory Simulation concepts Game theory Monte Carlo concepts Probability theory Sampling concepts Acceptance sampling Quality-control techniques Experimental design Statistical theory
Costs and cost control	Accounting concepts Inspection Budgets Control procedures Purchasing

edge from other scientific fields of endeavor. If these catch-all classifications were expanded in a similar manner, the list would give an even better indication of the vast variety of existing knowledge from which specific bits must be retrieved to assist in reaching objectives. With such a vast variety of fields of activity, it should surprise no one that expert practitioners of some specialty frequently tend to lose sight of problems and seem to be exercising the technology, or science, for its own sake.

A summary may now be made. Decision making has been indicated as central to control and as the focus of managerial jobs. The situations requiring decisions occur in the operation of the control systems, which have been described in previous chapters. The usual decision concerns the making of a selection from a variety of alternatives, concerning one or more of the following: man-jobs, physical plant, product, materials, the society of the industrial plant, the design of man-jobs, the design of product and process, the design of plant, the selection of materials, and the performance of any step in any of the control systems. The items listed are seldom independent. Time and money are usually among the criteria used in making a selection. Implicit in the task of making a selection is the task of generating a list of alternatives. Various techniques of management science may be used to assist in the generation of such a list, but they only assist.

The generation of a list of alternatives may result in an amplification of the criteria for selection; a better understanding of the limitations, or that which is not feasible; and a better understanding of the areas in which choice exists.

The control systems of the organization, the techniques of intelligence gathering, and the techniques of management science will be used to gain sufficient knowledge and intelligence to assist in selecting the most desirable alternative, with a reasonable knowledge of the probable consequences. The higher the risk in making the decision, the higher the degree of obviousness usually sought, although it cannot always be obtained. In complex situations, much cooperative effort will be needed among a variety of man-jobs to furnish the necessary input of knowledge and intelligence to the man-job having the final responsibility.

When a tentative decision is reached, the techniques of management science may be used to assist in testing more fully the desirability of the selected alternative and evaluating the various dimensions of risk. Of course, the lower the importance of the risk, the less likely this will take place; conversely, the higher the risk, the more likely.

The decision is subsequently tried, and the results watched and compared with the desired results. If a mistake is made, subsequent action is directed at minimizing the magnitude and finality of the risk. Not all risks are revokable. Some businesses fail. The mere application of the technology of management science is no assurance of success. The available techniques, procedures, and systems must be used with intelligence, in the more usual sense of the word.

However, as has been said, management is both a science and an art: a science in that much can be predicted on a causal basis; an art in that the relative importance of problems is often hard to ascertain; an art in that problems do not "lie around waiting to be picked up"; an art in that it involves dealing with people, and people do not respond in a mechanistic fashion; all of these aspects must be kept in the proper perspective.

REFERENCE TOPICS

Decision making	Simulation
Models of man	Logic
Models	The scientific method
Dimensional analysis	Operations research
Linear programming	Management analysis
Queuing	Value judgment
Monte Carlo models	

SUGGESTED THEMES

1. Take an assigned situation and create a model of it, making the model
   Time scalar
   Predictive
   Simulative
   Idealized
2. Describe the method of arriving at a decision for an assigned situation, giving the method of performing and the conclusions reached at each phase.
3. Analyze the probable factors and methods used to arrive at the final configuration of some selected product.
4. Find and compare models proposed for determining the desirability of replacing production equipment.
5. Find and compare models proposed for the determination of the economic lot size for production.

SUGGESTED CASES

Cruickshank, H. M., and K. Davis, *Cases in Management*, 3d ed. Homewood, Ill.: Richard D. Irwin, Inc., 1962. Cases beginning on pages 19, 175, 177, 185, 249, 263.

Mantel, S. J., Jr., *Cases in Managerial Decisions*. Englewood Cliffs, N.J.: Prentice-Hall, Inc., 1964. Cases beginning on pages 89, 98, 115, 146.

Terry, G. R., *Case Problems in Business and Industrial Management*, 2d ed. Dubuque, Iowa: William C. Brown Company, Publishers, 1955. Cases beginning on pages 19, 153, 179, 180, 182.

INDEX